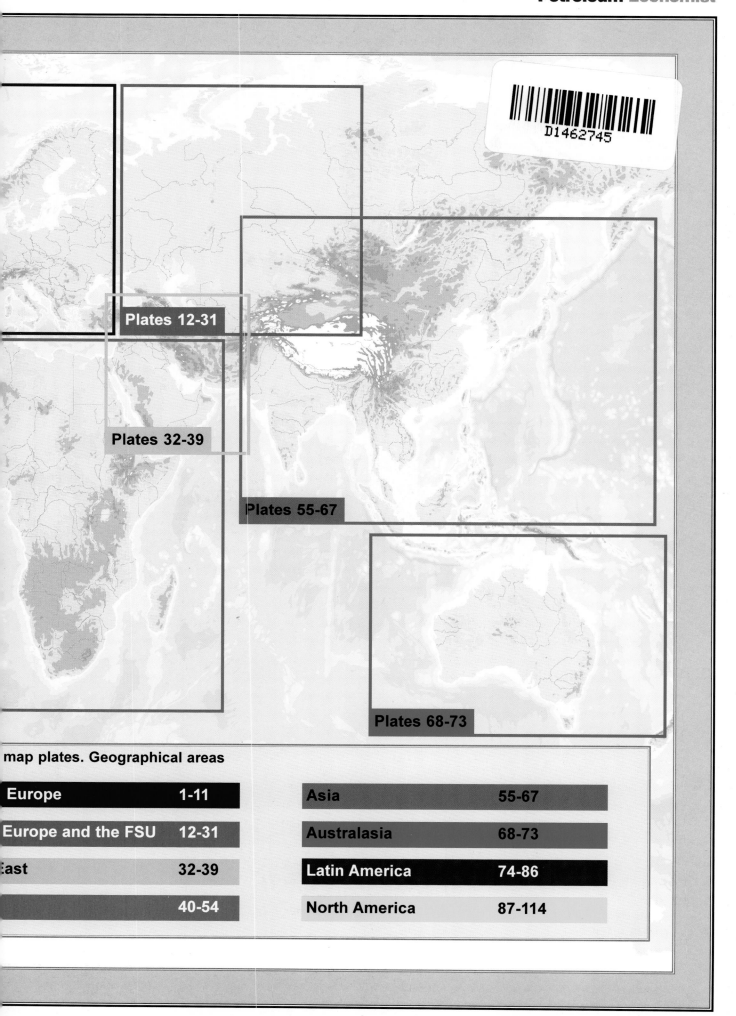

D1462745

Plates 12-31

Plates 32-39

Plates 55-67

Plates 68-73

map plates. Geographical areas

Europe	1-11	Asia	55-67
Europe and the FSU	12-31	Australasia	68-73
East	32-39	Latin America	74-86
	40-54	North America	87-114

The Petroleum Economist Ltd

WORLD
ENERGY
ATLAS

Petroleum Economist Cartographic
part of The Petroleum Economist Ltd

PETROLEUM
ECONOMIST
Cartographic
ENERGY MAPS

Acknowledgements

Published in 2001 by:
Petroleum Economist
Baird House
15/17 St Cross Street
London EC1N 8UW

Maps prepared in Great Britain by
Petroleum Economist
Cartographic

Managing Director
Crispian McCredie

Editorial
Derek Bamber

General Manager, Business Development
Edouard de Guitaut

Maps drawn and researched by
Peregrine Bush
Kevin Fuller

Production Editor
Euan Soutar

Index compiled by
Peregrine Bush
Rebekah Slater

Researcher
Rebekah Slater

ISBN 1 86186 137 0

The publishers would like to extend their grateful thanks to the following:

Schlumberger
Andersen
BG Group
BP
BP Statistical Review of World Energy
Cedigaz, Paris
Energy Research Institute RAS, Moscow
Gazprom
Infield Systems
International Energy Agency
Oil and Gas Journal
Opec
Penspen
Petrobras
Petroconsultants (IHS), London/Geneva
Ruhrgas
RNGS - Rosneftegrazstroy
Shell
Sonatrach
Wood Mackenzie
United Nations

Department of Trade and Industry, United Kingdom
Royal Ministry of Petroleum and Energy, Norway
Ministry of Environment and Energy, Danish Energy Agency

In the production of this atlas:
Grange Press
PW Reproprint
Colourscan Consulting
Direct CD Marketing

Contents

* former Soviet Union

www.petroleum-economist.com

WESTERN EUROPE

EASTERN EUROPE AND THE FSU*

Contents

Contents

Contents

Contents

Foreword

It is now two years since we produced *Petroleum Economist*'s first energy atlas, so our second edition incorporates numerous changes. The atlas now covers the new deep-water developments that are taking place, as well as providing a detailed listing of all projects within the atlas index. There are numerous revisions to the plates, including Siberia, Sakhalin Island, Trinidad and Tobago, West Coast Africa and the Gulf of Mexico, to name but a few. All LNG import terminals and export facilities have been updated, as have pipeline networks. *Petroleum Economist*'s cartographic team has also completely redrawn the base map to provide more topographical information throughout the atlas.

Once again, I must thank the many organisations that provided feedback on our first edition. We have received a great deal of first-hand information, often hand-drawn, on the maps we display at the many trade shows and exhibitions that we have attended around the world in the last two years. To all of you, we are indebted.

Crispian McCredie
Managing Director
Petroleum Economist

Schlumberger

Schlumberger is a global technology services company with more than 75,000 people in 160 countries around the world.

Schlumberger is organized into two segments:

SchlumbergerSema is a leading information technology services company providing IT consulting, systems integration, managed services, products and IP network security solutions serving the oil and gas, telecommunications, utility, finance, transport and public sector markets and is the leading supplier of smart card technology.

Schlumberger Oilfield Services is the leading provider of services, solutions and technology to the international petroleum industry.

Schlumberger

SchlumbergerSema

SchlumbergerSema is a global network of over 30,000 local experts in more than 100 countries providing services to six major market segments:

- oil and gas
- telecommunications
- utilities
- finance
- transport
- public sector

SchlumbergerSema provides:

IT Consulting

Helping our customers transform their business processes to improve efficiency and become more competitive and profitable

Systems Integration

Building complex mission-critical and large-scale technical business systems

Managed Services

Partnering with clients to manage business-critical processes

Products

- Smart cards for wireless, finance, telecommunication, transport, identification and network security applications
- Web payphones
- Point-of-sale, parking and mass transit terminals and associated management systems
- Customer care and billing systems
- Energy generation exchange boards

As the technology systems integrator for the 2002-2008 Olympic Games, SchlumbergerSema will provide systems to ensure the seamless operation of the summer and winter Olympic Games while supplying information to broadcasters, media, spectators and Web users worldwide.

Helping you

Schlumberger Oilfield Services

Schlumberger Oilfield Services provides virtually every type of service to the upstream exploration and production industry through a diverse, multicultural and highly trained workforce of over 45,000. We operate in more than 100 countries, with an established record of joint value creation and service excellence.

Schlumberger Oilfield Services is organized into two core product groups, which together bring a unique set of technology, expertise and experience to the Exploration and Production (E&P) business:

Reservoir Evaluation and Development combines wireline, seismic and all services relevant to well construction and productivity including directional and MWD/LWD drilling, pressure pumping, drilling fluids, testing, drill bits, pumps and completions products

Schlumberger Oil and Gas Information Solutions provides complete information solution business workflows. These range from secure IT infrastructure solutions to software applications, information management and expert products and consulting services.

Our advantage is your advantage

Schlumberger is an independent service company, which holds no equity stake in the development of oil and gas reserves.

Schlumberger is committed to being the leading oilfield services company, providing products and services that address the full spectrum of oil company needs for cost-effective, value-added reservoir solutions from discovery through to abandonment.

Schlumberger holds a major position in every significant E&P sector throughout the world. By utilizing the full potential of our workforce, we provide seamless integration of the products and services needed to enhance the value of your discoveries.

t the most
from your reservoir

Reservoir Evaluation and Development

Schlumberger provides services to increase the productivity of oil and gas reservoirs, from exploration through field development and management:

- surface seismic (WesternGeco)
- directional drilling and real-time drilling analysis
- drill bits
- drilling fluids (M-I)
- openhole logging
- cementing and stimulation
- cased hole logging and perforating
- well completion services and equipment
- production systems engineering
- subsea and topside facilities (Syntheseas)
- well testing
- well intervention
- electrical submersible pumps

Our Integrated Project Management (IPM) group is a multidisciplinary organization with comprehensive engineering, quality, safety and project management support systems, integrated through processes focused on improving oilfield business efficiency and maximizing asset value. IPM combines value-sharing models with unrivalled operational expertise to optimize the flow of hydrocarbons from pore to pipeline.

WesternGeco

WesternGeco is a joint venture company providing seismic services for exploration, reservoir imaging and field development. By combining the superior acquisition and data processing technologies, services and resources of the two industry leaders, Schlumberger and Baker Hughes have created the world's premier geophysical company. Services include high-resolution 2D and 3D imaging, time-lapse 4-D surveys for reservoir monitoring and management and multicomponent seismic for stratigraphic and pore-fill analysis.

The company also offers the industry's largest multiclient seismic library of high-quality data for oil and gas exploration in the world's most promising prospects.

www.westerngeco.com

M-I

M-I is a Smith International and Schlumberger joint venture company providing drilling fluids, drill-in fluids, completion and workover fluids, and additives as well as field engineering and technical support. M-I is also a producer of barite and bentonite for the oilfield industry and industrial markets. Swaco, a division of M-I, is the industry leader in solids control, pressure control and oilfield waste management equipment and services. M-I Integrated Fluids Engineering combines all fluids and fluids-related products and services into a unique planning-to-production program.

www.midf.com

Syntheseas

Syntheseas is a joint venture company providing integrated solutions to improve reserve recoveries from subsea fields using a range of ABB and Schlumberger technologies, products and services from reservoir evaluation and development, through subsea production to topside facilities. In addition, the company provides life-of-field management expertise. As a single-point contracting entity, Syntheseas can supply everything needed from reservoir to delivery point, through goal-aligned contract terms. Syntheseas is focused on earlier first oil dates and higher net present value (NPV) to improve the economics of offshore developments.

www.syntheseas.com

Schlumberger Oil & Gas Information Solutions

Schlumberger Oil & Gas Information Solutions (SIS) is the preferred partner to support oil and gas companies through the fundamental transformations required for the e-business age. SIS supports right-time decision making through its comprehensive offering of software products, data management, expert consulting services and information technologies.

Information Management

SIS manages customer E&P data on-site and in our Data Management Centers, which are hubs for secure delivery of not only data but also applications through LiveQuest* Application Service Provision (ASP), e-commerce tools and support services.

Information Technology

Through Schlumberger Network Solutions, SIS provides integrated IT systems to support E&P product and service technology. Services range from network and security technologies to wireless application integration and consulting, including end-to-end responsibility for all network elements from design and service provision to liaison with suppliers and network operators.

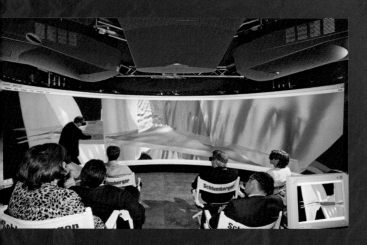

Software

The GeoQuest software division of SIS delivers leading-edge tools to model complex reservoirs and update those models with new data and interpretations to improve reservoir performance. Integrated data management software ensures on-time delivery of E&P asset information. SIS also provides a complete suite of economics evaluation, decision-making, capital planning and portfolio optimization software to optimize oil and gas production while increasing return on capital expenditure.

E&P Expert Services

SIS has a depth of multidomain expertise unmatched in the industry. We provide expert services to clients in a broad spectrum of disciplines including workflow analysis, business optimization, education, knowledge management, information management, custom development and technical services.

SIS provides the full spectrum of services, from in-time wellsite acquisition support and delivery of answer products to integrated data analysis and interpretation for full-field reservoir characterization, optimization, and cross-disciplinary reservoir and production solutions.

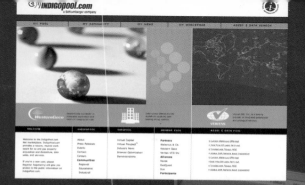

IndigoPool.com

IndigoPool* brings a proven enterprise-class e-commerce platform and associated business solutions to the global oil and gas industry and related financial institutions. The IndigoPool.com e-marketplace provides a secure, neutral, collaborative workspace for oil and gas property acquisition and divestiture, company portfolio administration and E&P data marketing. IndigoPool.com also markets industry information and online services to registered site users.
www.indigopool.com

Network of Excellence in Training (NExT)

NExT* has created a network of recognized excellence in petroleum industry education through an association of industry and academia to provide the transfer of leading-edge and established technologies.

The NExT consortium of Heriot-Watt University in Scotland, Texas A&M University in the USA, The University of Oklahoma in the USA and Schlumberger Oilfield Services has developed unique, advanced accredited training for oil and gas industry professionals.

Tailored to individual client needs and conducted at NExT locations and client locations worldwide, courses can incorporate company data, problems and software. In addition to these closed or open courses, NExT offers media-rich computer-based training (CBT). NExT also provides competence and skill gap assessments, pinpointing knowledge gaps to help oil companies develop their most valuable asset – their people.
www.next.ie

Schlumberger GeoMarkets

Our worldwide network of 27 GeoMarkets, grouped into three geographic areas, ensures efficient and cost-effective delivery of the services developed by our business units. Each GeoMarket is geographically positioned and organized to focus on local needs and provide customized solutions.

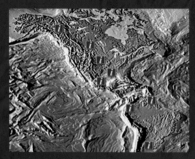

North and South America

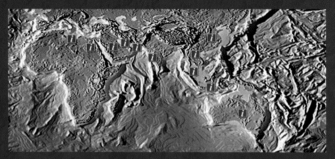

Middle East and Asia

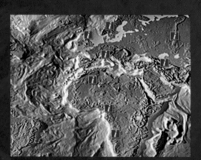

Europe, CIS and Africa

Every person in Schlumberger is committed to deliver the best possible performance – anytime, anywhere. Our culturally diverse teams innovate to create new standards of excellence that surpass our customers' expectations.

i GeoMarket Headquarters

At Schlumberger, what matters is
getting the job done right.

LEGEND

Gasfield	●
Gas pipeline	——————
Gas pipeline under construction, planned or proposed	− − − − −
Oilfield	◑
Oil pipeline	——————
Oil pipeline under construction, planned or proposed	− − − − −
Condensate field	◑
Condensate pipeline	——————
Oilshale field	●
Gas processing plant	◕
Underground gas storage	⊡
Gas processing plant under construction	◔
Underground gas storage under construction	⊟
Oil refinery	�
Tanker terminal	⛴

Coastline/river	∿
International borders	— ·· — · — · —
Other borders	— · — · —
Graticule	————
Capital city/Major city	■
City/Major town	●

The scale is indicated on the bottom of each page.
For instance, the annotation 1: 1,000,000 means that 1mm* on the map equals 1,000,000mm* in actual scale or 1 mm* equals 1 km**.

* mm = millimetre, ** km = kilometre

★ LNG export plant

☆ LNG export plant under construction

☆ LNG export plant planned or proposed

☆ LNG export plant speculative

★ LNG import terminal

★ LNG import terminal under construction

★ LNG import terminal planned or proposed

☆ LNG import terminal speculative

☆ LNG import terminal mothballed

RELIEF

+6,000 metres	
+4,000 metres	
+2,000 metres	
+1,000 metres	
+500 metres	
land/sea level	
depression	
sea / -500 metres*	
-1,000 metres*	
-2,000 metres*	
-3,000 metres*	
- 4,000 metres*	
-5,000 metres*	

* Bathymetry is only shown on maps with deepwater fields

WESTERN
EUROPE

Scale: 1:18,000,000

WESTERN EUROPE

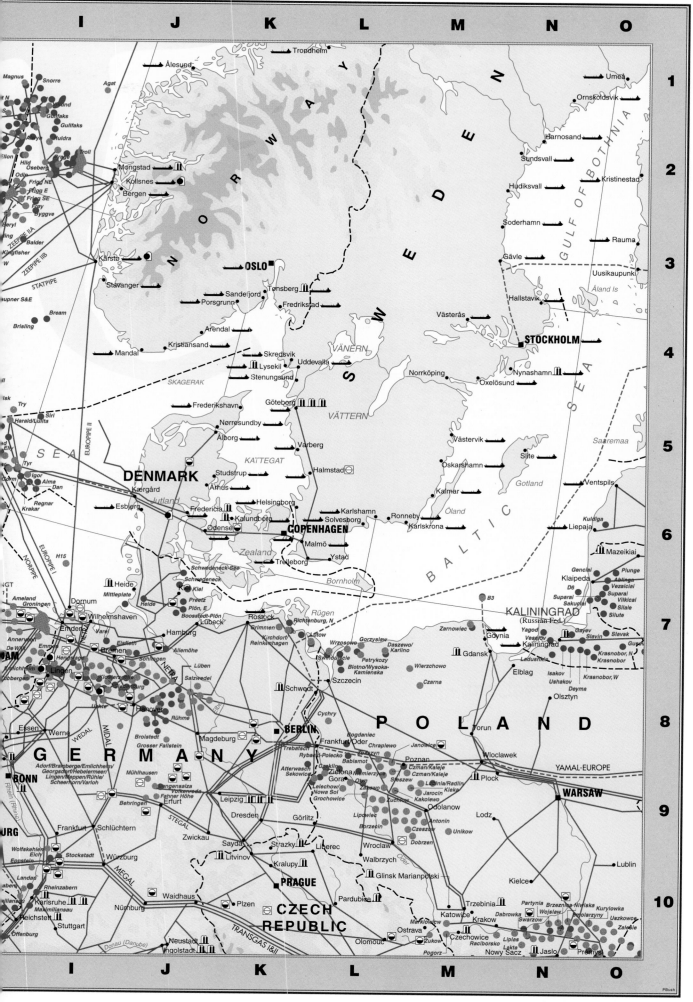

WESTERN EUROPE

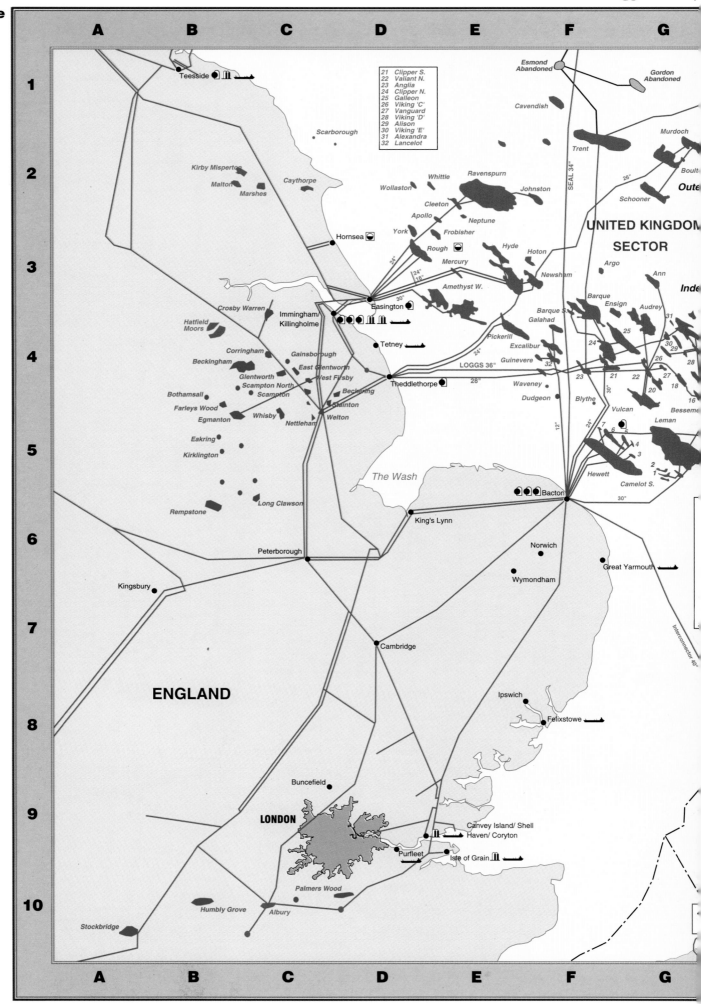

Scale: 1:1,650,000

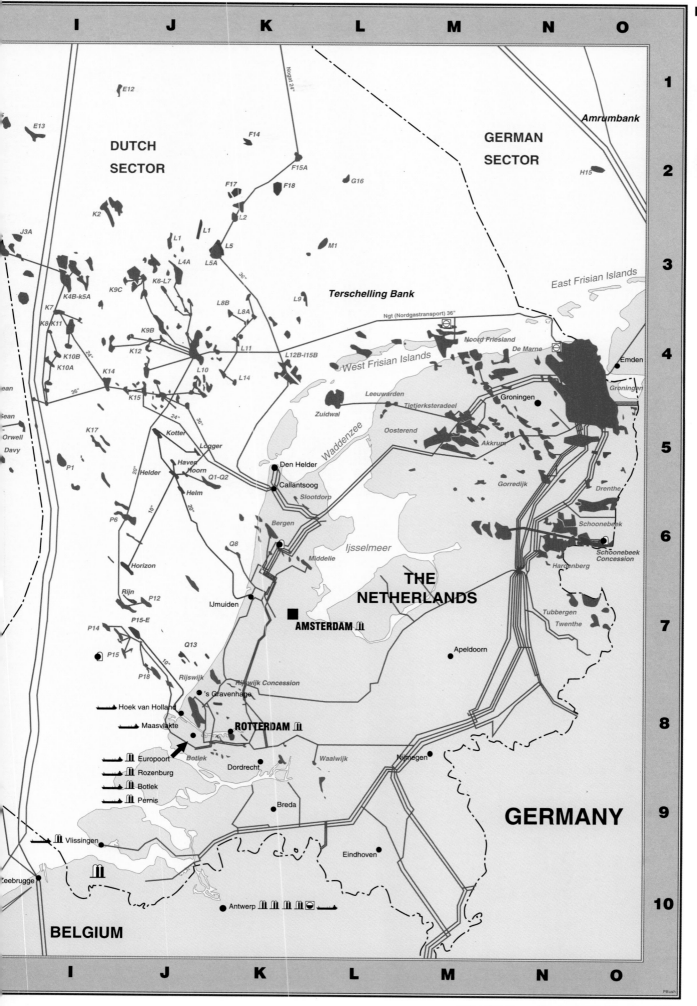

Plate
4

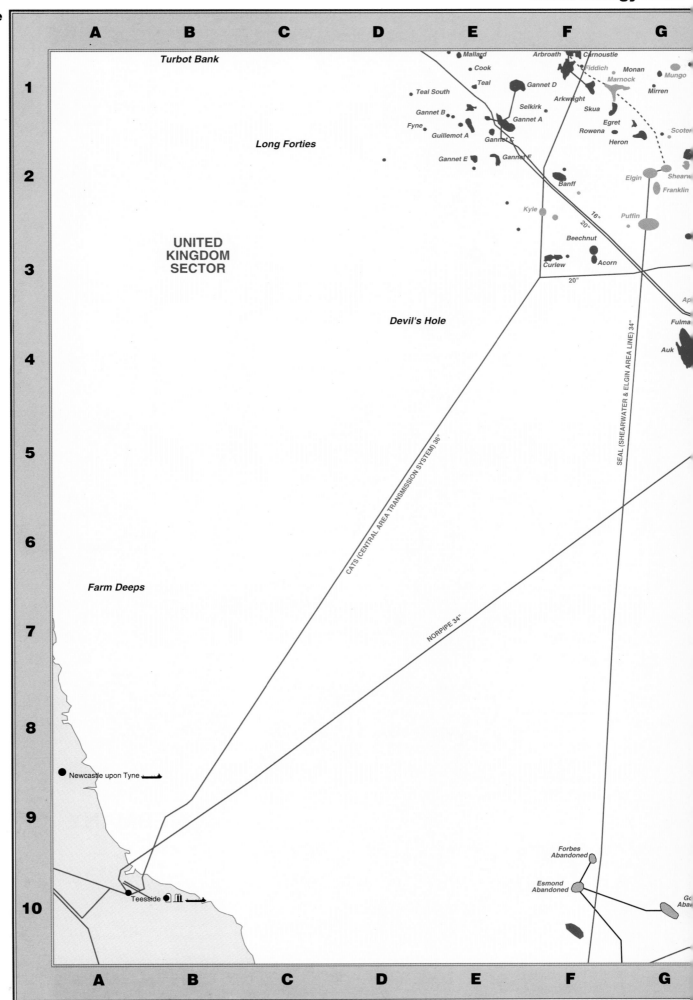

Turbot Bank

Mallard
Cook
Teal
Teal South
Gannet D
Gannet B
Selkirk
Fyne
Guillemot A
Gannet A
Gannet C
Gannet E
Gannet F
Arbroath
Carnoustie
Fiddich
Monan
Marnock
Mungo
Mirren
Skua
Egret
Rowena
Heron
Scoter

Long Forties

Banff
Elgin
Shearw
Franklin
Kyle
16"
20"
Puffin
Beechnut
Curlew
Acorn
20"

UNITED
KINGDOM
SECTOR

Devil's Hole

Ap
Fulma
Auk

CATS (CENTRAL AREA TRANSMISSION SYSTEM) 36"

SEAL (SHEARWATER & ELGIN AREA LINE) 34"

Farm Deeps

NORPIPE 34"

Newcastle upon Tyne

Forbes
Abandoned

Esmond
Abandoned

Go
Ab

Teesside

Scale: 1:1,400,000

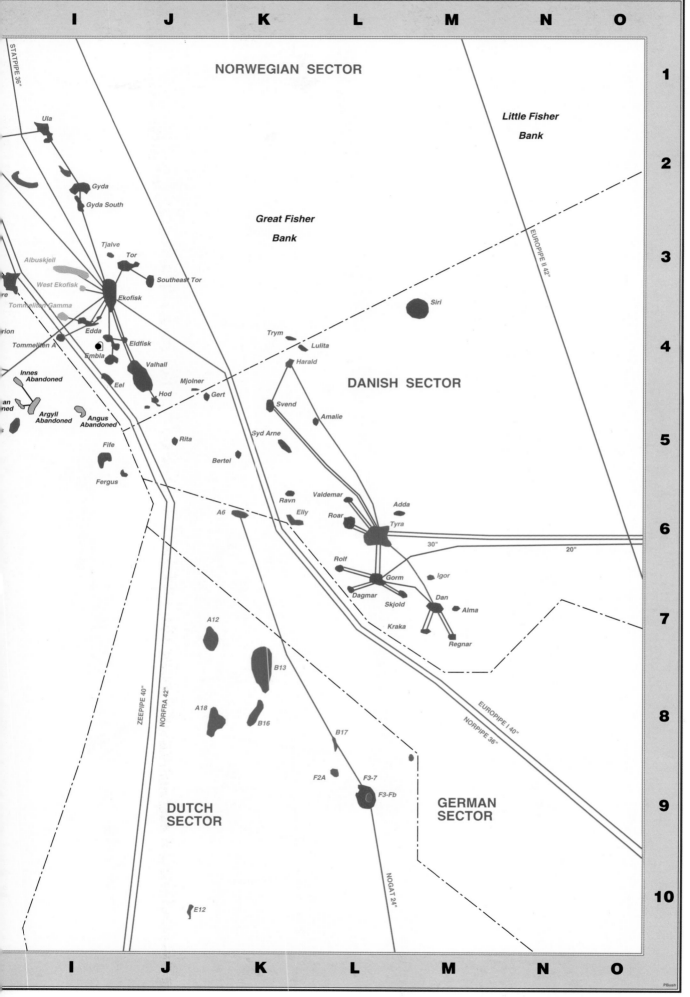

WESTERN EUROPE

NORWEGIAN SECTOR

Little Fisher Bank

Great Fisher Bank

STATPIPE 36"

Ula

Gyda
Gyda South

Albuskjell
Tjalve
Tor
West Ekofisk
Southeast Tor
Tommeliten Gamma
Ekofisk
Siri
Edda
Trym
Lulita
Tommeliten A
Eldfisk
Harald
Embla
Valhall
DANISH SECTOR
Innes
Abandoned
Eel
Mjolner
Svend
Hod
Gert
Amalie
Argyll
Abandoned
Angus
Abandoned
Syd Arne
Rita
Fife
Bertel
Valdemar
Adda
Fergus
Ravn
Roar
Tyra
A6
Elly
30"
20"
Rolf
Igor
Gorm
Dagmar
Dan
Alma
A12
Skjold
Kraka
B13
Regnar
A18
B16
B17
EUROPIPE I 40"
NORPIPE 36"
F2A
F3-7
ZEEPIPE 40"
NORFRA 42"
F3-Fb
DUTCH
SECTOR
GERMAN
SECTOR
EUROPIPE II 42"
NOGAT 24"
E12

CENTRAL NORTH NORTH SEA

Plate 5

WESTERN EUROPE

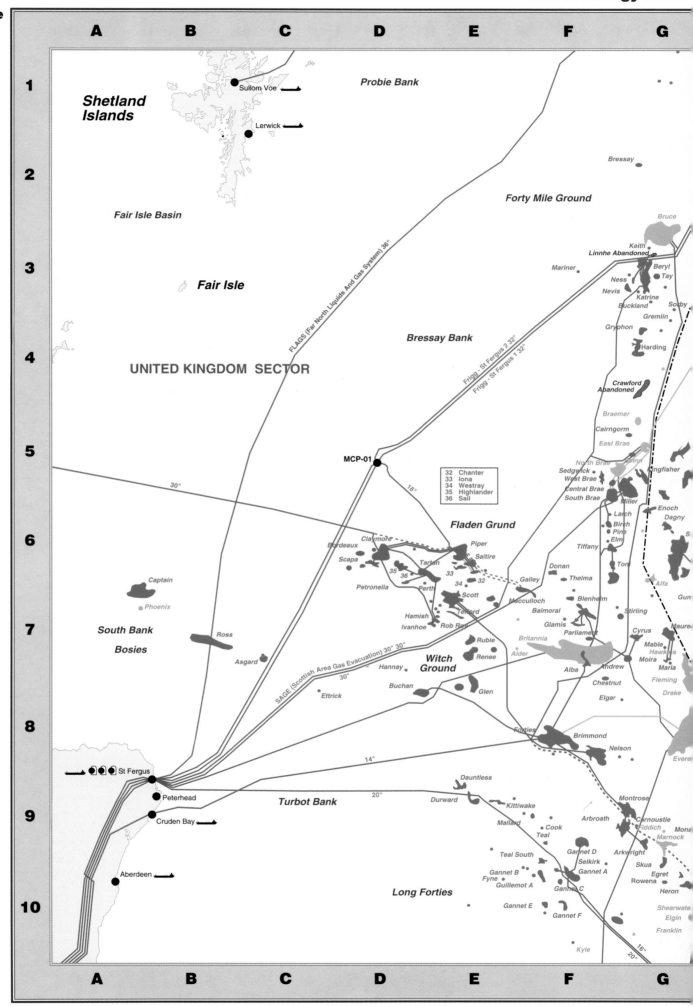

Scale: 1:1,420,000

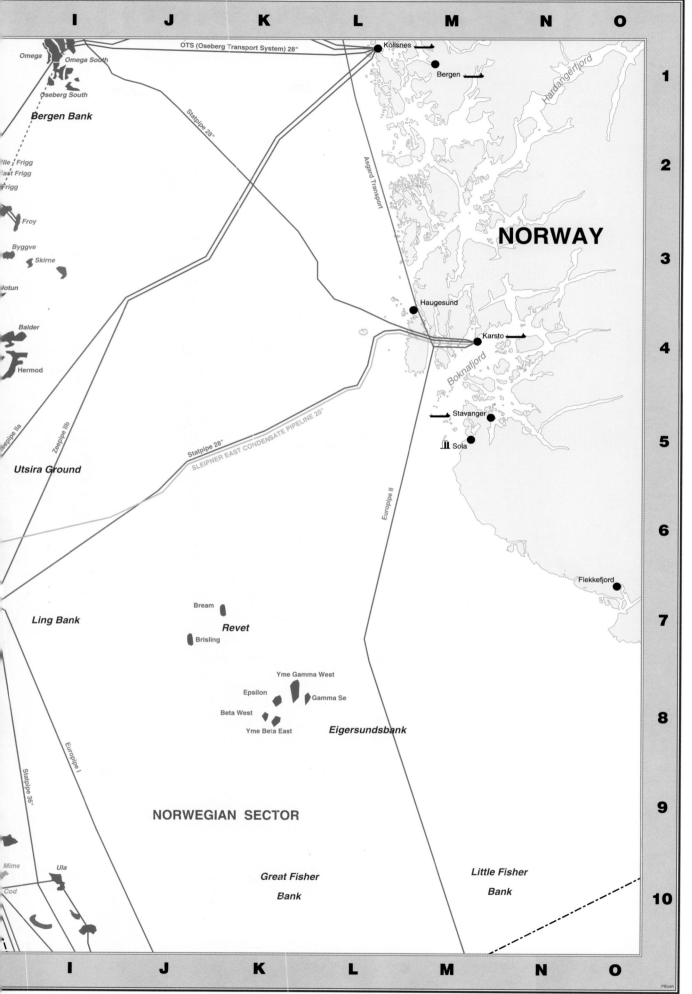

NORWAY

Omega
Omega South
Oseberg South
Bergen Bank
OTS (Oseberg Transport System) 28"
Kollsnes
Bergen
Hardangerfjord

Statpipe 28"
Asgard Transport

Ille Frigg
East Frigg
Frigg
Froy
Byggve
Skirne
Jotun
Balder
Hermod

Haugesund
Karsto
Boknafjord

Zeepipe IIa
Zeepipe IIb
Utsira Ground

Statpipe 28"
SLEIPNER EAST CONDENSATE PIPELINE 20"
Europipe II

Stavanger
Sola

Flekkefjord

Ling Bank
Bream
Revet
Brisling

Yme Gamma West
Epsilon
Gamma Se
Beta West
Yme Beta East
Eigersundsbank

Europipe I
Statpipe 36"

NORWEGIAN SECTOR

Mime
Ula
Cod
**Great Fisher
Bank**
**Little Fisher
Bank**

Plate
6

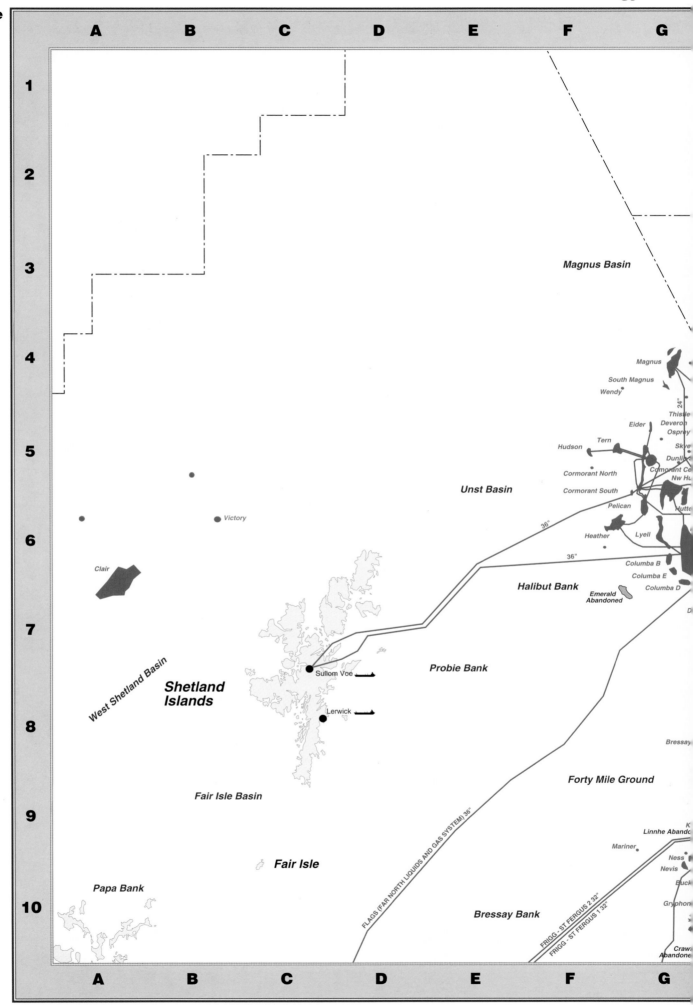

Magnus Basin

Magnus

South Magnus

Wendy

Thistle
Deveron
Osprey

Eider

Tern

Skye

Hudson

Dunlin

Cormorant Ce

Cormorant North

Nw Hu

Unst Basin

Cormorant South

Pelican

Hutte

36"

Heather

Lyell

36"

Columba B

Columba E

Halibut Bank

Emerald
Abandoned

Columba D

Di

Victory

Clair

Probie Bank

Bressay

West Shetland Basin

Shetland
Islands

Sullom Voe

Lerwick

Forty Mile Ground

Fair Isle Basin

FLAGS (FAR NORTH LIQUIDS AND GAS SYSTEM) 36"

Linnhe Abando

K'

Mariner

Ness

Nevis

Fair Isle

Buck

Papa Bank

Gryphon

FRIGG - ST FERGUS 2 32"

FRIGG - ST FERGUS 1 32"

Bressay Bank

Craw
Abandone

Scale: 1:1,460,000

Aktivneset

Ålesund

Storfjord

Agat

Nordfjord

Florø

Snorre

Vigdis

Visund

tfjord E.

Tordis

Gullfaks

Sognefjord

Gullfaks South

lvieg

Kvitebjørn

mfaks

Gamma

Huldra

35/8-1

35/9-1

35/8-2

35/11-2

Fram

Troll West

Troll East

Mongstad

Troll Oil Pipeline

ng
nk

Veslefrikk

Oseberg East

Sture

Brage

TROLL GAS PIPELINE 26"+26"

Oseberg West

Kollsnes

STATPIPE 28"

Kappa

OTS (Oseberg Transport System) 28"

Oseberg

Bergen

Omega

Omega South

Oseberg South

STATPIPE 28"

Bergen Bank

Hild

Lille- Frigg

East Frigg

SE-Frigg

Frigg

Frøy

S Vale

NORWAY

ndal

Byggve

Skirne

Jotun

Haugesund

Balder

Karsto

STATPIPE 36"

Hermod

Hardangerfjord

Plate
7

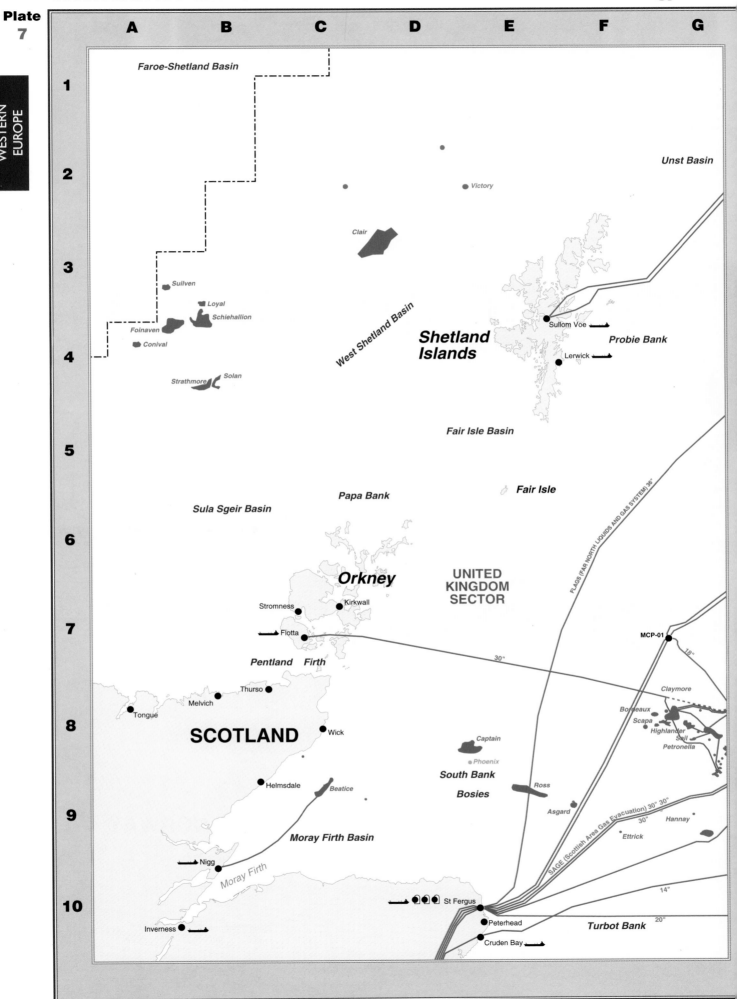

A B C D E F G

1

Faroe-Shetland Basin

Unst Basin

2

Victory

Clair

3

Suilven

Loyal

Schiehallion

Foinaven

Conival

West Shetland Basin

Shetland Islands

Sullom Voe

Probie Bank

Lerwick

4

Strathmore *Solan*

Fair Isle Basin

5

Fair Isle

Papa Bank

Sula Sgeir Basin

6

Orkney

UNITED KINGDOM SECTOR

FLAGS (FAR NORTH LIQUIDS AND GAS SYSTEM) 36"

Stromness

Kirkwall

7

Flotta

30"

MCP-01

18"

Claymore

Pentland Firth

Thurso

Bordeaux

Scapa

Melvich

Highlander

Sail

Tongue

8

Wick

Captain

Petronella

SCOTLAND

Phoenix

Helmsdale

Beatice

South Bank

Bosies

Ross

Asgard

SAGE (Scottish Area Gas Evacuation) 30" 30"

Hannay

9

30"

Ettrick

Moray Firth Basin

Nigg

Moray Firth

14"

10

St Fergus

Peterhead

20"

Inverness

Turbot Bank

Cruden Bay

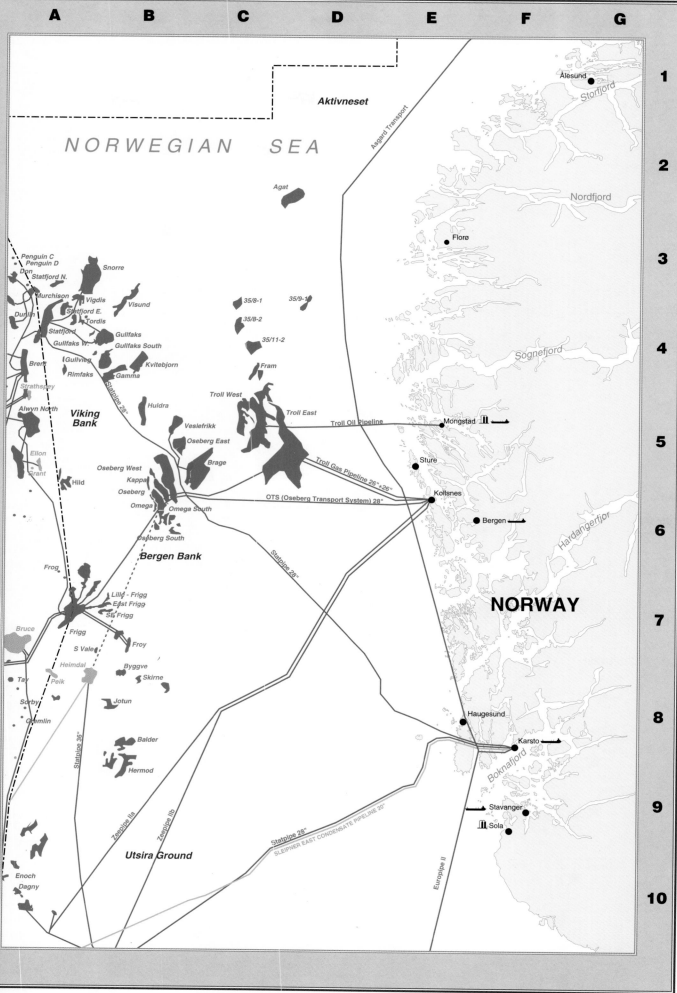

A   B   C   D   E   F   G

1   2   3   4   5   6   7   8   9   10

Aktivneset

NORWEGIAN SEA

Ålesund

Storfjord

Nordfjord

Florø

Agat

35/8-1   35/9-1
35/8-2
35/11-2
Fram

Sognefjord

Penguin C
Penguin D
Don   Statfjord N.
Murchison   Snorre
Dunlin   Vigdis
Statfjord E.   Visund
Statfjord   Tordis
Gullfaks
Gullfaks W.   Gullfaks South
Brent   Gullveig   Kvitebjorn
Strathspey   Rimfaks   Gamma
Alwyn North   Huldra
Viking Bank   Troll West
Ellon   Troll East
Grant   Hild   Veslefrikk
Oseberg East
Oseberg West   Brage
Kappa   Bergen Bank
Oseberg
Omega   Omega South
Oseberg South
Frog
Bruce   Lille - Frigg
East Frigg
SE Frigg
Frigg   Froy
S Vale   Byggve
Heimdal   Skirne
Tay   Peik   Jotun
Sorby
Gremlin   Balder
Hermod
Enoch
Dagny   Utsira Ground

Statpipe 29"
Statpipe 28"
Statpipe 36"
Zeepipe IIa
Zeepipe IIb
Statpipe 28"
SLEIPNER EAST CONDENSATE PIPELINE 20"
Europipe II

Åsgard Transport
Troll Oil Pipeline
Troll Gas Pipeline 26" +26"
OTS (Oseberg Transport System) 28"

Mongstad
Sture
Kollsnes
Bergen

NORWAY

Haugesund
Karsto
Boknafjord
Stavanger
Sola

Hardangerfjord

Scale: 1:1,900,000

Plate 9

WESTERN EUROPE

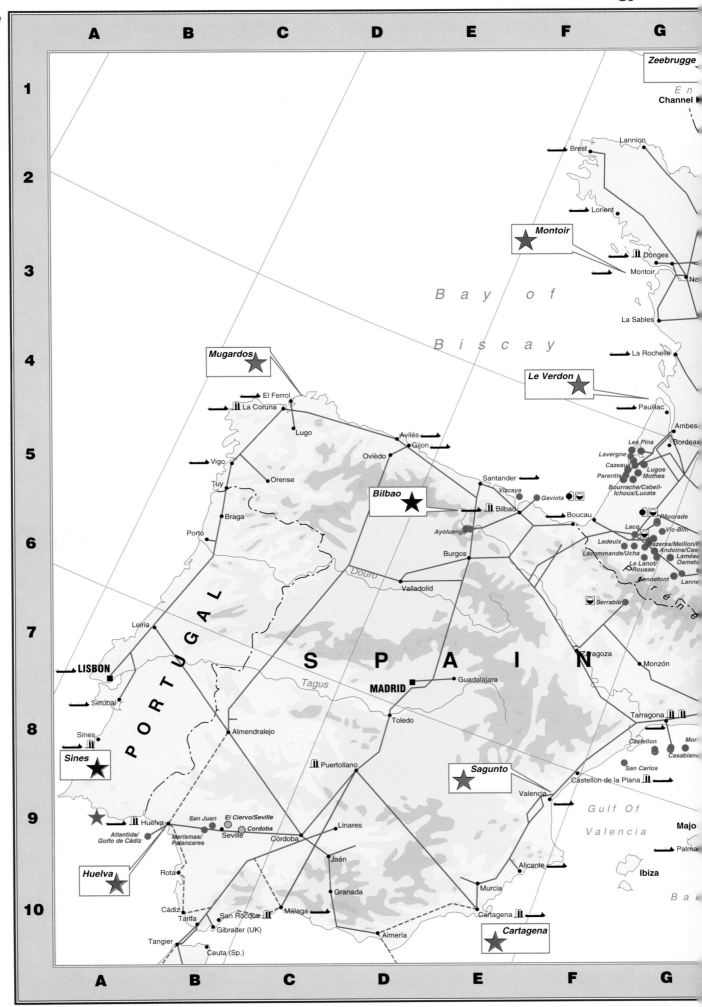

Scale: 1:6,000,000

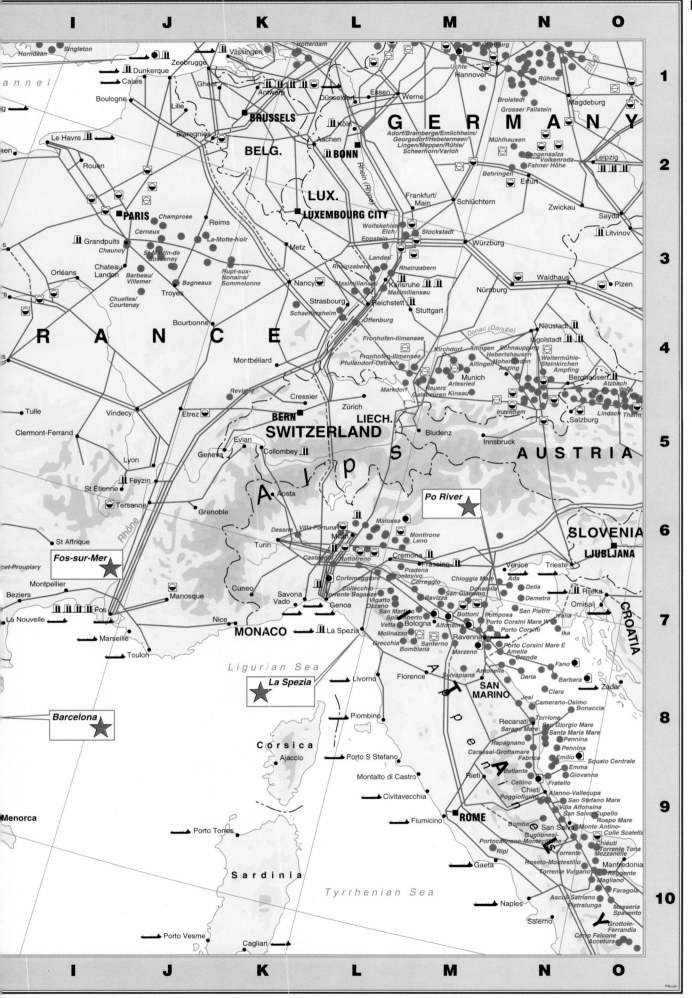

Plate
10

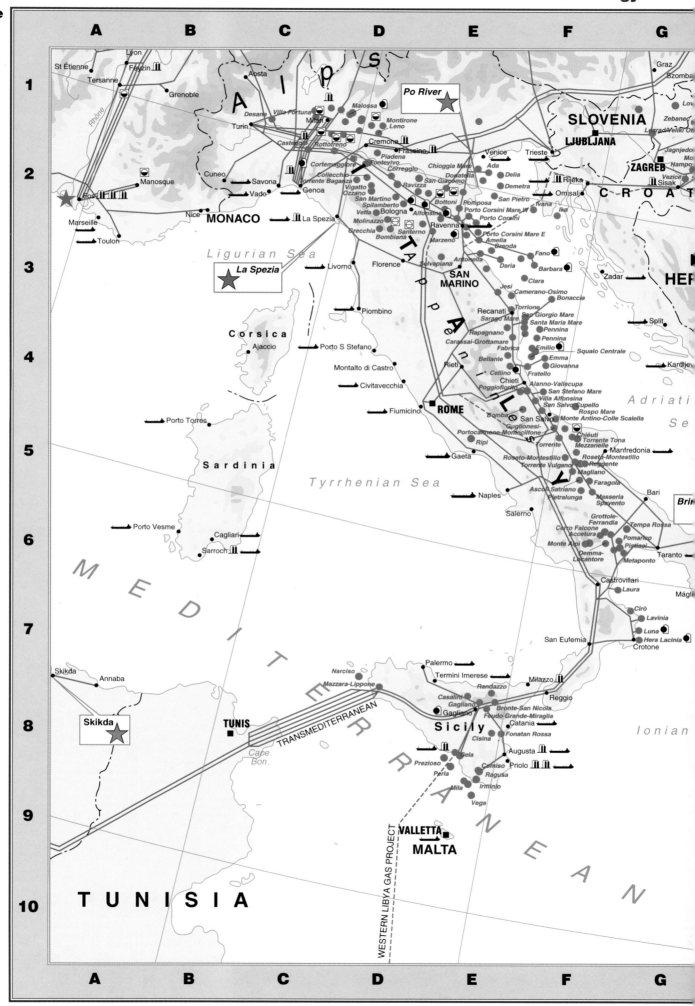

Scale: 1:5,550,000

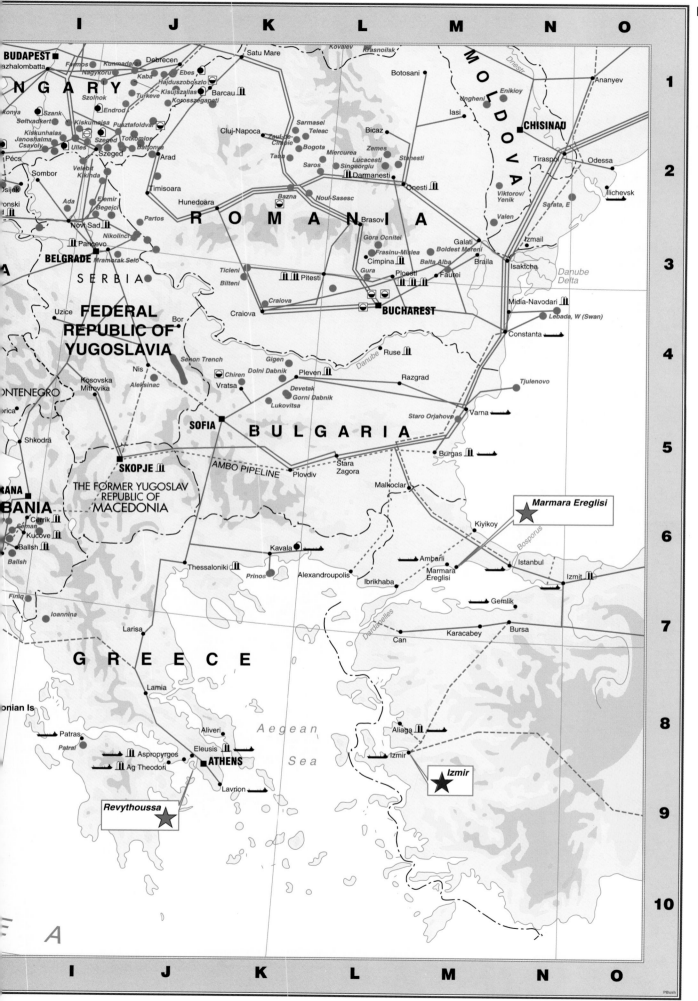

BUDAPEST
azhalombatta
Fabops
Kunmadaras
Debrecen
Satu Mare
Kovalev
Krasnoilsk
Botosani
Ananyev

1

NGARY
Nagykoru
Ebes
Kaba
Hajduszoboszlo
Kisujszallas
Barcau
Szolnok
Turkeve
Korosszegapati
Cluj-Napoca
Zaul-de-Cimpie
Sarmasel
Teleac
Bicaz
Ungheni
Enikioy
Iasi
CHISINAU

Pécs
konya
Szank
Soltvadkert
Kiskunmajsa
Pusztafoldvar
Szeged
Totkomlos
Battonya
Arad
Bogota
Tada
Miercurea
Singeorgiu
Saros
Zemes
Stanesti
Tiraspol
Odessa
Ilichevsk

2

Sombor
osijek
onski
Ada
Elemir
Begejci
Partos
Timisoara
Hunedoara
Bazna
Noul-Sasesc
Darmanesti
Onesti
Viktorov/
Yenik
Valen
Safata, E
Izmail

Novi Sad
Nikolinch
Pancevo
ROMANIA
Brasov
Gora Ocnitel
Frasinu-Mislea
Cimpina
Galati
Boldest Mereni
Balta Alba
Braila
Isaktcha
Danube
Delta

3

BELGRADE
Mramarak Selo
SERBIA
Ticleni
Bilteni
Pitesti
Gura
Gigen
Ploesti
Fautei
Midia-Navodari
Lebada, W (Swan)

FEDERAL
REPUBLIC OF
YUGOSLAVIA
Uzice
Bor
Senon Trench
Craiova
Craiova
BUCHAREST
Constanta

4

MONTENEGRO
orica
Kosovska
Mitrovika
Nis
Aleksinac
Chiren
Vratsa
Dolni Dabnik
Devetak
Gorni Dabnik
Lukovitsa
Pleven
Danube
Ruse
Razgrad
Tjulenovo
Staro Orjahove
Varna

Shkodrä
SOFIA
BULGARIA
Burgas

5

RANA
BANIA
SKOPJE
THE FORMER YUGOSLAV
REPUBLIC OF
MACEDONIA
AMBO PIPELINE
Plovdiv
Stara
Zagora
Malkoclar

Cerrik
Séman
Kucove
Balish
Ballsh
Kavala
Kiyikoy
Marmara Ereglisi
Bosporus

6

Finiq
Thessaloniki
Prinos
Alexandroupolis
Ibrikhaba
Marmara
Ereglisi
Ambarli
Istanbul
Izmit

Ioannina
Larisa
Gemlik

7

GREECE
Can
Karacabey
Bursa
Dardanelles

Lamia

onian Is
Aliveri
Aegean
Aliaga
Izmir

8

Patras
Patrai
Aspropyrgos
Eleusis
ATHENS
Sea
Izmir
Izmir

Ag Theodori
Lavrion

Revythoussa

9

A

10

Plate
11

WESTERN EUROPE

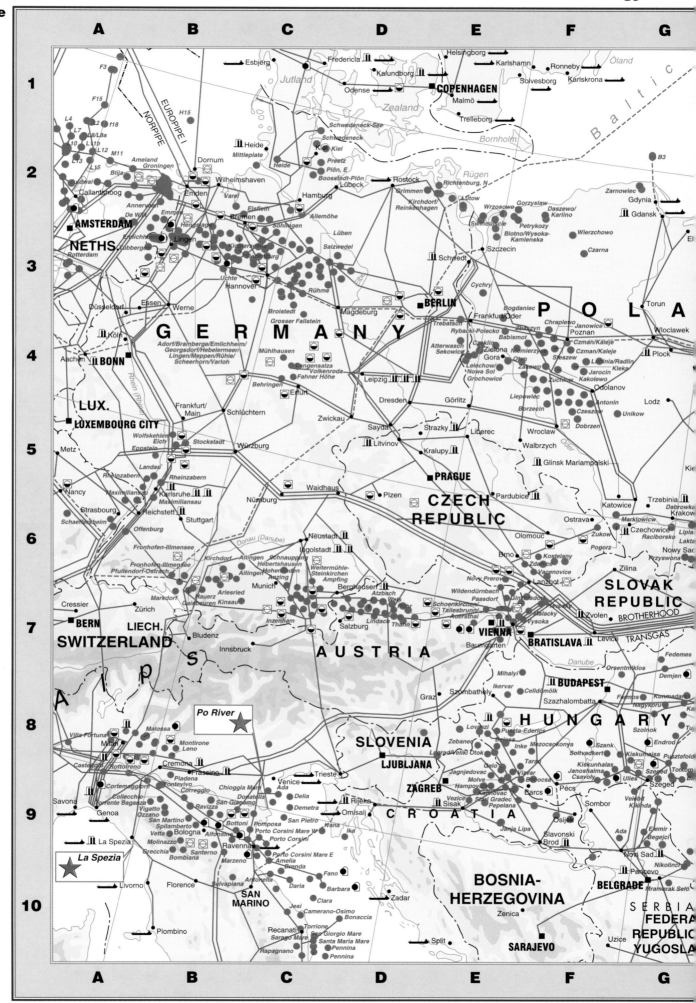

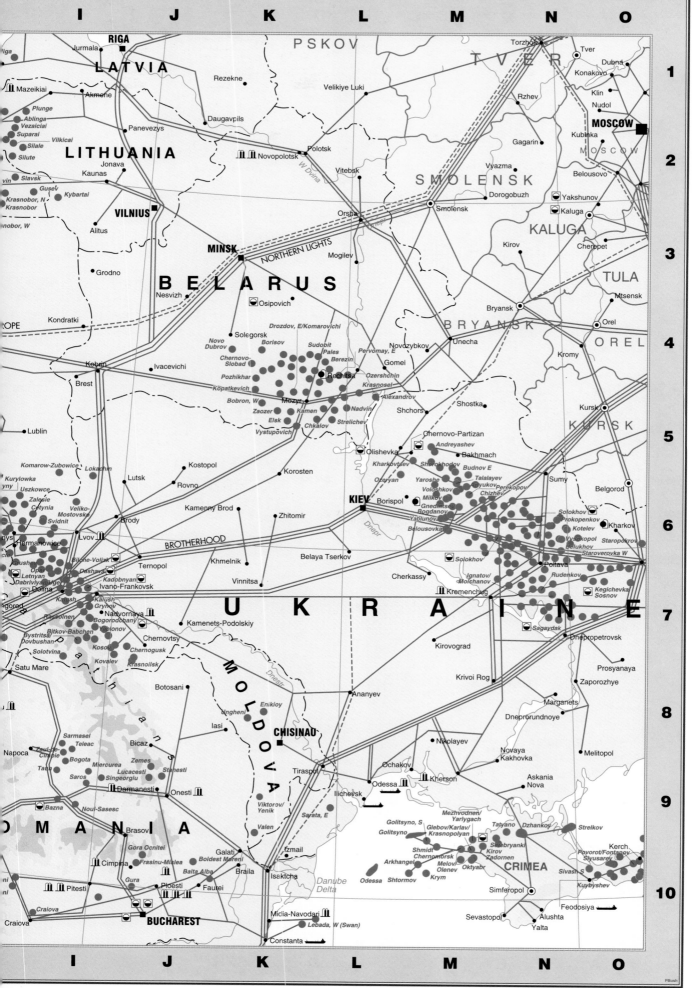

EASTERN EUROPE AND THE FSU

Plate
12

EASTERN EUROPE
& THE FSU

Scale: 1:20,300,000

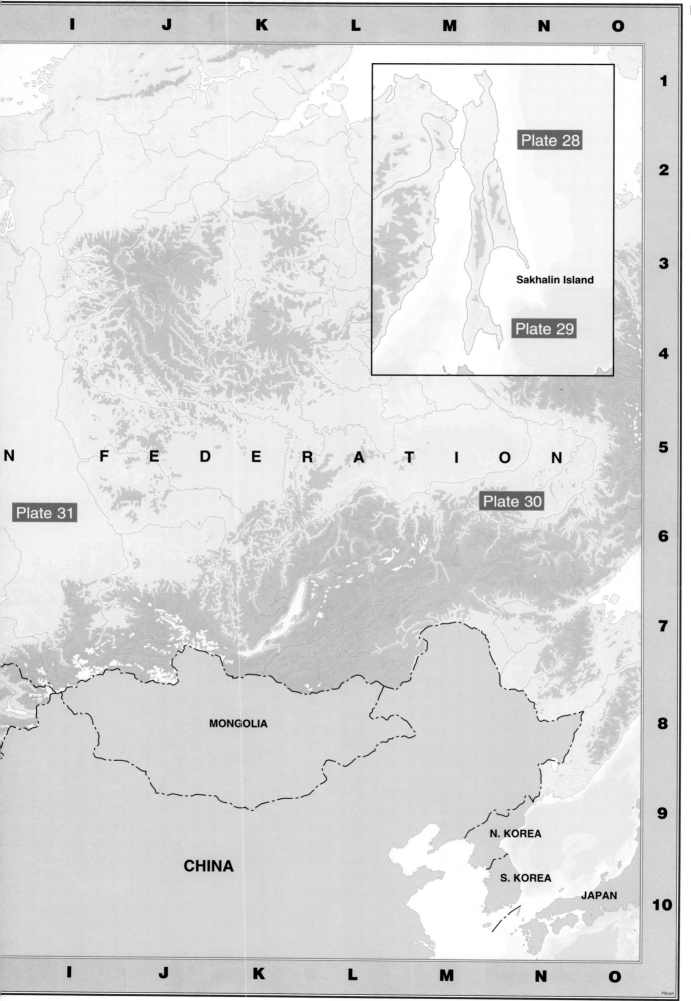

I   J   K   L   M   N   O

1

Plate 28

2

Sakhalin Island

3

Plate 29

4

N   F E D E R A T I O N   5

Plate 31

Plate 30

6

7

8

MONGOLIA

9

N. KOREA

CHINA

S. KOREA

JAPAN

10

I   J   K   L   M   N   O

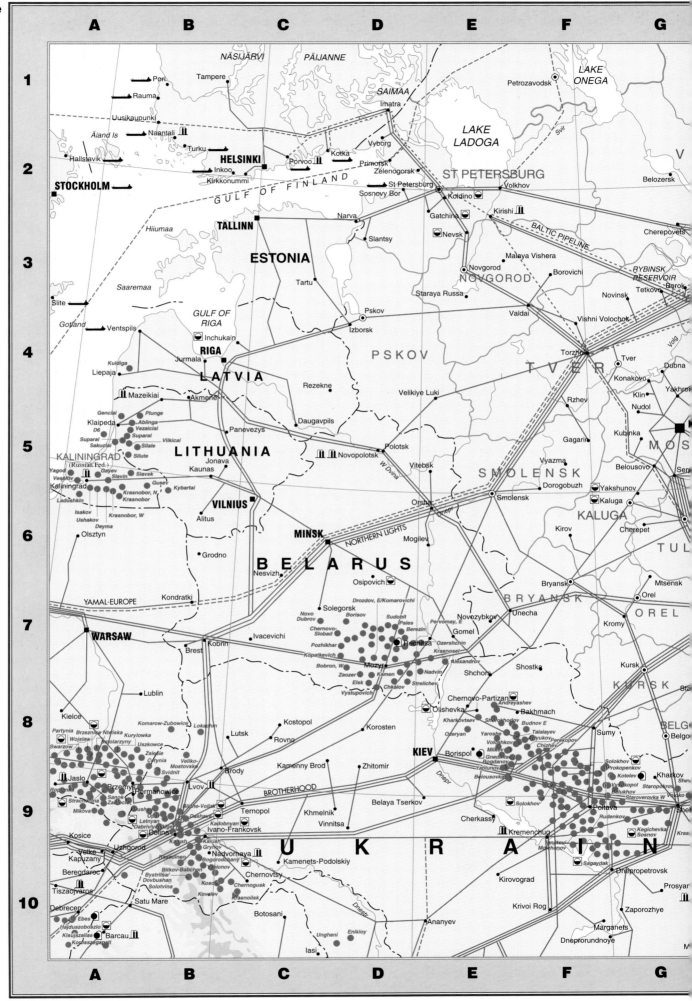

Scale: 1:7,000,000

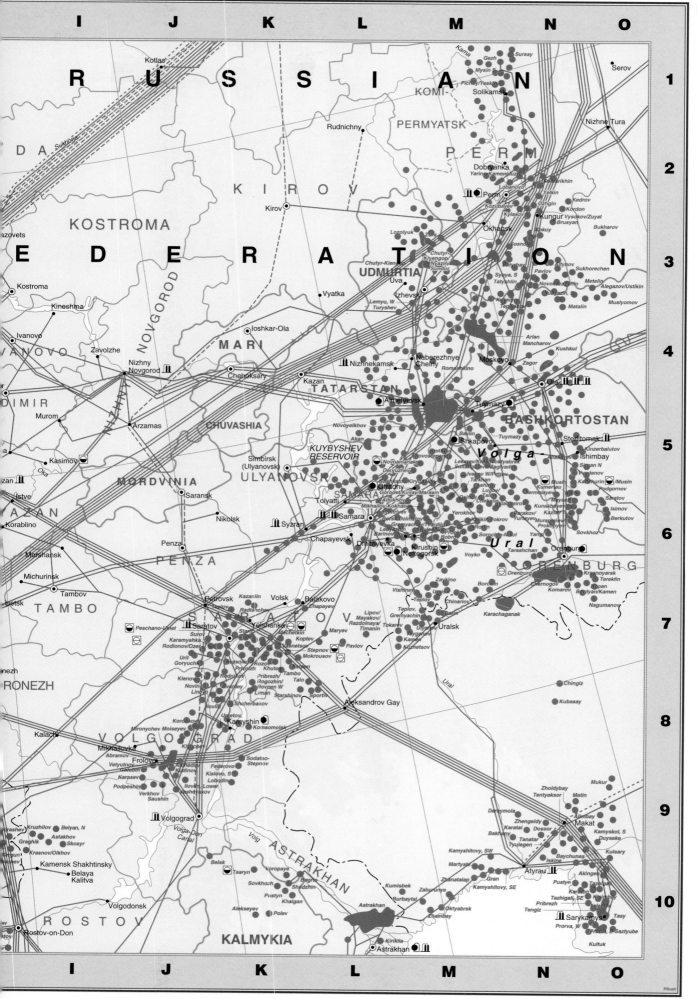

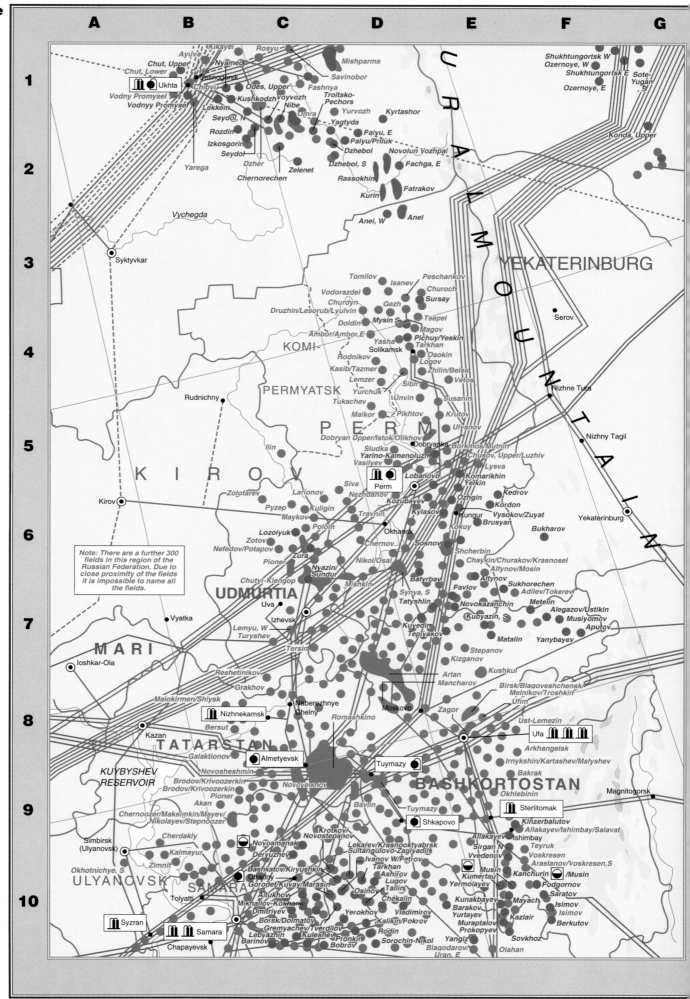

EASTERN EUROPE & THE FSU

Note: There are a further 300 fields in this region of the Russian Federation. Due to close proximity of the fields it is impossible to name all the fields.

Scale: 1:5,000,000

Plate
15

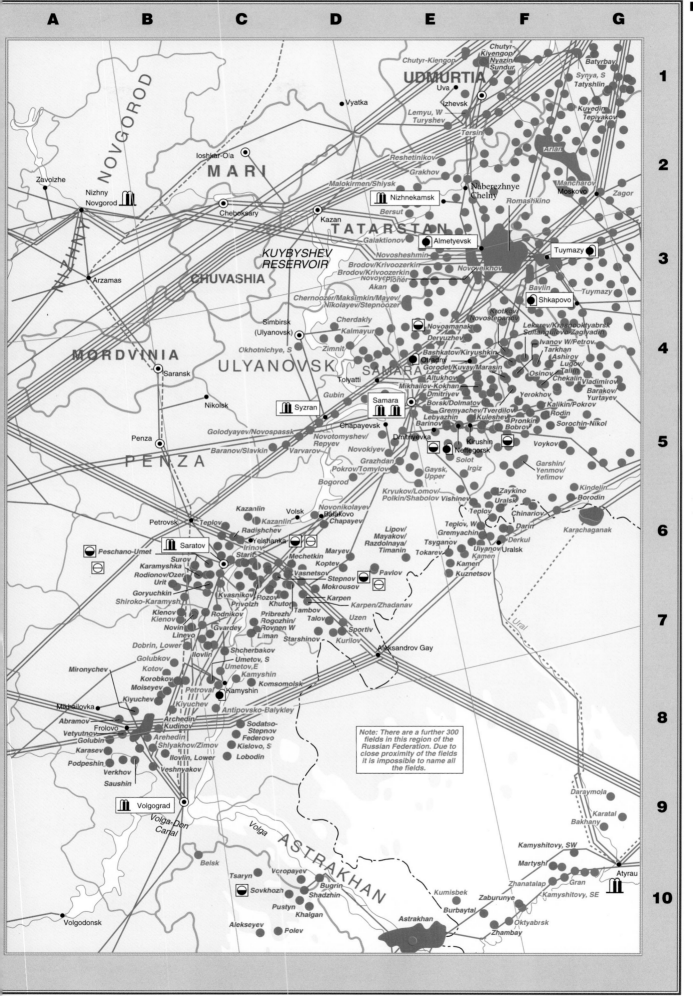

EASTERN EUROPE
& THE FSU

Note: There are a further 300
fields in this region of the
Russian Federation. Due to
close proximity of the fields
it is impossible to name all
the fields.

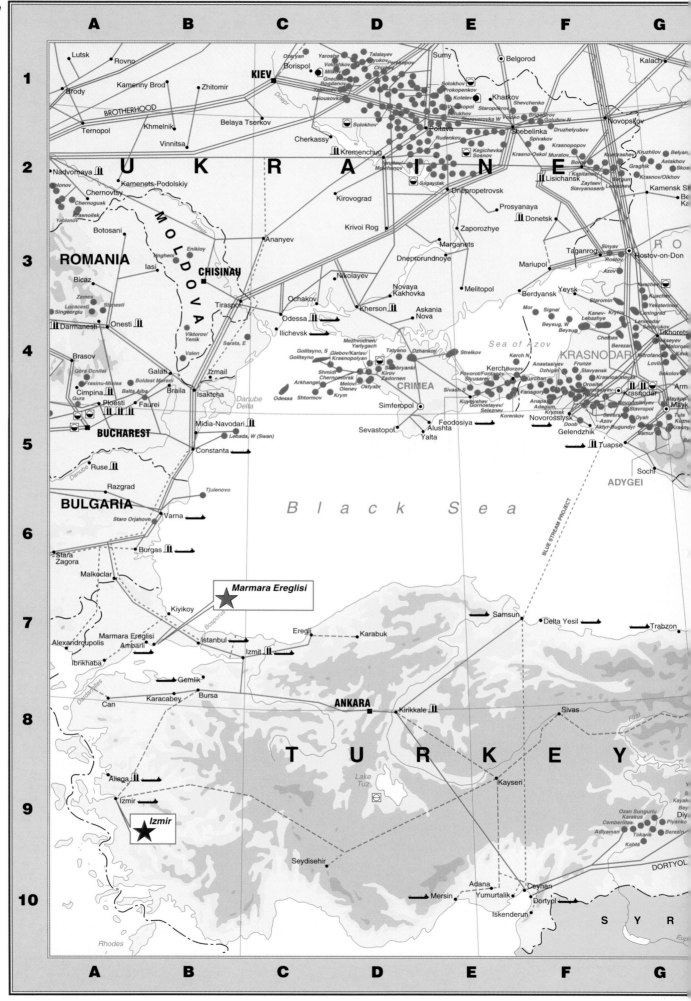

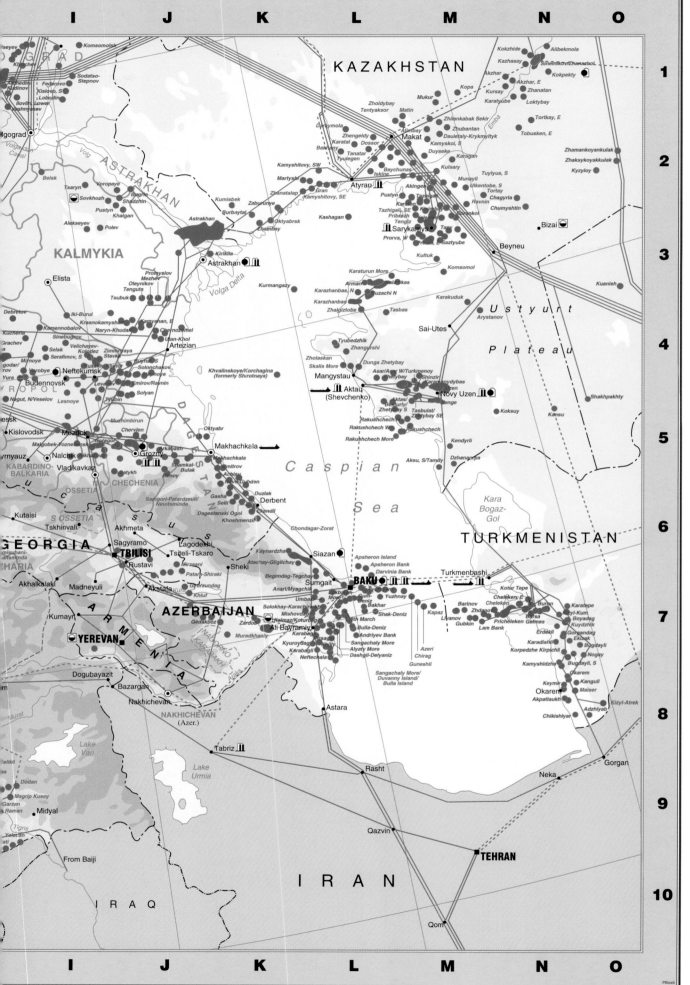

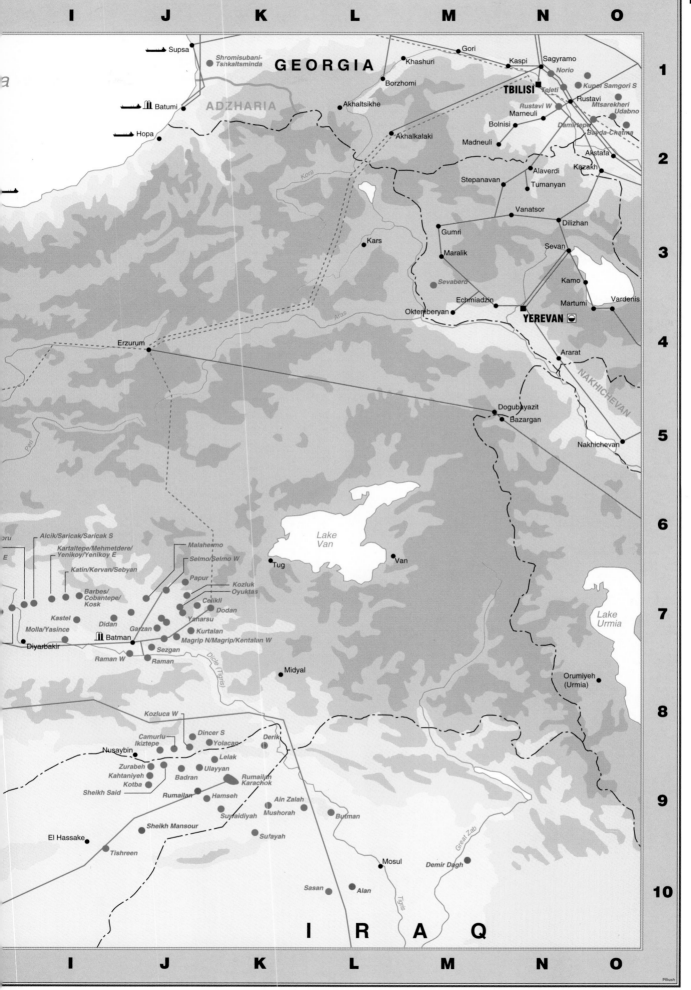

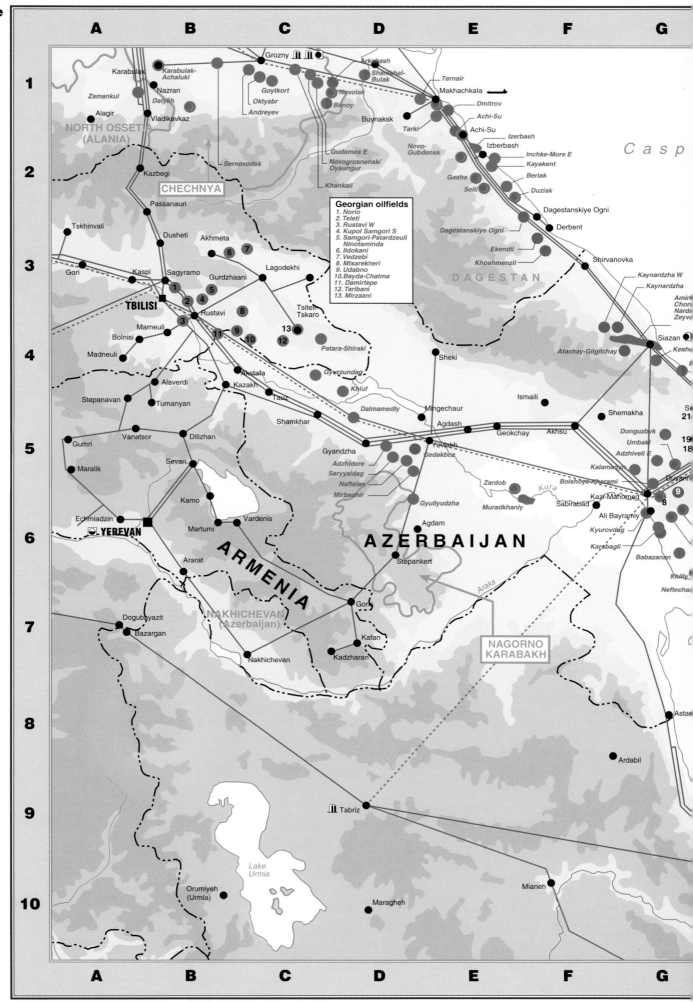

Georgian oilfields
1. Norio
2. Teleti
3. Rustavi W
4. Kupol Samgori S
5. Samgori-Patardzeuli
   Ninotsminda
6. Ildokani
7. Vedzebi
8. Mtsarekheri
9. Udabno
10. Bayda-Chatma
11. Damirtepe
12. Taribani
13. Mirzaani

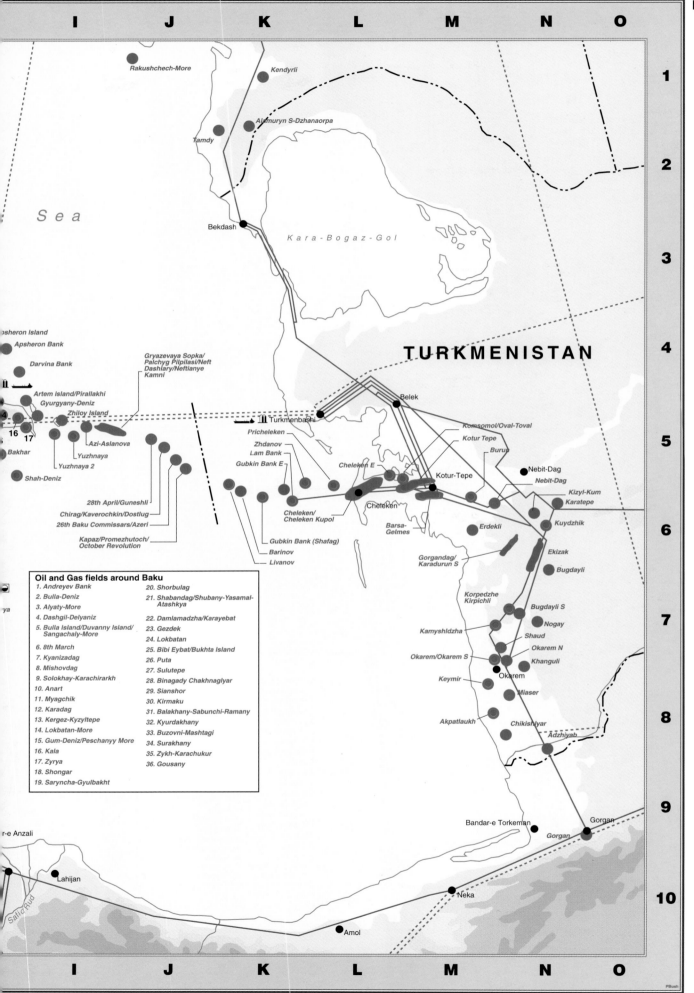

I J K L M N O

1

Rakushchech-More

Kendyrli

Alamuryn S-Dzhanaorpa

Tamdy

2

Sea

Bekdash

Kara-Bogaz-Gol

3

Apsheron Island
Apsheron Bank

TURKMENISTAN

4

Darvina Bank

Gryazevaya Sopka/
Palchyg Pilpilasi/Neft
Dashlary/Neftianye
Kamni

Belek

Artem Island/Pirallakhi
Gyurgyany-Deniz
Zhiloy Island

Turkmenbashi

Pricheleken

Komsomol/Oval-Toval
Kotur Tepe
Burun

5

16 17
Bakhar

Azi-Aslanova
Yuzhnaya
Yuzhnaya 2

Zhdanov
Lam Bank
Gubkin Bank E

Cheleken E

Kotur-Tepe

Nebit-Dag
Nebit-Dag

Shah-Deniz

Cheleken/
Cheleken Kupol

Cheleken

Kizyl-Kum
Karatepe

28th April/Guneshli
Chirag/Kaverochkin/Dostlug
26th Baku Commissars/Azeri

Barsa-
Gelmes

Erdekli

Kuydzhik

6

Kapaz/Promezhutoch/
October Revolution

Gubkin Bank (Shafag)

Gorgandag/
Karadurun S

Ekizak

Barinov
Livanov

Bugdayli

Oil and Gas fields around Baku

1. Andreyev Bank	20. Shorbulag
2. Bulla-Deniz	21. Shabandag/Shubany-Yasamal-Atashkya
3. Alyaty-More	
4. Dashgil-Delyaniz	22. Damlamadzha/Karayebat
5. Bulla Island/Duvanny Island/ Sangachaly-More	23. Gezdek
	24. Lokbatan
6. 8th March	25. Bibi Eybat/Bukhta Island
7. Kyanizadag	26. Puta
8. Mishovdag	27. Sulutepe
9. Solokhay-Karachirarkh	28. Binagady Chakhnaglyar
10. Anart	29. Sianshor
11. Myagchik	30. Kirmaku
12. Karadag	31. Balakhany-Sabunchi-Ramany
13. Kergez-Kyzyltepe	32. Kyurdakhany
14. Lokbatan-More	33. Buzovni-Mashtagi
15. Gum-Deniz/Peschanyy More	34. Surakhany
16. Kala	35. Zykh-Karachukur
17. Zyrya	36. Gousany
18. Shongar	
19. Saryncha-Gyulbakht	

Korpedzhe
Kirpichli

Bugdayli S
Nogay

Kamyshldzha
Shaud

7

Okarem/Okarem S
Okarem N
Khanguli

Keymir
Okarem

Miaser

Akpatlaukh
Chikishlyar

Adzhiyab

8

r-e Anzali

Bandar-e Torkeman
Gorgan
Gorgan

9

Lahijan

Neka

10

SafīdRūd

Amol

I J K L M N O

Plate
19

EASTERN EUROPE & THE FSU

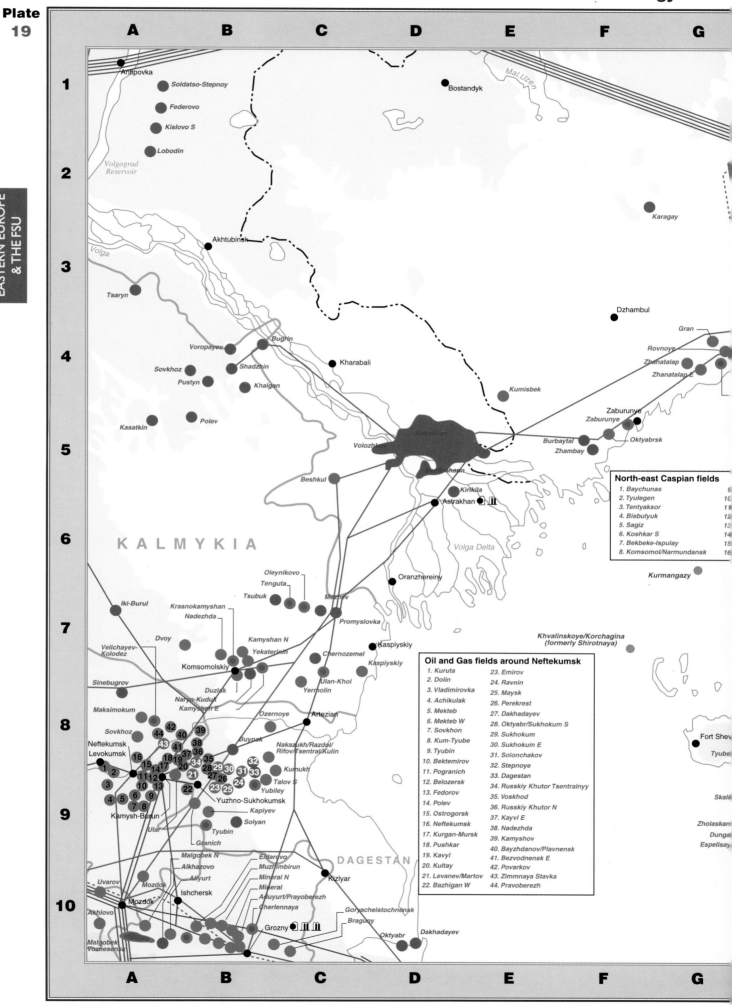

North-east Caspian fields

1. Baychunas
2. Tyulegen
3. Tentyaksor
4. Bisbulyuk
5. Sagiz
6. Koshkar S
7. Bekbeke-Ispulay
8. Komsomol/Narmundansk

Oil and Gas fields around Neftekumsk

1. Kuruta	23. Emirov
2. Dolin	24. Ravnin
3. Vladimirovka	25. Maysk
4. Achikulak	26. Perekrest
5. Mekteb	27. Dakhadayev
6. Mekteb W	28. Oktyabr/Sukhokum S
7. Sovkhon	29. Sukhokum
8. Kum-Tyube	30. Sukhokum E
9. Tyubin	31. Solonchakov
10. Bektemirov	32. Stepnoye
11. Pogranich	33. Dagestan
12. Belozersk	34. Russkiy Khutor Tsentralnyy
13. Fedorov	35. Voskhod
14. Polev	36. Russkiy Khutor N
15. Ostrogorsk	37. Kayvl E
16. Neftekumsk	38. Nadezhda
17. Kurgan-Mursk	39. Kamyshov
18. Pushkar	40. Bayzhdanov/Plavnensk
19. Kavyl	41. Bezvodnensk E
20. Kultay	42. Povarkov
21. Levanev/Martov	43. Zimmnaya Stavka
22. Bazhigan W	44. Pravoberezh

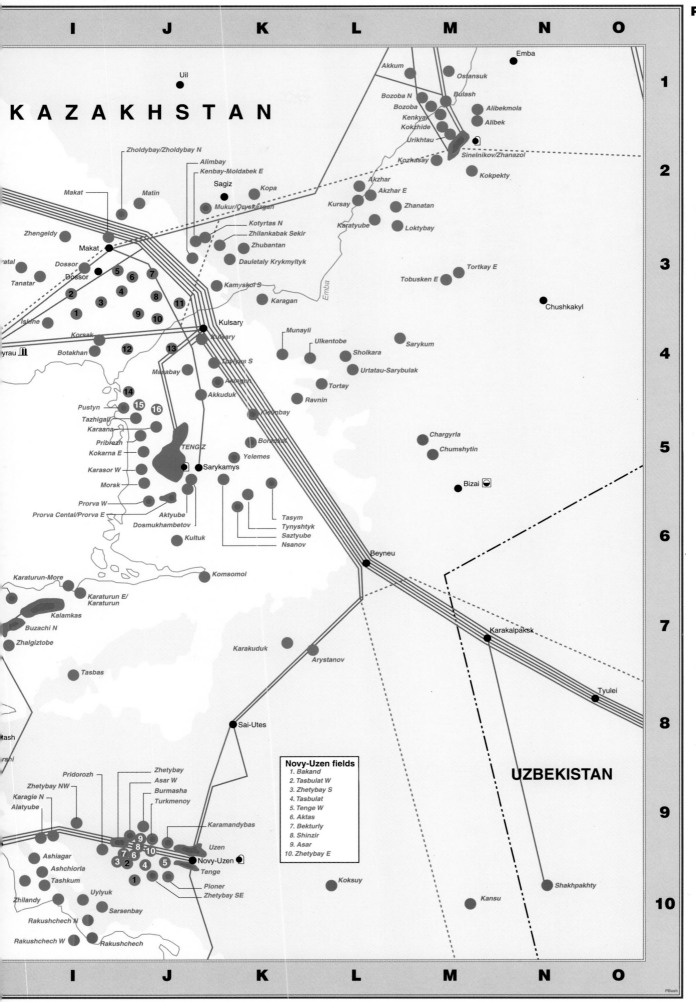

EASTERN EUROPE
& THE FSU

KAZAKHSTAN

Uil

Emba

I J K L M N O

1

Akkum
Ostansuk
Bozoba N
Bozoba
Kenkyak
Kokzhide
Urikhtau
Bulash
Alibekmola
Alibek
Sinelnikov/Zhanazol

Zholdybay/Zholdybay N
Alimbay
Kenbay-Moldabek E
Sagiz
Matin
Kopa
Mukur/Oyskazgan
Kozhasay
Kokpekty

2

Akzhar
Akzhar E
Kursay
Zhanatan
Karatyube
Loktybay

Makat

Zhengeldy
Kotyrtas N
Zhilankabak Sekir
Zhubantan
Dauletaly Krykmyltyk

Makat
Dossor
Dossor
5   6   7
4
2   3
8
1   9   11
10

Iskine
Korsak
Botakhan
12   13

yrau

Kamyskol S
Karagan

Emba

Tobusken E
Tortkay E

Chushkakyl

3

Kulsary
Kulsary
Munayli
Ulkentobe
Sarykum

Tuplyus S
Asingen
Akkuduk
Sholkara
Urtatau-Sarybulak
Tortay
Ravnin

4

Masabay

14

Pustyn
Tazhigali
Karaana
15   16
Kleonbay

Chargyrla
Chumshytin

5

Pribrezh
Kokarna E
Karasor W
Morsk
TENGIZ
Sarykamys
Boranqol
Yelemes

Bizai

Prorva W
Prorva Cental/Prorva E
Aktyube
Dosmukhambetov
Kultuk
Tasym
Tynyshtyk
Saztyube
Nsanov

6

Komsomol

Beyneu

7

Karaturun-More
Karaturun E/
Karaturun
Kalamkas
Buzachi N
Zhalgiztobe
Karakalpaksk

Tasbas

Karakuduk
Arystanov

Tyulei

8

Sai-Utes

UZBEKISTAN

9

Pridorozh
Zhetybay
Asar W
Burmasha
Turkmenoy
Zhetybay NW
Karagie N
Alatyube
Karamandybas
Uzen

9
8   10
7   6
3   2   4   5
1
Novy-Uzen
Tenge
Pioner
Zhetybay SE

Koksuy

Shakhpakhty

Ashiagar
Ashchiorla
Tashkum
Zhilandy
Uylyuk
Sarsenbay
Rakushchech N
Rakushchech W
Rakushchech

Kansu

10

Novy-Uzen fields
1. Bakand
2. Tasbulat W
3. Zhetybay S
4. Tasbulat
5. Tenge W
6. Aktas
7. Bekturly
8. Shinzir
9. Asar
10. Zhetybay E

I J K L M N O

EASTERN EUROPE
& THE FSU

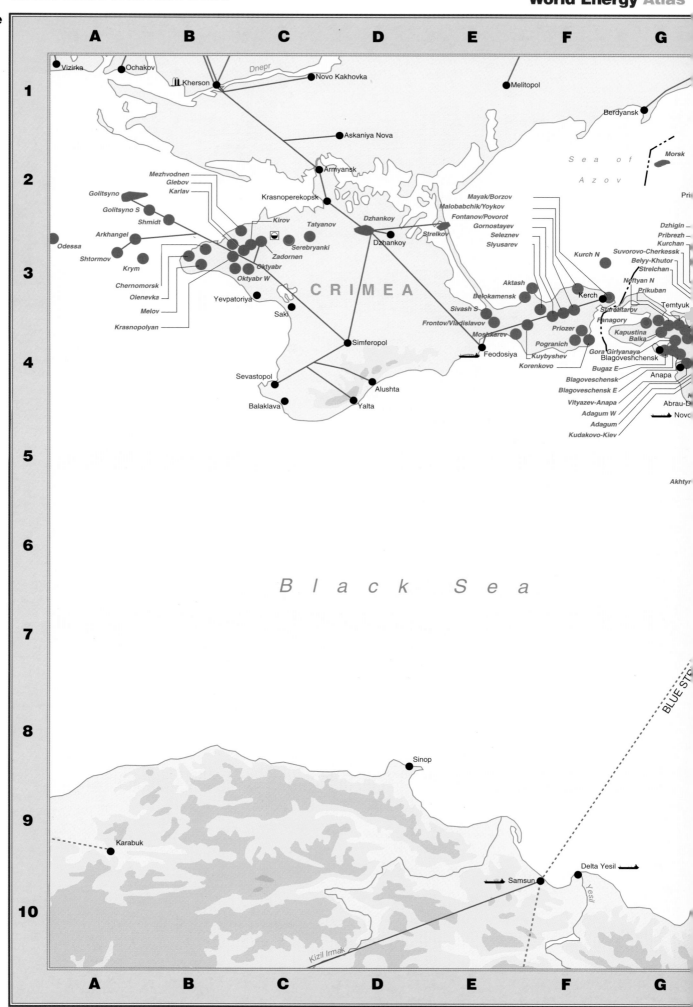

Scale: 1:2,880,000

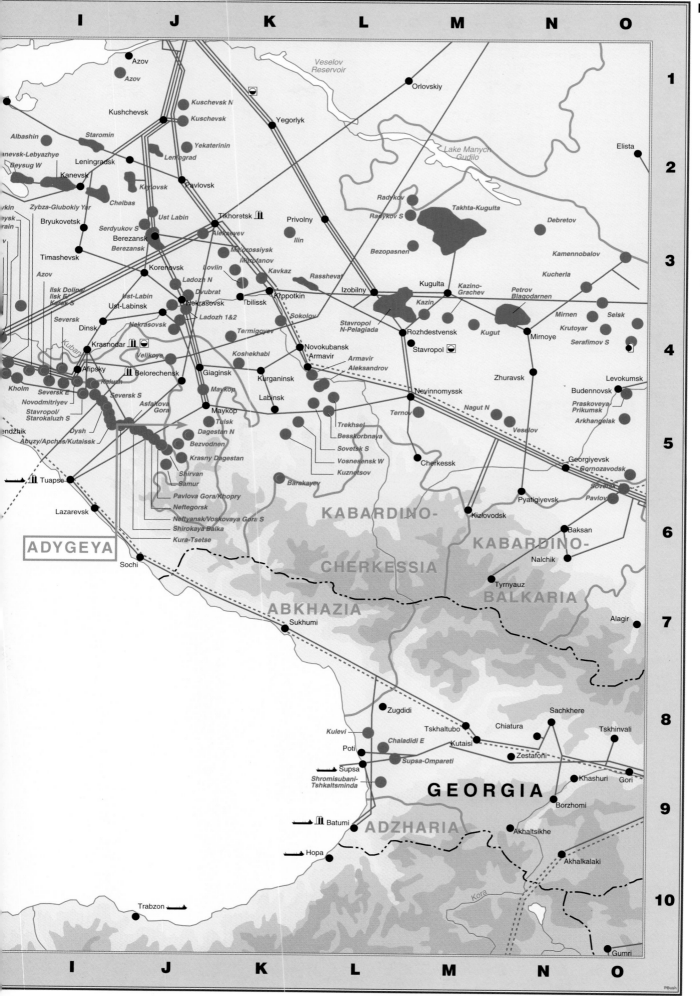

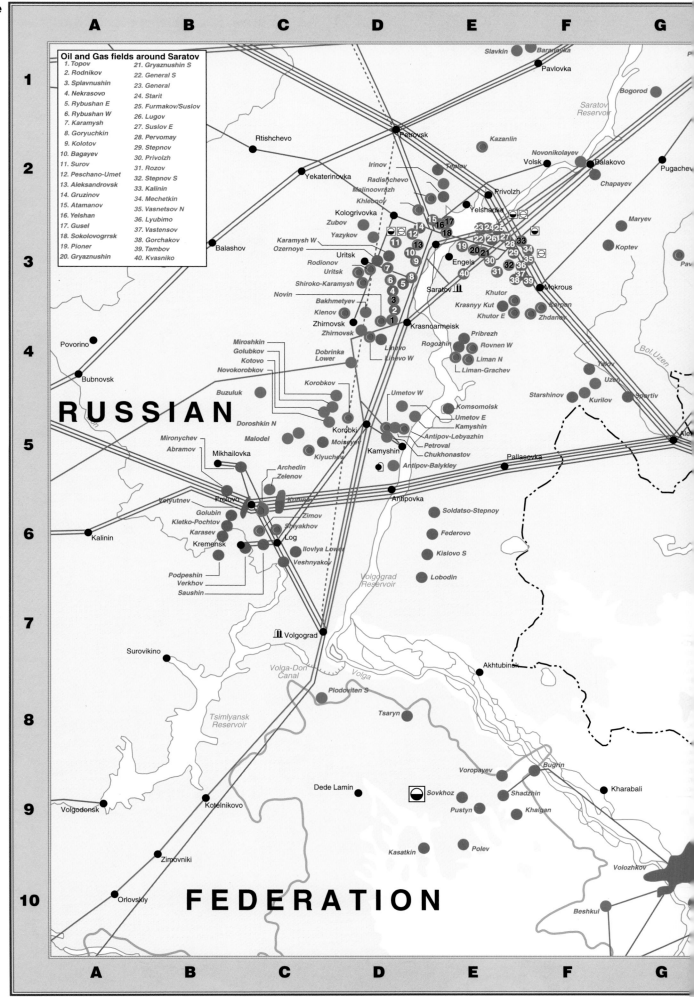

Oil and Gas fields around Saratov

1. Topov	21. Gryaznushin S
2. Rodnikov	22. General S
3. Splavnushin	23. General
4. Nekrasovo	24. Starit
5. Rybushan E	25. Furmakov/Suslov
6. Rybushan W	26. Lugov
7. Karamysh	27. Suslov E
8. Goryuchkin	28. Pervomay
9. Kolotov	29. Stepnov
10. Bagayev	30. Privolzh
11. Surov	31. Rozov
12. Peschano-Umet	32. Stepnov S
13. Aleksandrovsk	33. Kalinin
14. Gruzinov	34. Mechetkin
15. Atamanov	35. Vasnetsov N
16. Yelshan	36. Lyubimo
17. Gusel	37. Vastensov
18. Sokolovogrrsk	38. Gorchakov
19. Pioner	39. Tambov
20. Gryaznushin	40. Kvasniko

Scale: 1:2,800,000

EASTERN EUROPE
& THE FSU

KAZAKHSTAN

Dmitrievka Oil Fields
Dmitrievka
Yezhov
Irgiz
Mnogopol
Bobrov
Sorochinsk
Shveytsar W
Yefimov
Yefimov E
Rykobayev
Grachev
Shveytsar
Shirokodol
Garshin
Flerov
Konchevnen
Konnov
Zaykino
Zorin
Rostashin
Davidov
Miroshkin
Zaykino E
Teplov W
nyachin E
nyachin W
Vishnev
Dolin
nyachin S
Teplov
Ulyanov
Teplov S
Tsyganov
Darin
Tokarev
Berkul
Kamen
Uralsk
Kuznetsov
zha

Uran Upper
Kolgan
Kitayam
Salmysh
Olshan
Karinov
Dachno-Repla
Tarashchan
Radov S
Shevalov
Donetsk
Syrtov
Orenburg
Kindelin
Tashla
Alekseyevka
Borodin
Kuznetso
Orenburg
Rozhdestven
Chkalov
Chernigov
Terektin
Komarov
Krasnoyarsk
Kopan
Kopan N
Kamen
Berdyan
Karachaganak
Sol-Iletsk
Nagumanov
Ural

Mergenevo
Ural

Chingiz
Karatobe
Kubasay
Uil

Mal.Uzen

Inderborskiy

Zholdybay/Zholdybay N
Alimbay
Kenbay-Moldabek E
Sagiz
Kopa
Makat
Matin
Mukur/Oryskazgan
Karagay
Kotyrtas N
Daraymola
Zhilankabak Sekir
Zhengeldy
Zhubantan
Makat
Dauletaly Krykmyltyk
Karatal
Dossor
Baklany
Kamyskol S
Tanatar
Dossor
5
6
7
Karagan
2
4
8
3
11
1
9
10
Kulsary
Iskine
Kulsary
Munayli
Korsak
Botakhan
12
13
Tbylyss S
Masabay
Atangel
Tortay
Akkuduk
14
Kleimbay
Pustyn
15
16
Tazhigall
Karaana
Borankol
Pribrezh
Yelemes
Kokarna E
TENGIZ
Karasor W
Sarykamys
Tasym
Morsk
Prorva W
Prorva Cental/Prorva E
Aktyube

th-east Caspian fields
aychunas
vulegen
entyaksor
isbulyuk
agiz
oshkar S
ekbeke-Ispulay
omsomol/Narmundansk
aratakyz
ltykol-Kyzylkala
uyseke
yrankul
oschagyl
erenozek W
azhigali
araton
Kumisbek
Dzhambul
Gran
Kamyshitovy 6W
Rovnoye
Zhanatalap
Zhanatalap E
Kamyshitovy SE
Atyrau
Gryadov
Martyshi
Zaburunye
Zaburunye
Burbaytal
Oktyabrsk
Zhambay

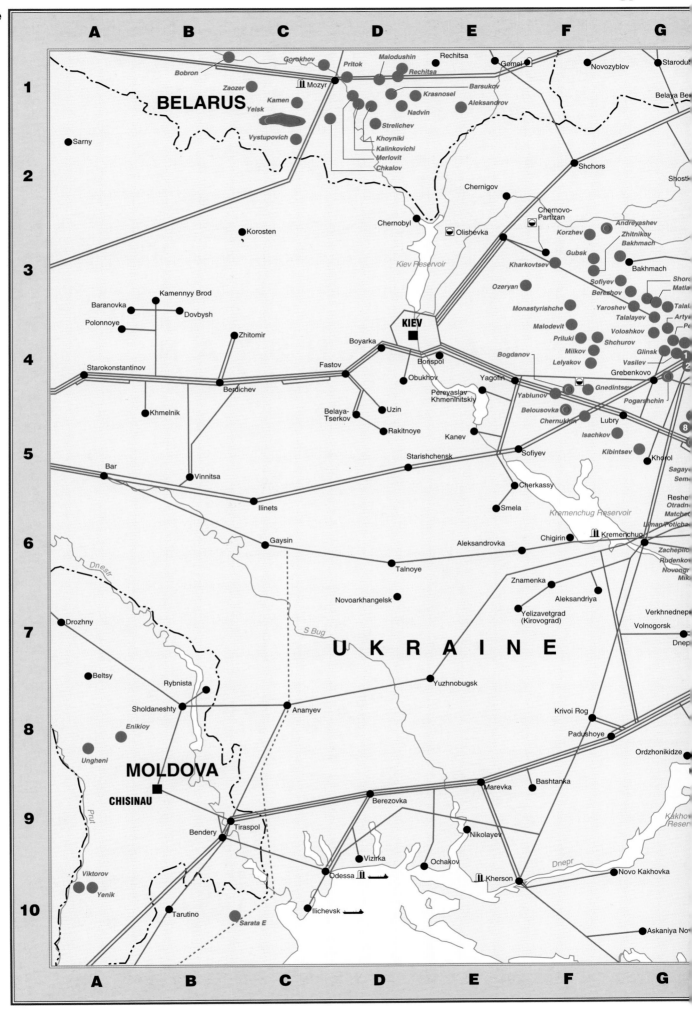

A B C D E F G

BELARUS

Sarny

Bobron
Gorokhov
Pritok
Malodushin
Rechitsa
Gomel
Novozyblov
Starodub
Zaozer
Mozyr
Rechitsa
Barsukov
Belaya Be
Kamen
Yelsk
Krasnosel
Aleksandrov
Vystupovich
Nadvin
Strelichev
Khoyniki
Kalinkovichi
Merlovit
Chkalov

Korosten

Chernigov
Shchors
Shostk

Chernobyl
Chernovo-Partizan
Korzhev
Andreyashev
Zhitnikov
Bakhmach
Olishevka
Gubsk
Kharkovtsev
Bakhmach
Ozeryan
Sofiyev
Shor
Matia
Kiev Reservoir
Bereshov
Monastyrishche
Yaroshev
Talala
Malodevit
Talalayev
Arty
Pe
Kamennyy Brod
Priluki
Voloshkov
Baranovka
Dovbysh
KIEV
Bogdanov
Milkov
Shchurov
Glinsk
1
Polonnoye
Boyarka
Lelyakov
Vasilev
2
Zhitomir
Borispol
Grebenkovo
Starokonstantinov
Fastov
Obukhov
Yagotin
Yablunov
Gnedintsev
Pogarshchin
Berdichev
Pereyaslav Khmelnitskiy
Belousovka
Khmelnik
Belaya-Tserkov
Uzin
Chernukhin
Lubry
8
Rakitnoye
Isachkov
Kanev
Kibintsev
Khorol
Bar
Starishchensk
Sofiyev
Sagaye
Seme
Vinnitsa
Cherkassy
Reshe
Ilinets
Smela
Otradne
Matched
Kremenchug Reservoir
Liman/Poticha
Gaysin
Aleksandrovka
Chigirin
Kremenchug
Zachepilo
Rudenko
Talnoye
Novongr
Miki
Novoarkhangelsk
Znamenka
U K R A I N E
Aleksandriya
Verkhnednepr
Yelizavetgrad (Kirovograd)
Volnogorsk
Drozhny
Dnep
Beltsy
Yuzhnobugsk
Rybnista
Krivoi Rog
Sholdaneshty
Ananyev
Padushoye
Enikioy
Ordzhonikidze
Ungheni
Bashtanka
MOLDOVA
Marevka
CHISINAU
Berezovka
Bendery
Tiraspol
Nikolayev
Kakho
Reser
Vizirka
Ochakov
Dnepr
Viktorov
Odessa
Kherson
Novo Kakhovka
Yenik
Tarutino
Ilichevsk
Prut
Sarata E
Askaniya Nov
Dnestr
S Bug

A B C D E F G

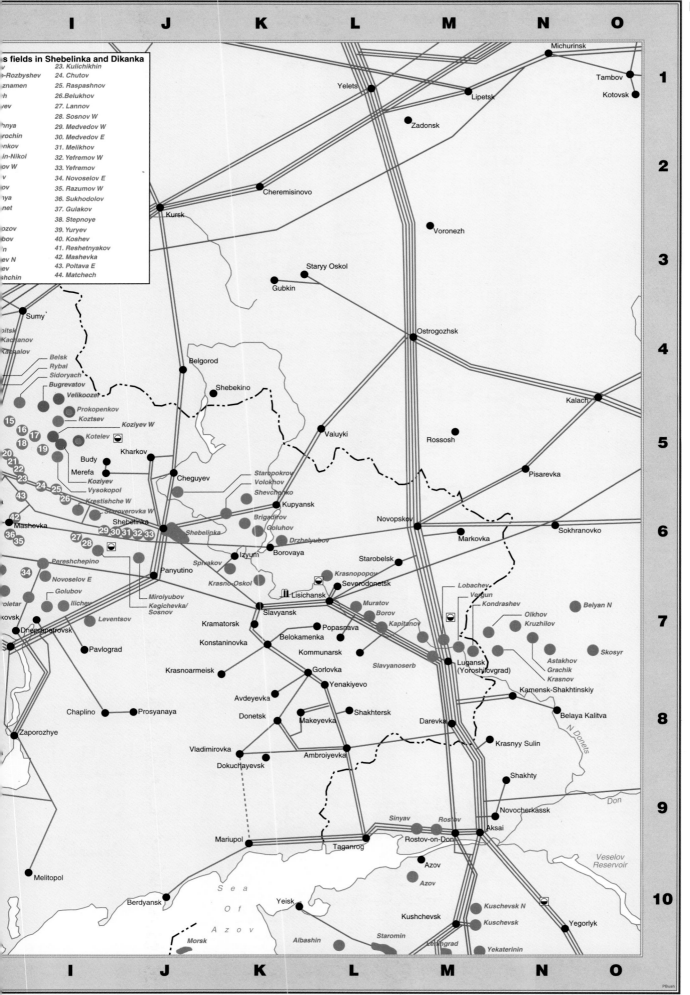

EASTERN EUROPE & THE FSU

s fields in Shebelinka and Dikanka
- 23. Kulichikhin
- 24. Chutov
- 25. Raspashnov
- 26. Belukhov
- 27. Lannov
- 28. Sosnov W
- 29. Medvedov W
- 30. Medvedov E
- 31. Melikhov
- 32. Yefremov W
- 33. Yefremov
- 34. Novoselov E
- 35. Razumov W
- 36. Sukhodolov
- 37. Gulakov
- 38. Stepnoye
- 39. Yuryev
- 40. Koshev
- 41. Reshetnyakov
- 42. Mashevka
- 43. Poltava E
- 44. Matchech

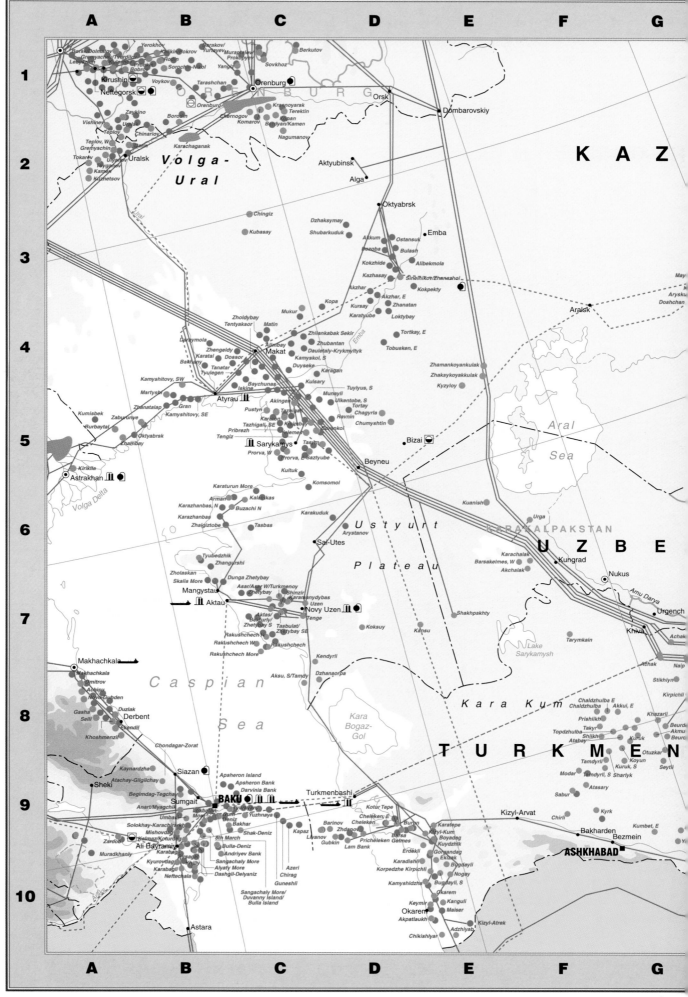

CENTRAL ASIAN REPUBLICS

Plate
23

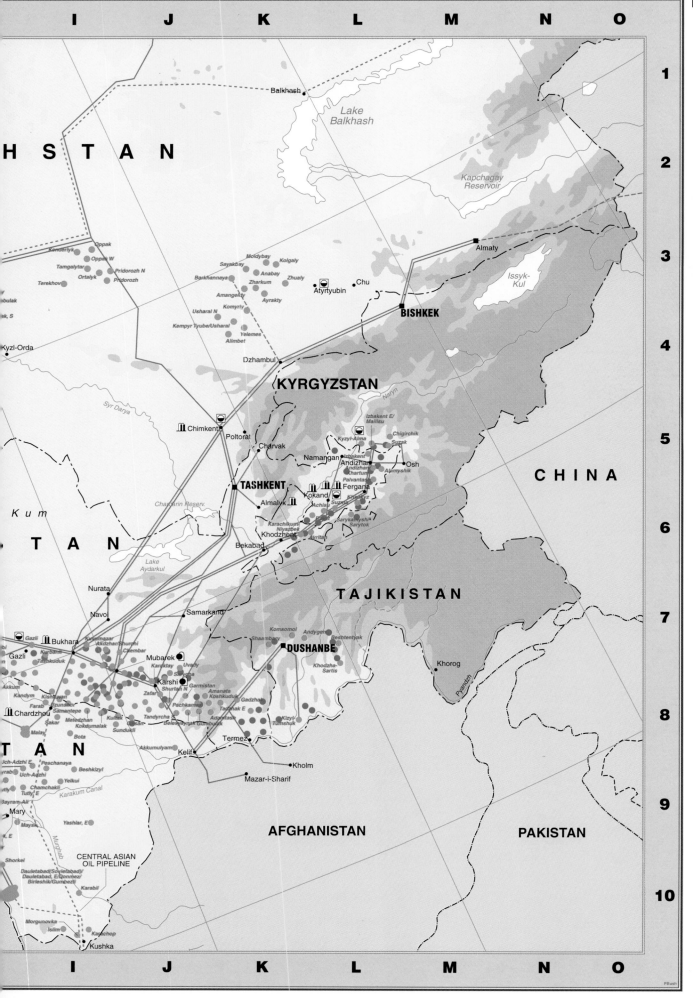

UZBEKISTAN & TURKMENISTAN

Plate 24

World Energy Atlas

EASTERN EUROPE & THE FSU

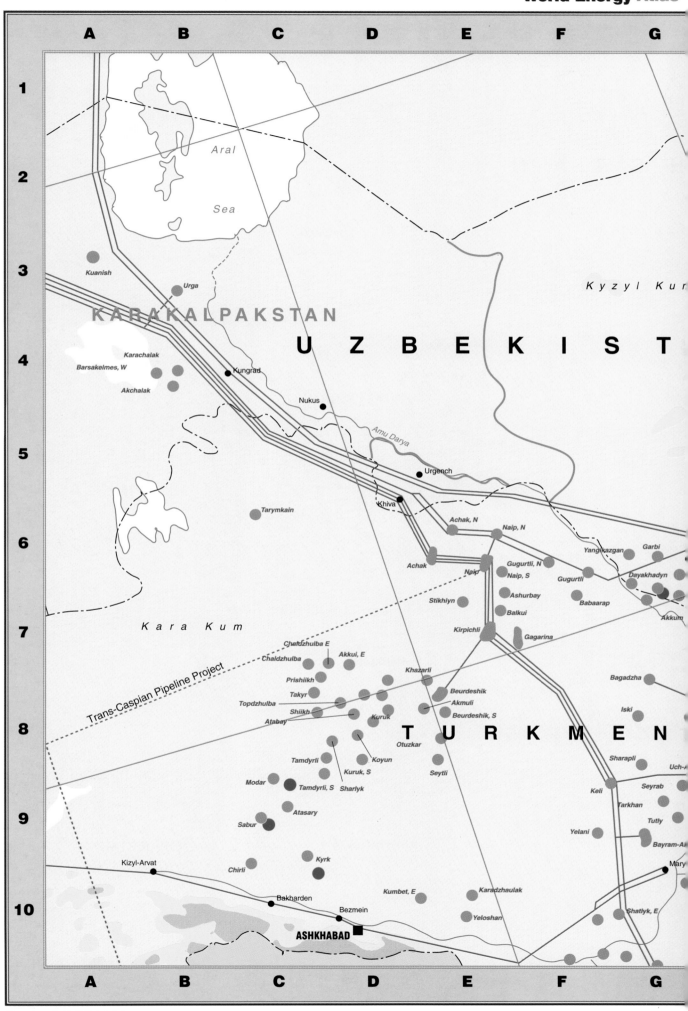

Scale: 1:3,680,000

TAJIKISTAN AND KYRGYZSTAN

Plate
24

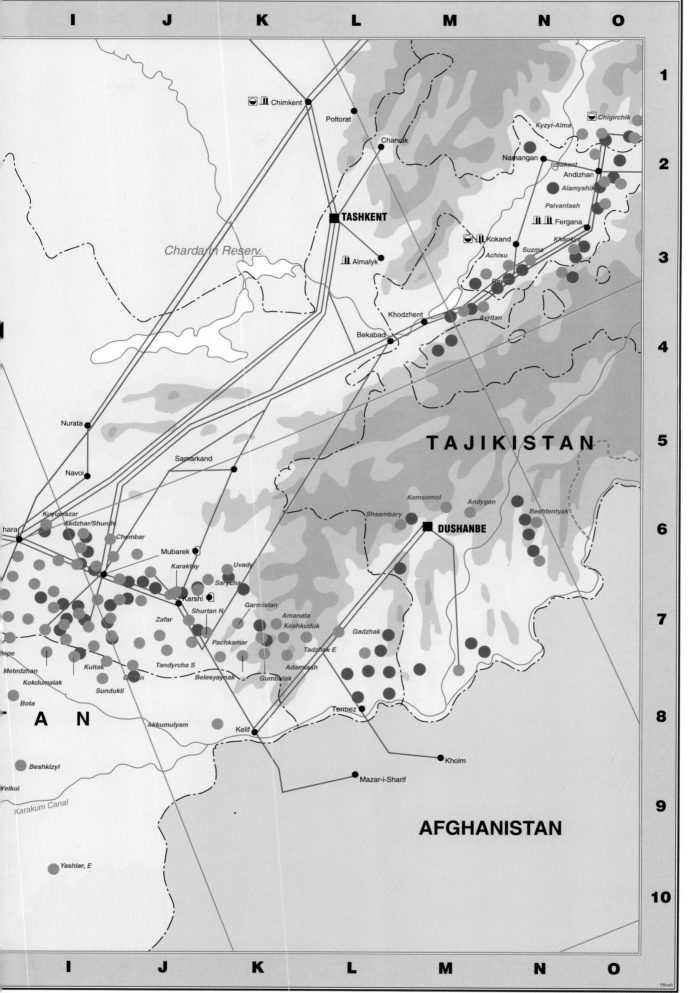

EASTERN EUROPE & THE FSU

Chimkent
Poltorat
Charvak
Kyzyl-Alma
Chigirchik
Namangan
Izbakent
Andizhan
Alamyshik
Palvantash
TASHKENT
Kokand
Fergana
Achisu
Khapkyz
Suzma
Almalyk
Ravat
Khodzhent
Ayritan
Bekabad

TAJIKISTAN

Nurata

Samarkand

Navoi

Komsomol
Andygen
Beshtentyak
Shaambary
Kuyumazar
Akdzhar/Shurch
DUSHANBE
hara
Chembar
Mubarek
Uvady
Karaktay
Sarycha
Karshi
Garmistan
Zafar
Shurtan N
Amanata
Koshkuduk
Gadzhak
Pachkamar
Tadzhak E
Tandyrcha S
Adamtash
epe
Belesyaynak
Gumbulak
Metedzhan
Kultak
Gissan
Kokdumalak
Sundukli
Bota
Termez

Beshkizyl

Akkumulyam
Kelif

AN

Kholm

Yelkui

Mazar-i-Sharif

Karakum Canal

AFGHANISTAN

Yashlar, E

Plate
25

Scale: 1:6,670,000

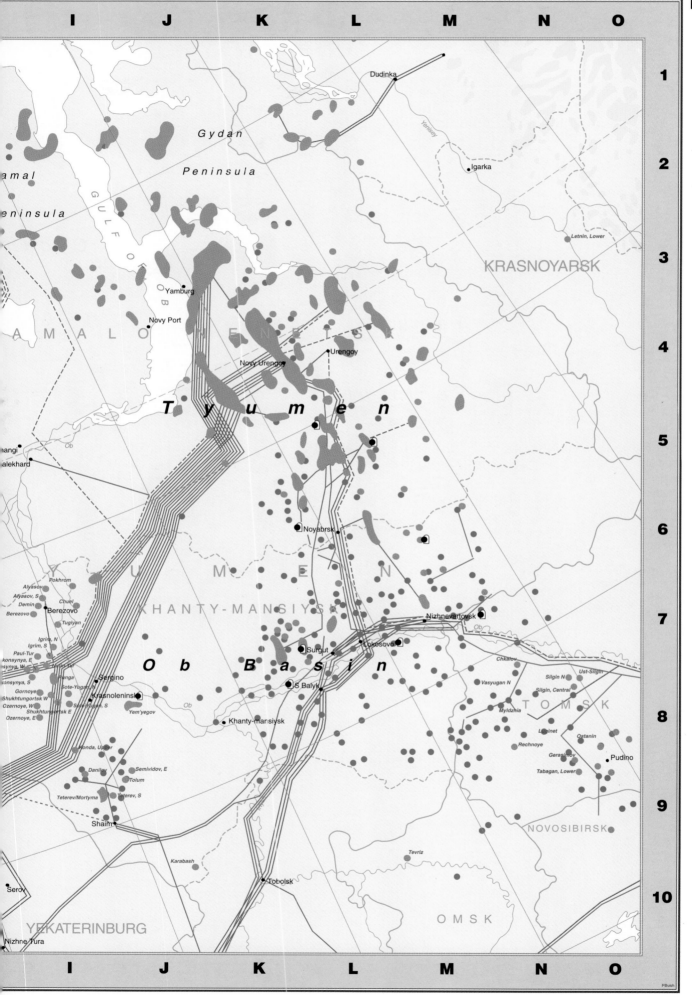

EASTERN EUROPE
& THE FSU

Gydan

Peninsula

Dudinka

Igarka

Letnin, Lower

KRASNOYARSK

Yenisey

Yamburg

Novy Port

Ob

Urengoy

Novy Urengoy

T y u m e n

Ob

hangi

alekhard

Noyabrsk

Alyasov
Alyasov, S
Demin
Berezovo
Chuel
Tuglyan
Pokhrom

Y U M E N

KHANTY-MANSIYSK

Nizhnevartovsk

Ob

Igrim, N
Igrim, S
Paul-Tur
konsynya, E
synya, W
synya, S
Gornoye
Shukhtungortsk W
Ozernoye, W
Shukhtungortsk E
Ozernoye, E

Surgut
Lokosovo

Chkalov

Ust-Silgin

O b   B a s i n

Sergino
Sote-Yugan, N
Sos-Yugan
Sote-Yugan, S
Yem'yegov

Krasnoleninsk

S Balyk

Ob

Silgin N
Vasyugan N
Silgin, Central

Khanty-mansiysk

Myldzhir

T O M S K

Lininet
Rechnoye
Ostanin

Honda, Upper

Danilov
Semividov, E
Tolum

Gerasimov
Tabagan, Lower

Pudino

Teterev/Mortyma
Teterev, S

Shaim

NOVOSIBIRSK

Karabash

Tevriz

Tobolsk

Serov

YEKATERINBURG

O M S K

Nizhne Tura

Plate
26

EASTERN EUROPE
& THE FSU

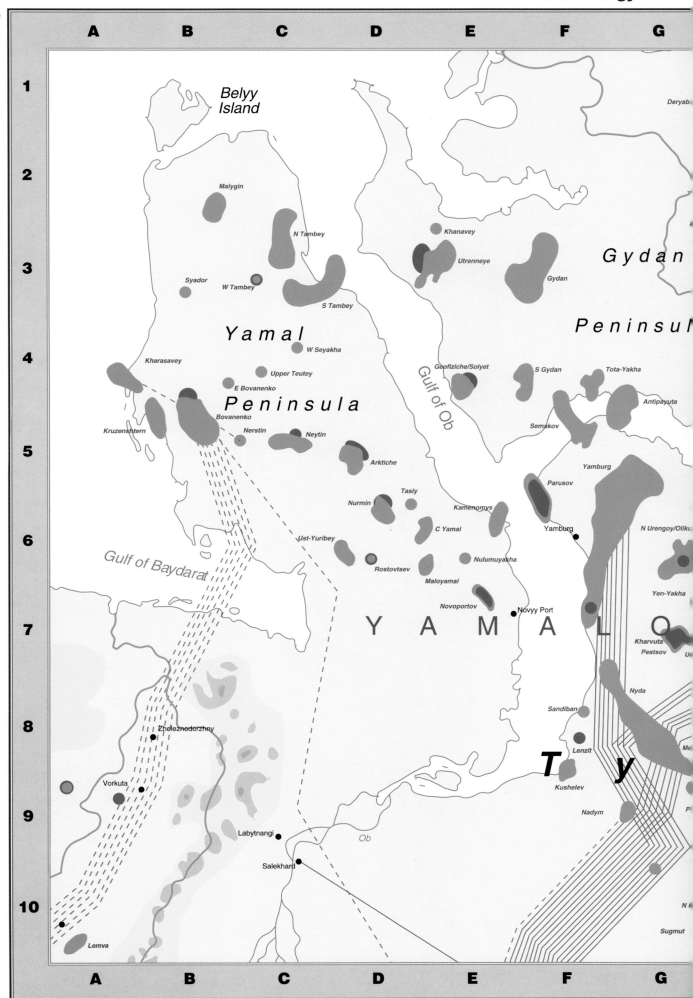

Belyy
Island

A B C D E F G

1

2

Malygin

N Tambey

Khanavey

Utrenneye

Gydan

3

Syador

W Tambey

S Tambey

Gydan

Y a m a l

P e n i n s u l

W Seyakha

Kharasavey

Geofiziche/Solyet

S Gydan

Tota-Yakha

4

P e n i n s u l a

Upper Teutey

E Bovanenko

Antipayuta

Bovanenko

Gulf of Ob

Nerstin

Neytin

Semakov

Kruzenshtern

Arktiche

Yamburg

5

Tasiy

Parusov

Nurmin

Kamenomys

N Urengoy/Oliku

C Yamal

Ust-Yuribey

Yamburg

6

Gulf of Baydarat

Nulumuyakha

Rostovtsev

Yen-Yakha

Maloyamal

Novoportov

Y   A   M   A   L   O

Novyy Port

7

Kharvuta

Pestsov

Nyda

Zheleznedorzhny

Sandiban

8

Lenzit

T   *y*

Vorkuta

Kushelev

Nadym

9

Labytnangi

Ob

Salekhard

10

Lemva

Sugmut

A B C D E F G

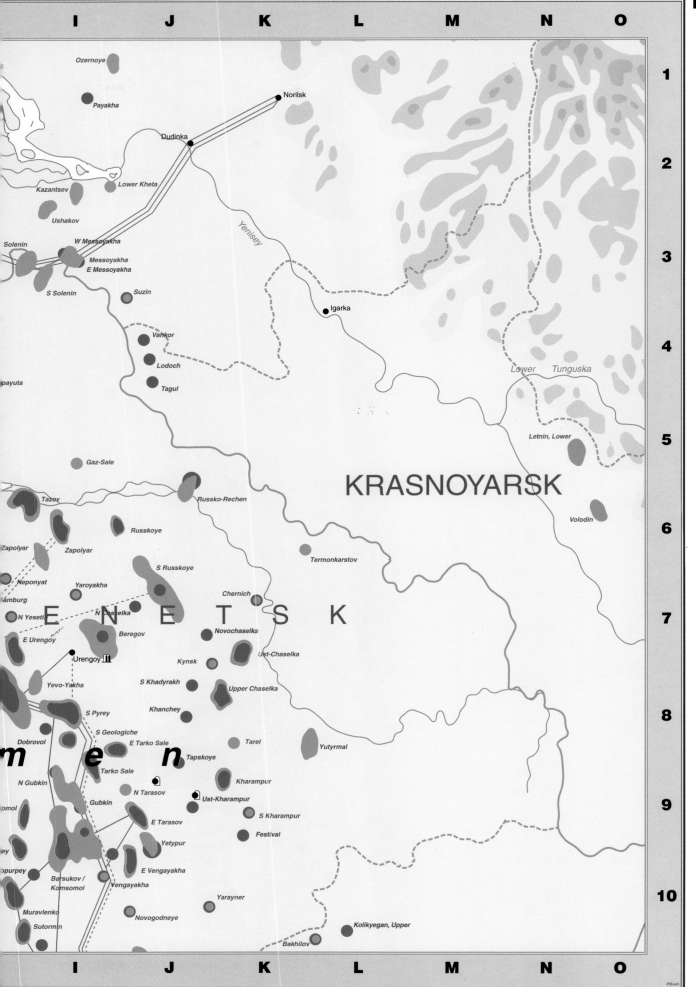

KRASNOYARSK

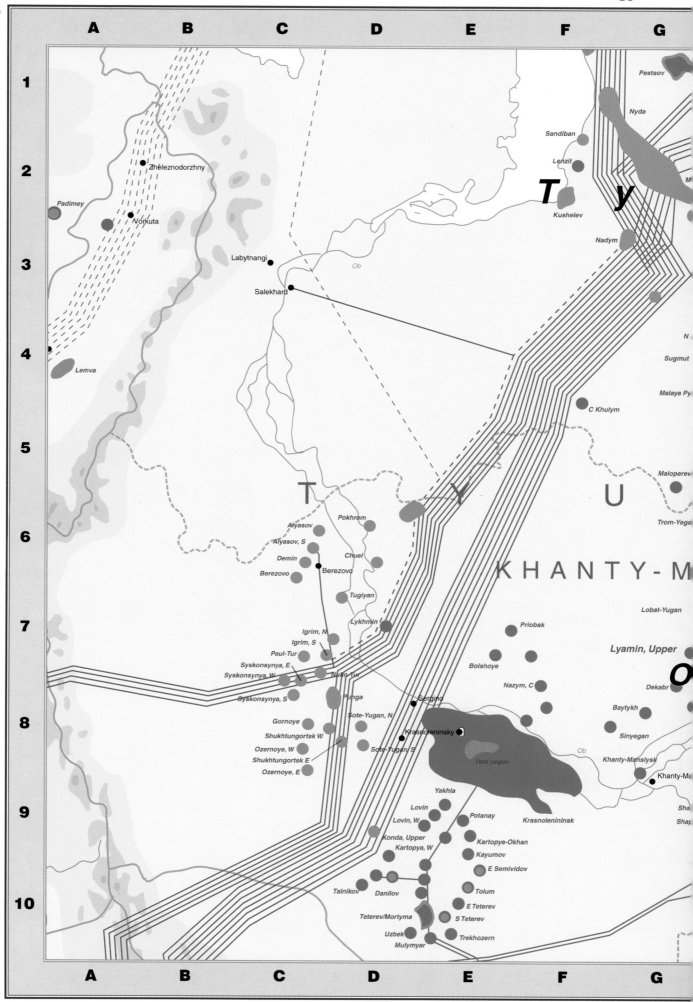

Scale: 1:3,770,000

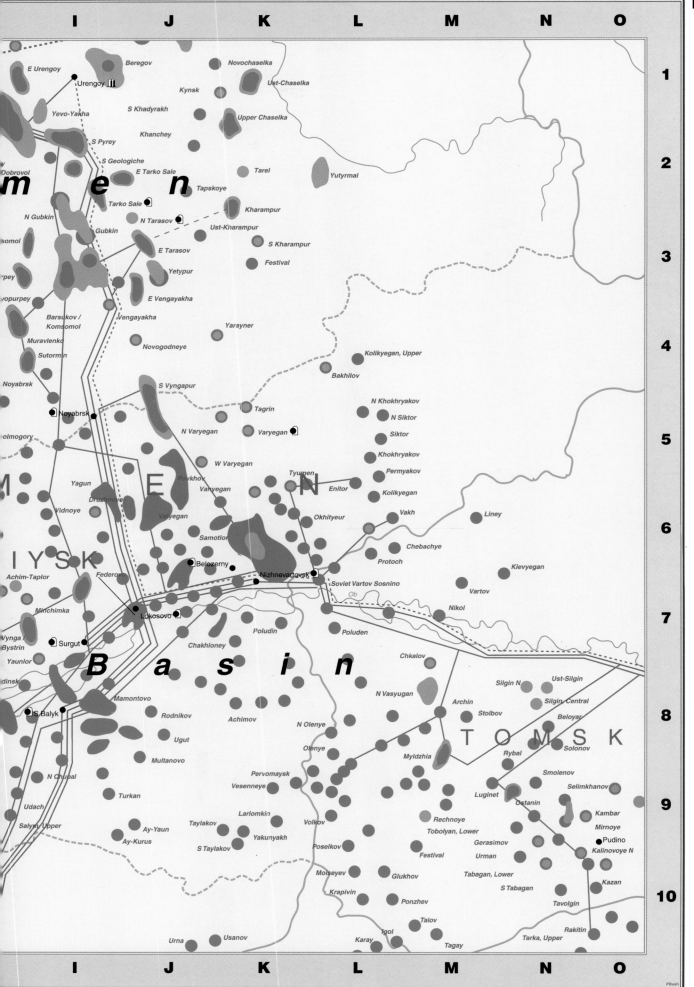

EASTERN EUROPE
& THE FSU

I J K L M N O

E Urengoy
Beregov
Novochaselka
Urengoy
Ust-Chaselka
1
Kynsk
Yevo-Yakha
S Khadyrakh
Upper Chaselka
Khanchey
S Pyrey
S Geologiche
E Tarko Sale
2
m e n
Tarel
Yutyrmal
Tapskoye
Dobrovol
Tarko Sale
Kharampur
N Gubkin
N Tarasov
Ust-Kharampur
somol
Gubkin
S Kharampur
3
E Tarasov
Festival
rpey
Yetypur
opurpey
E Vengayakha
Barsukov /
Komsomol
Vengayakha
Yarayner
4
Muravlenko
Novogodneye
Kolikyegan, Upper
Sutormin
Bakhilov
Noyabrsk
S Vyngapur
N Khokhryakov
Noyabrsk
Tagrin
N Siktor
olmogory
N Varyegan
Varyegan
Siktor
5
M
W Varyegan
Khokhryakov
Yagun
Povkhor
Tyumen
Permyakov
E
Vanyegan
Enitor
Kolikyegan
Vidnoye
Druzhnoye
N
Varyegan
Okhityeur
Vakh
Liney
6
Samotlor
Chebachye
IYSK
Belozerny
Protoch
Kievyegan
Achim-Taplor
Federovo
Nizhnevartovsk
Soviet Vartov Sosnino
Vartov
Ob
Nikol
7
Minchimka
Lokosovo
Poludin
Vynga /
Bystrin
Chakhloney
Poluden
Yaunlor
Surgut
Chkalov
Basin
dinsk
Mamontovo
N Vasyugan
Silgin N
Ust-Silgin
S Balyk
Rodnikov
Archin
Silgin Central
8
Achimov
Stolbov
Beloyar
Ugut
N Olenye
TOMSK
Multanovo
Olenye
Rybal
Solonov
Myldzhia
N Chupal
Pervomaysk
Smolenov
Vesenneye
Selimkhanov
Turkan
Luginet
Ostanin
9
Udach
Larlomkin
Volkov
Rechnoye
Kambar
Ay-Yaun
Taylakov
Yakunyakh
Tobolyan, Lower
Mirnoye
Salym Upper
Ay-Kurus
S Taylakov
Poselkov
Festival
Gerasimov
Pudino
Kalinovoye N
Urman
Molseyev
Tabagan, Lower
Kazan
Krapivin
Glukhov
S Tabagan
10
Urna
Usanov
Ponzhev
Tavolgin
Karay
Igol
Talov
Rakitin
Tagay
Tarka, Upper

I J K L M N O

PBush

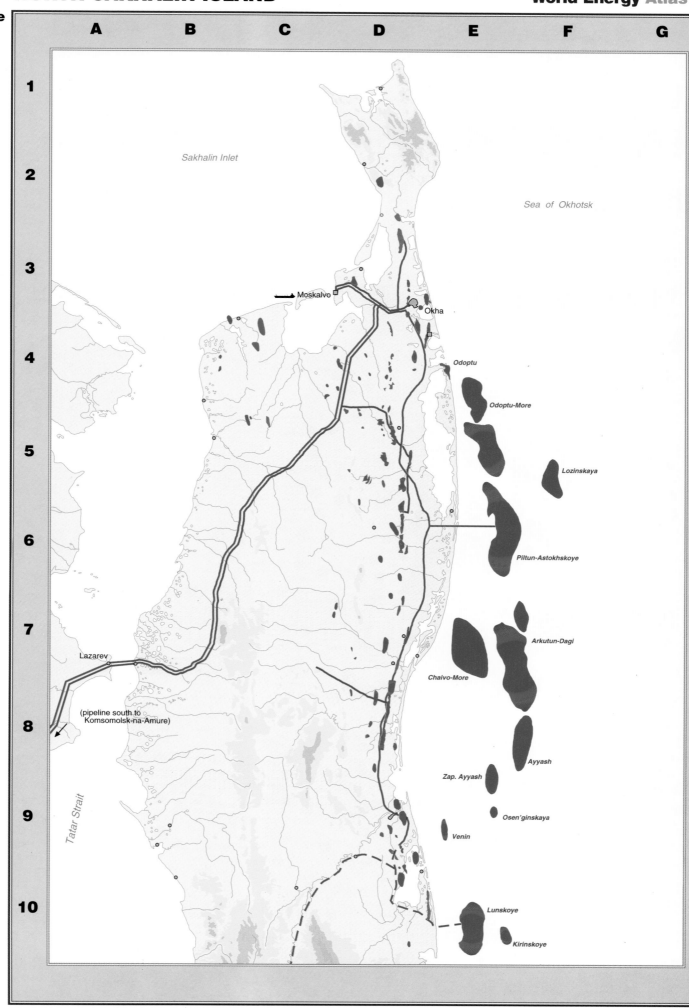

Sakhalin Inlet

Sea of Okhotsk

Moskalvo

Okha

Odoptu

Odoptu-More

Lozinskaya

Piltun-Astokhskoye

Arkutun-Dagi

Chaivo-More

Lazarev

(pipeline south to Komsomolsk-na-Amure)

Ayyash

Zap. Ayyash

Osen'ginskaya

Venin

Tatar Strait

Lunskoye

Kirinskoye

Scale: 1:1,285,000

SOUTH SAKHALIN ISLAND

Plate 29

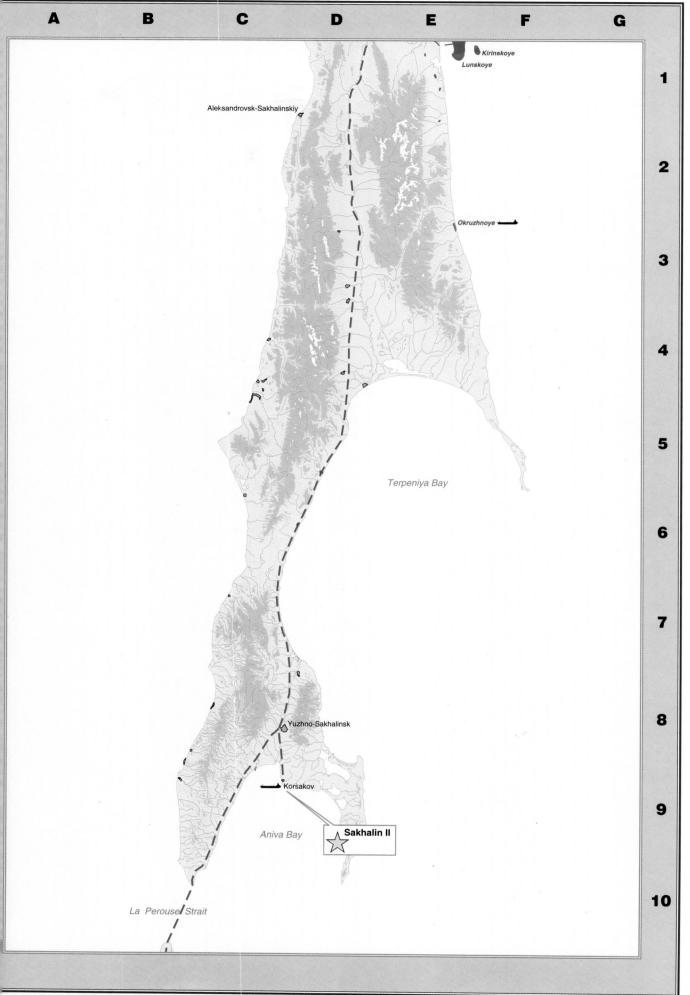

EASTERN EUROPE & THE FSU

Kirinskoye

Lunskoye

Aleksandrovsk-Sakhalinskiy

Okruzhnoye

Terpeniya Bay

Yuzhno-Sakhalinsk

Korsakov

Aniva Bay

Sakhalin II

La Perouse Strait

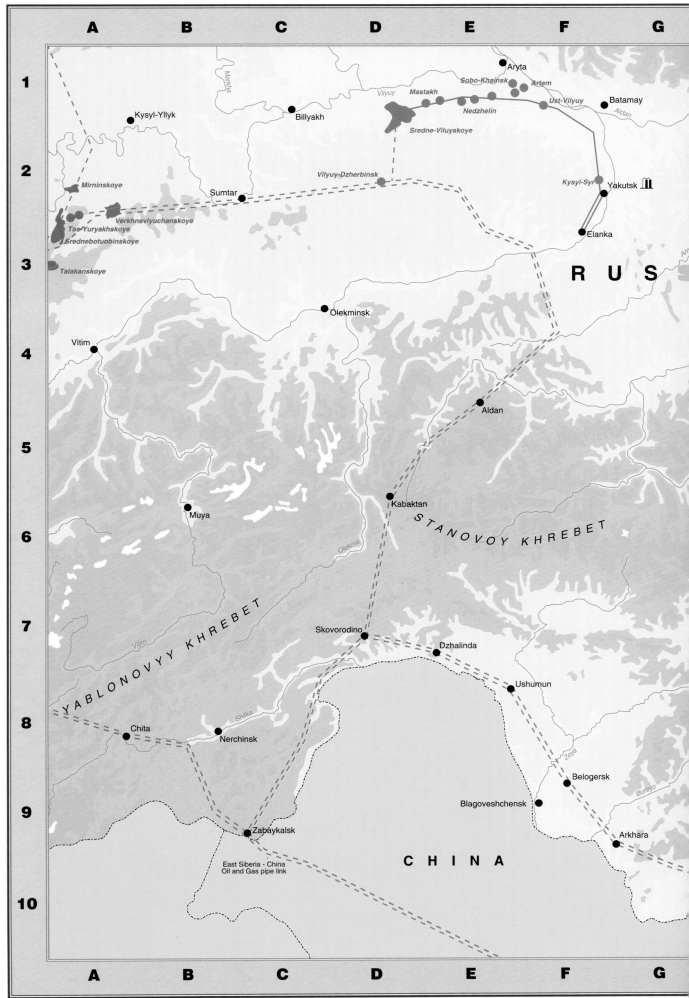

R U S

Kysyl-Yllyk

Billyakh

Vilyuy

Mastakh

Sobo-Khainsk

Artem

Aryta

Nedzhelin

Ust-Vilyuy

Batamay

Aldan

Sredne-Viluyskoye

Mirninskoye

Sumtar

Vilyuy-Dzherbinsk

Kysyl-Syr

Yakutsk

Verkhneviyuchanskoye

Tas-Yuryakhskoye

Srednebotuobinskoye

Elanka

Talakanskoye

Olekminsk

Vitim

Aldan

Vitim

Muya

Kabaktan

S T A N O V O Y   K H R E B E T

Olekma

Y A B L O N O V Y Y   K H R E B E T

Skovorodino

Dzhalinda

Ushumun

Chita

Shilka

Nerchinsk

Zeya

Belogersk

Blagoveshchensk

Bureyo

Arkhara

Zabaykalsk

East Siberia - China
Oil and Gas pipe link

C H I N A

Am

Scale: 1:8,450,000

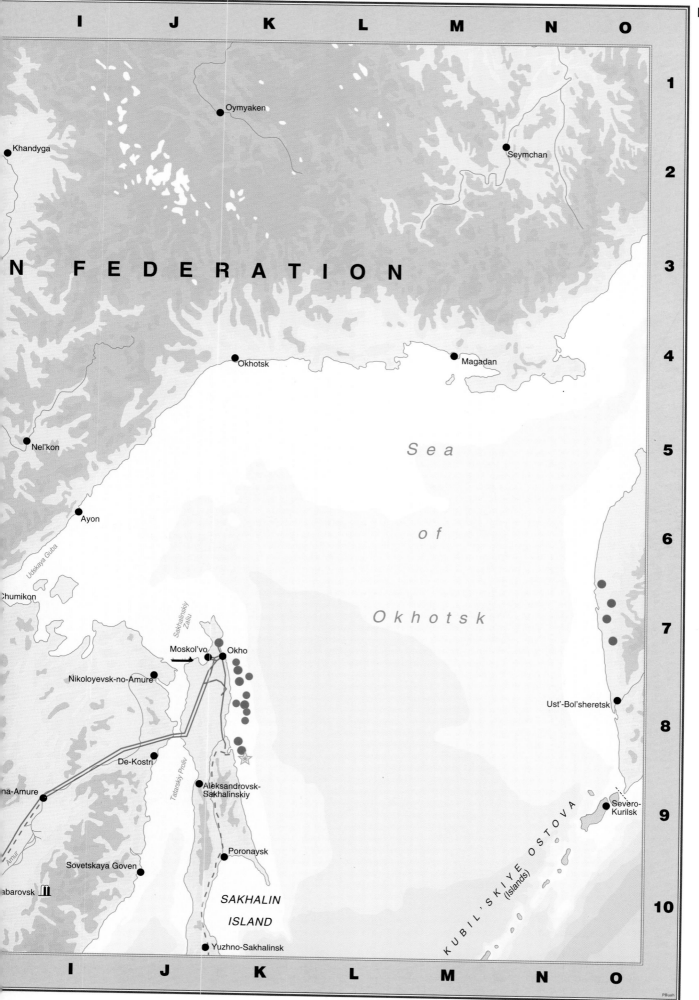

EASTERN EUROPE
& THE FSU

I J K L M N O

Oymyaken

Khandyga

Seymchan

1

2

N FEDERATION

3

Okhotsk

Magadan

4

Nel'kon

S e a

5

Ayon

o f

6

Udskaya Guba

Chumikon

O k h o t s k

7

Sakhalinskiy Zaliu

Moskol'vo   Okho

Nikoloyevsk-no-Amure

Ust'-Bol'sheretsk

De-Kostri

Tatarskiy Proliv

8

na-Amure

Aleksandrovsk-
Sakhalinskiy

Severo-
Kurilsk

9

Amur

Poronaysk

Sovetskaya Goven

KUBIL'SKIYE OSTOVA
(Islands)

abarovsk

*SAKHALIN
ISLAND*

10

Yuzhno-Sakhalinsk

I J K L M N O

PBush

A B C D E F G

1 Krasnosel'kup Turukhansk

Tembenchi

Vivi

2 *Nizhnyaya* Uchami

3 **R U S S I A N   F**

S

4 Baykit *Yurubcheno-Takhomskoye*
Paiginsk
Viktorovski
Yenisey

5

6 Lesosibirsk *Angara*

Ob

7 *Yenisey* Kansk Poima
Tomsk Achinsk Krasnoyarsk

8 Kemerovo
Novosibirskoye Vodokhranilishche Novosibirsk Nizhneudi

S A Y A N   M O U N T

9 Prokopyevsk
Barnaul Novokuznetsk Abakan
Biysk

10 Kyzyl

ALTAI MOUNTAINS

Semipalatinsk
Ust-Kamenogorsk

A B C D E F G

Scale: 1:5,770,000

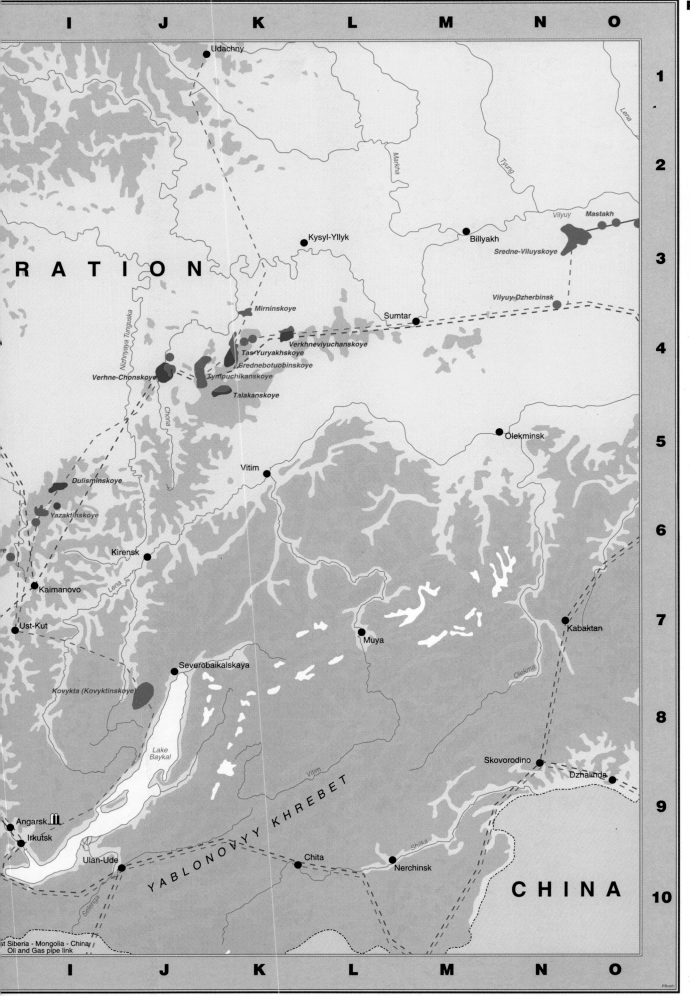

EASTERN EUROPE
& THE FSU

I   J   K   L   M   N   O

1

2

Udachny

Markha

Lena

Tyung

Vilyuy   *Mastakh*

Kysyl-Yllyk   Billyakh   *Srene-Viluyskoye*

R A T I O N

3

Vilyuy-Dzherbinsk

Nizhnyaya Tunguska

Mirninskoye   Sumtar

Verkhneviyuchanskoye   4

Tas'Yuryakhskoye

Srednebotuobinskoye

Verhne-Chonskoye   *Tympuchikanskoye*

Talakanskoye

Chona

Olekminsk   5

Dulisminskoye   Vitim

Yazaktinskoye   6

Kirensk

Lena

Kaimanovo

Ust-Kut   7

Kabaktan

Muya

Severobaikalskaya   Olekma

Kovykta (Kovyktinskoye)

8

*Lake
Baykal*

Skovorodino   9
Dzhalinda

Vitim

Angarsk

Irkutsk   **Y A B L O N O V Y Y   K H R E B E T**   9

Chita   Shilka

Ulan-Ude   Nerchinsk

C H I N A   10

Selenga

st Siberia - Mongolia - China/
Oil and Gas pipe link

I   J   K   L   M   N   O

PBush

Plate
32

THE MIDDLE EAST

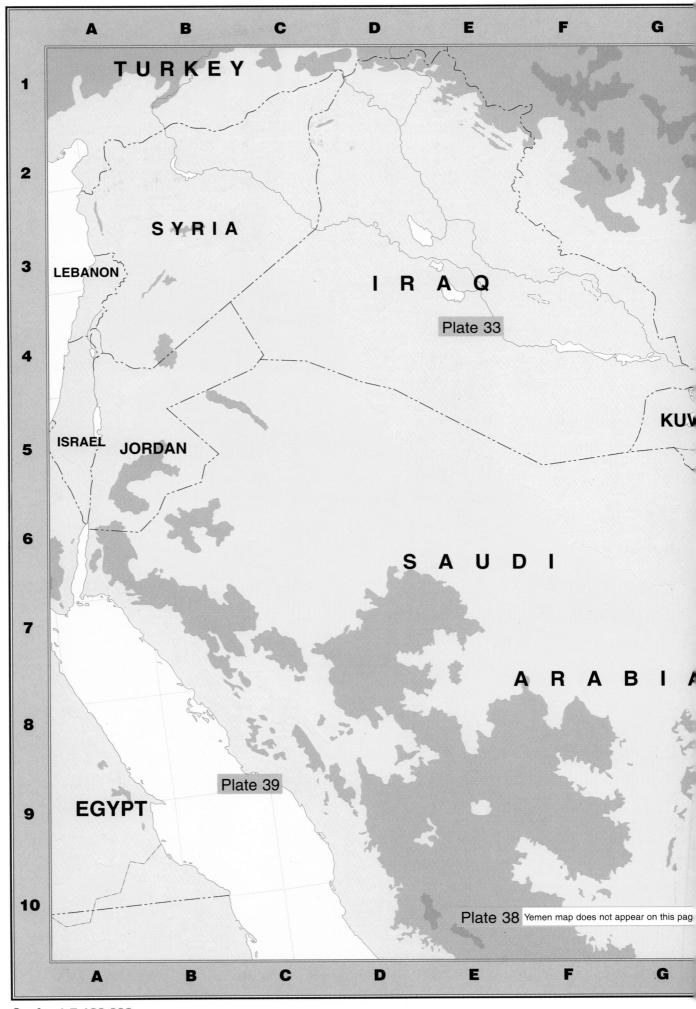

Scale: 1:7,120,000

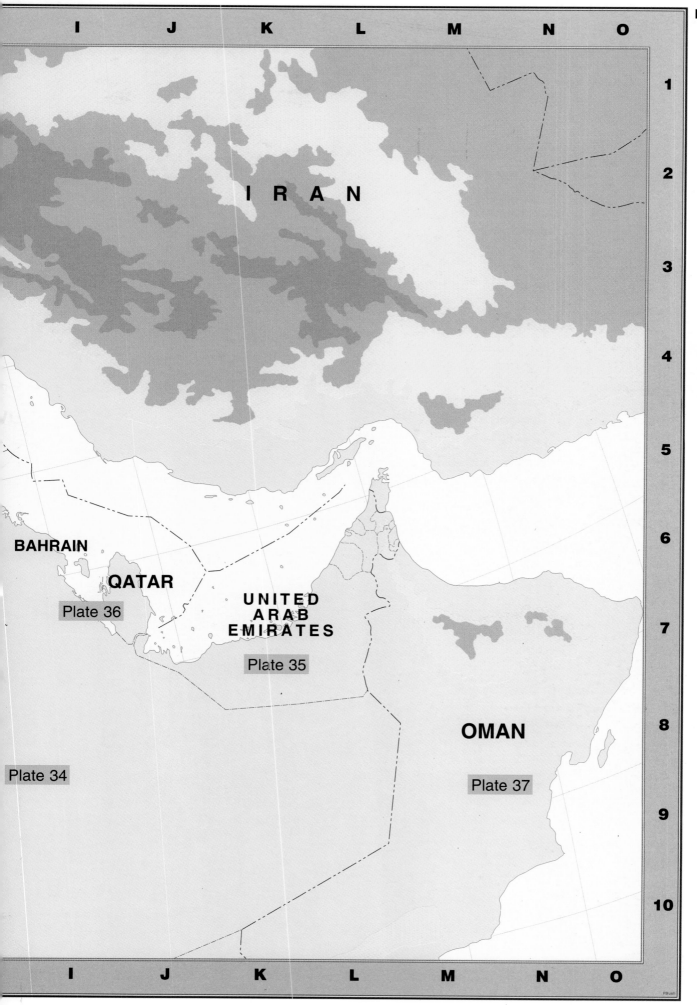

THE MIDDLE EAST

IRAN

BAHRAIN

QATAR

Plate 36

UNITED
ARAB
EMIRATES

Plate 35

OMAN

Plate 34

Plate 37

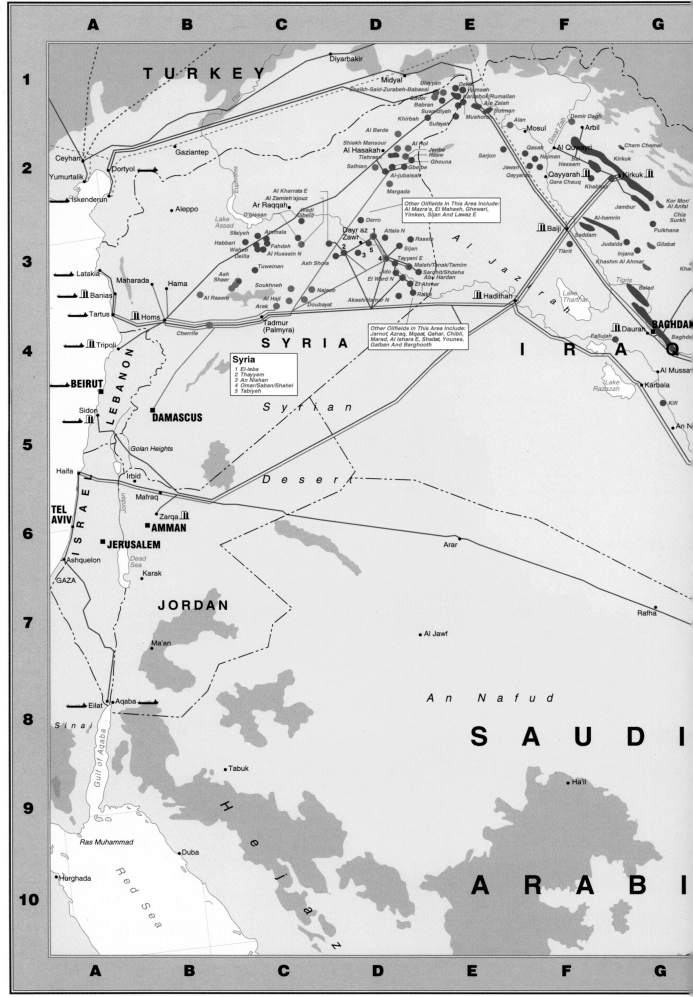

THE MIDDLE EAST

Scale: 1:5,595,000

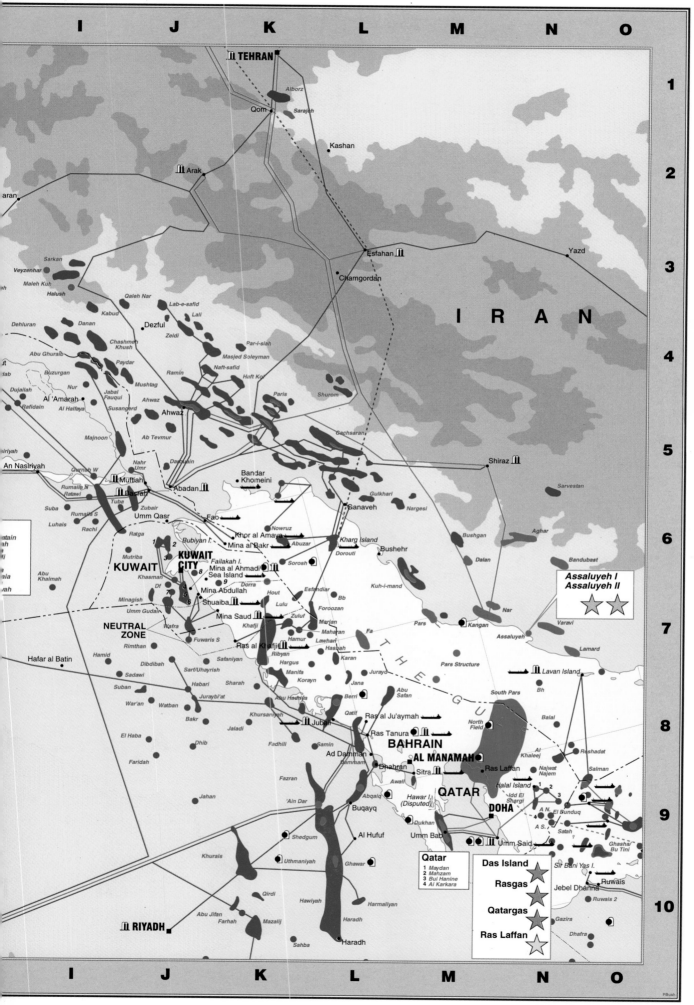

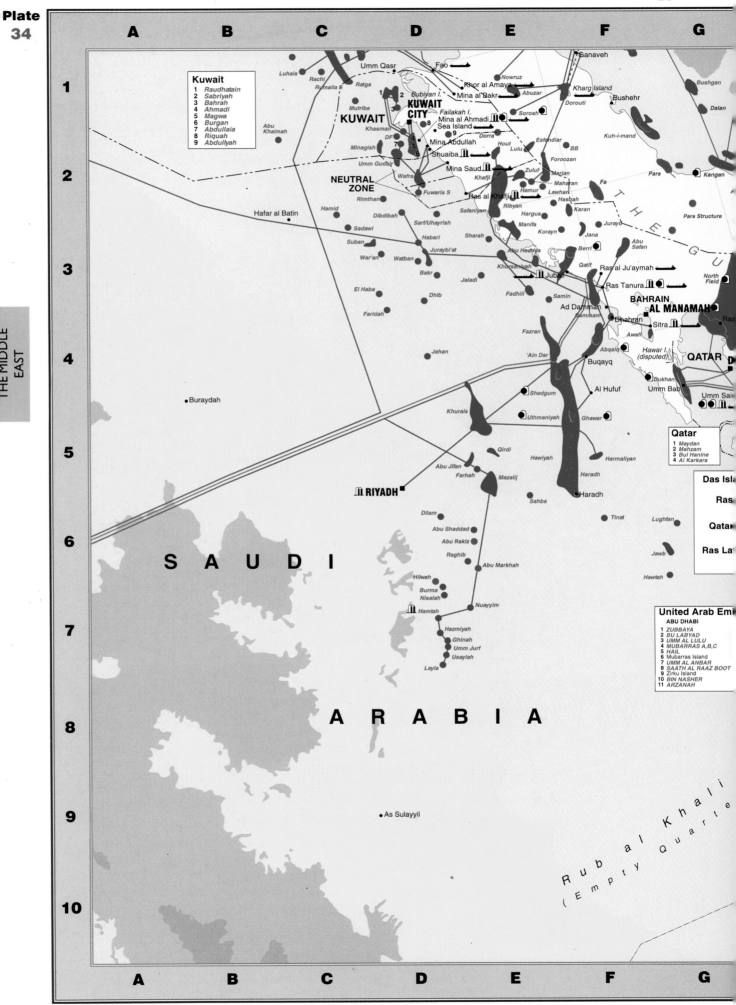

Kuwait
1 Raudhatain
2 Sabriyah
3 Bahrah
4 Ahmadi
5 Magwa
6 Burgan
7 Abdullaia
8 Riquah
9 Abdullyah

Qatar
1 Maydan
2 Mahzam
3 Bul Hanine
4 Al Karkara

Das Isla

Ras

Qatar

Ras La

United Arab Emi
ABU DHABI
1 ZUBBAYA
2 BU LABYAD
3 UMM AL LULU
4 MUBARRAS A,B,C
5 HAIL
6 Mubarras Island
7 UMM AL ANBAR
8 SAATH AL RAAZ BOOT
9 Zirku Island
10 BIN NASHER
11 ARZANAH

SAUDI

ARABIA

Rub al Khali
(Empty Quarte

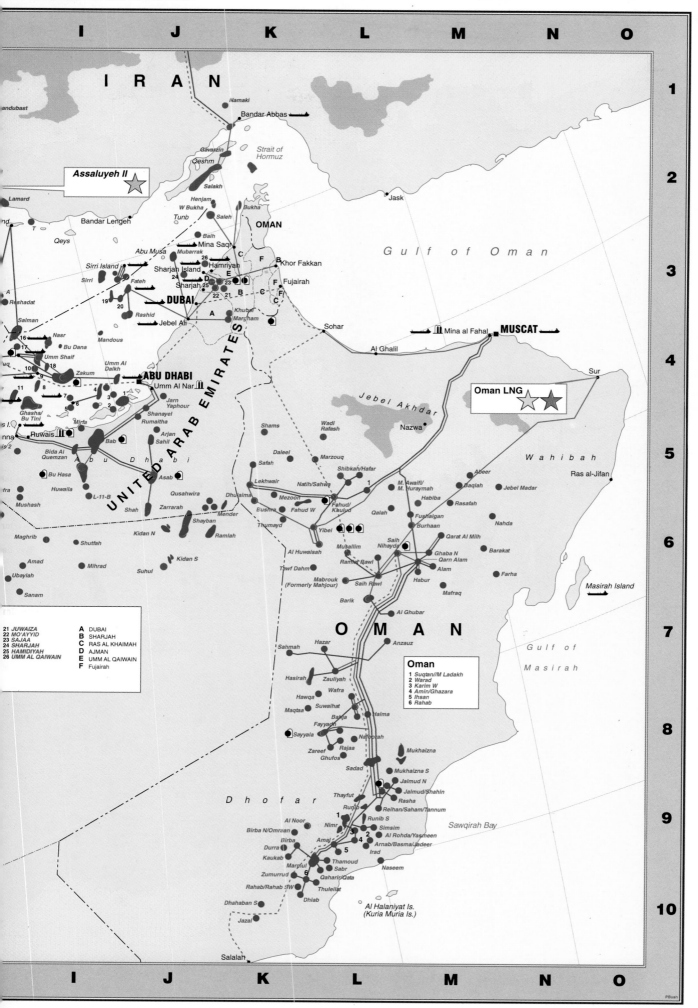

THE MIDDLE
EAST

Plate
35

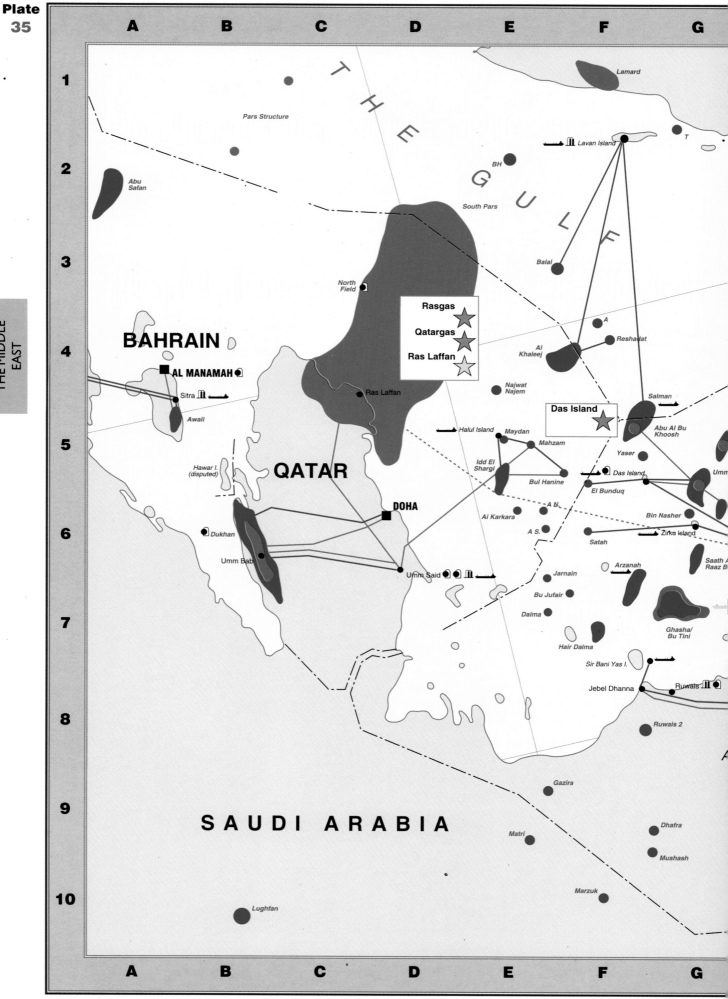

BAHRAIN

QATAR

DOHA

SAUDI ARABIA

THE GULF

Lamard

Pars Structure

Abu Safan

South Pars

BH

Lavan Island

T

Balal

A

Reshadat

North Field

Rasgas
Qatargas
Ras Laffan

Al Khaleej

Salman

Ras Laffan

Najwat Najem

Das Island

Abu Al Bu Khoosh

AL MANAMAH

Sitra

Awali

Halul Island

Maydan

Mahzam

Yaser

Das Island

Umm

Idd El Shargi

Bul Hanine

El Bunduq

Hawar I.
(disputed)

Bin Nasher

A N.

Satah

Zirku Island

Dukhan

A S.

Umm Bab

Arzanah

Saath A
Raaz B

Umm Said

Jarnain

Bu Jufair

Dalma

Ghasha/
Bu Tini

Hair Dalma

Sir Bani Yas I.

Jebel Dhanna

Ruwais

Ruwais 2

Gazira

Matri

Dhafra

Mushash

Marzuk

Lughfan

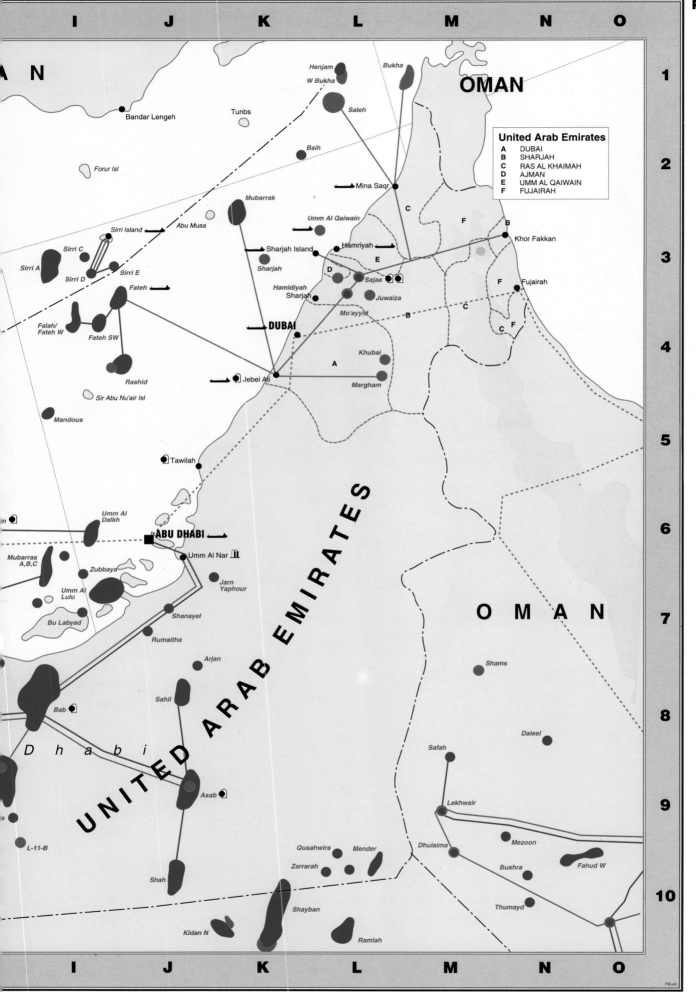

THE MIDDLE EAST

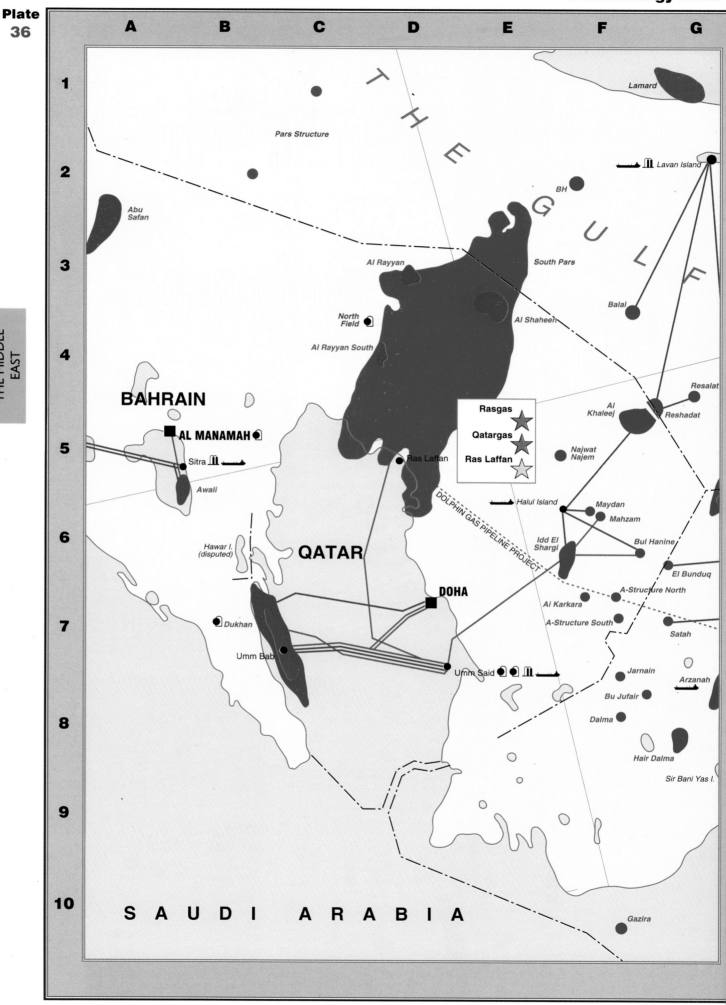

THE MIDDLE EAST

A B C D E F G

1

THE

Pars Structure

Lamard

2

GULF

Abu
Safan

Lavan Island

BH

3

Al Rayyan

South Pars

Balal

Al Shaheen

North
Field

4

Al Rayyan South

Resalat

BAHRAIN

Al
Khaleej

Reshadat

5

AL MANAMAH

Rasgas

Qatargas

Najwat
Najem

Ras Laffan

Sitra

Awali

Halul Island

Maydan

DOLPHIN GAS PIPELINE PROJECT

Mahzam

6

Hawar I.
(disputed)

QATAR

Idd El
Shargi

Bul Hanine

El Bunduq

DOHA

A-Structure North

Ai Karkara

7

Dukhan

A-Structure South

Satah

Umm Bab

Jarnain

Arzanah

Umm Said

Bu Jufair

8

Dalma

Hair Dalma

Sir Bani Yas I.

9

10

SAUDI ARABIA

Gazira

Scale: 1:830,000

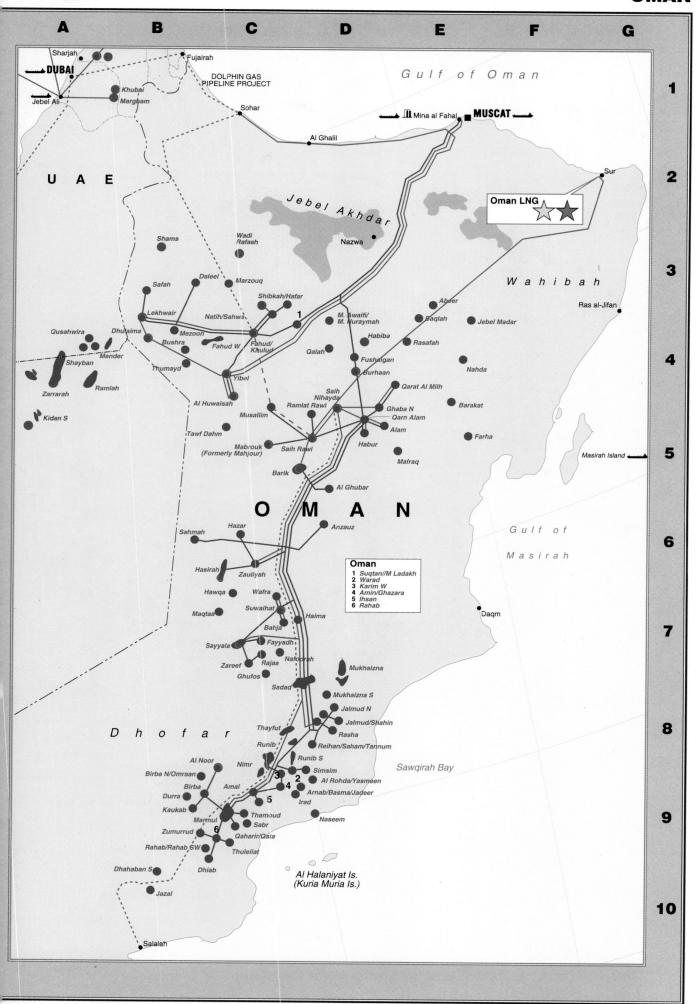

THE MIDDLE
EAST

Oman LNG

Oman
1 Suqtan//M Ladakh
2 Warad
3 Karim W
4 Amin/Ghazara
5 Ihsan
6 Rahab

DOLPHIN GAS
PIPELINE PROJECT

Gulf of Oman

Jebel Akhdar

Wahibah

*Gulf of
Masirah*

O M A N

Dhofar

Sawqirah Bay

*Al Halaniyat Is.
(Kuria Muria Is.)*

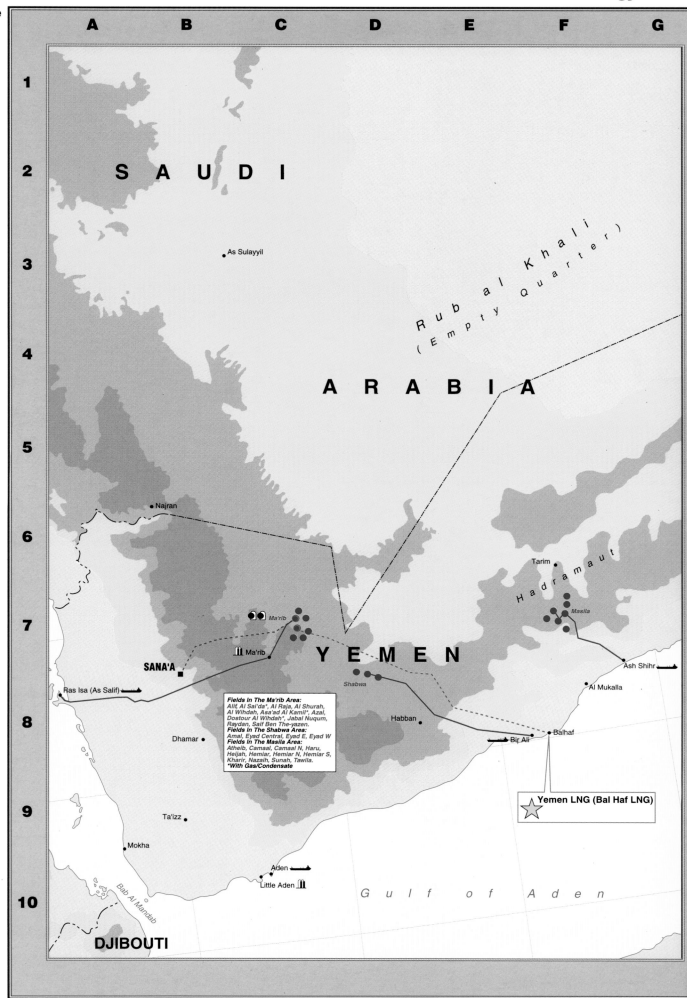

SAUDI

ARABIA

Rub al Khali
(Empty Quarter)

• As Sulayyil

• Najran

Hadramaut

Tarim •

Masila

Ma'rib

SANA'A ■

Ma'rib

YEMEN

Ash Shihr

Ras Isa (As Salif)

Shabwa

Al Mukalla

Fields In The Ma'rib Area:
Alif, Al Sai'da, Al Raja, Al Shurah,
Al Wihdah, Asa'ad Al Kamil*, Azal,
Dostour Al Wihdah*, Jabal Nuqum,
Raydan, Saif Ben The-yazen.*
Fields In The Shabwa Area:
Amal, Eyad Central, Eyad E, Eyad W
Fields In The Masila Area:
*Atheib, Camaal, Camaal N, Haru,
Heijah, Hemiar, Hemiar N, Hemiar S,
Kharir, Nazaih, Sunah, Tawila.*
***With Gas/Condensate**

Habban •

Bir Ali

Balhaf

Dhamar •

★ **Yemen LNG (Bal Haf LNG)**

Ta'izz •

Mokha •

Aden

Little Aden

Gulf of Aden

Bab Al Mandab

DJIBOUTI

Scale: 1:4,620,000

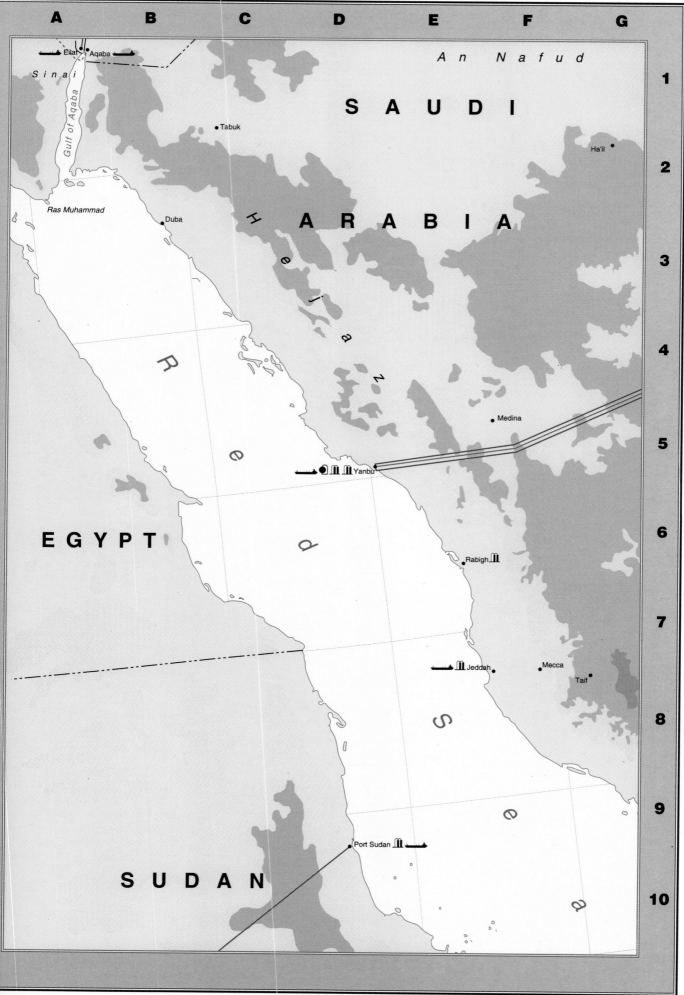

Scale: 1:4,760,000

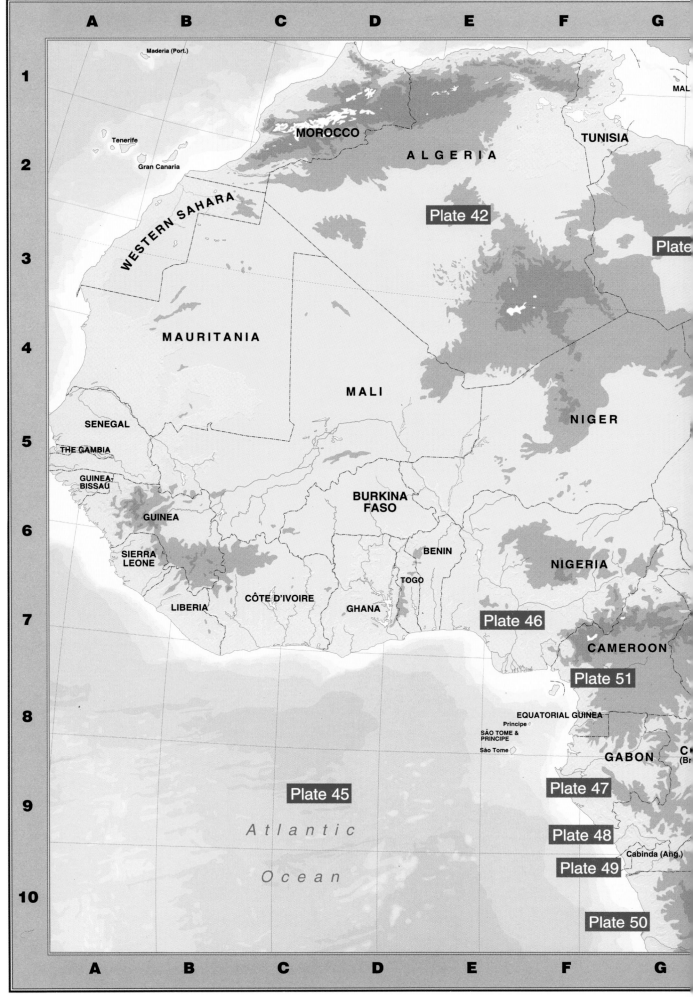

AFRICA

A B C D E F G

1
2
3
4
5
6
7
8
9
10

Maderia (Port.)

Tenerife

Gran Canaria

WESTERN SAHARA

MOROCCO

A L G E R I A

TUNISIA

MAL

Plate 42

Plate

MAURITANIA

MALI

NIGER

SENEGAL

THE GAMBIA

GUINEA BISSAU

GUINEA

SIERRA LEONE

LIBERIA

CÔTE D'IVOIRE

BURKINA FASO

BENIN

TOGO

GHANA

NIGERIA

Plate 46

CAMEROON

Plate 51

EQUATORIAL GUINEA

Principe

SÃO TOME & PRINCIPE

São Tome

GABON

C
(Br

Plate 45

Plate 47

A t l a n t i c

Plate 48

Cabinda (Ang.)

Plate 49

O c e a n

Plate 50

Scale: 1:20,000,000

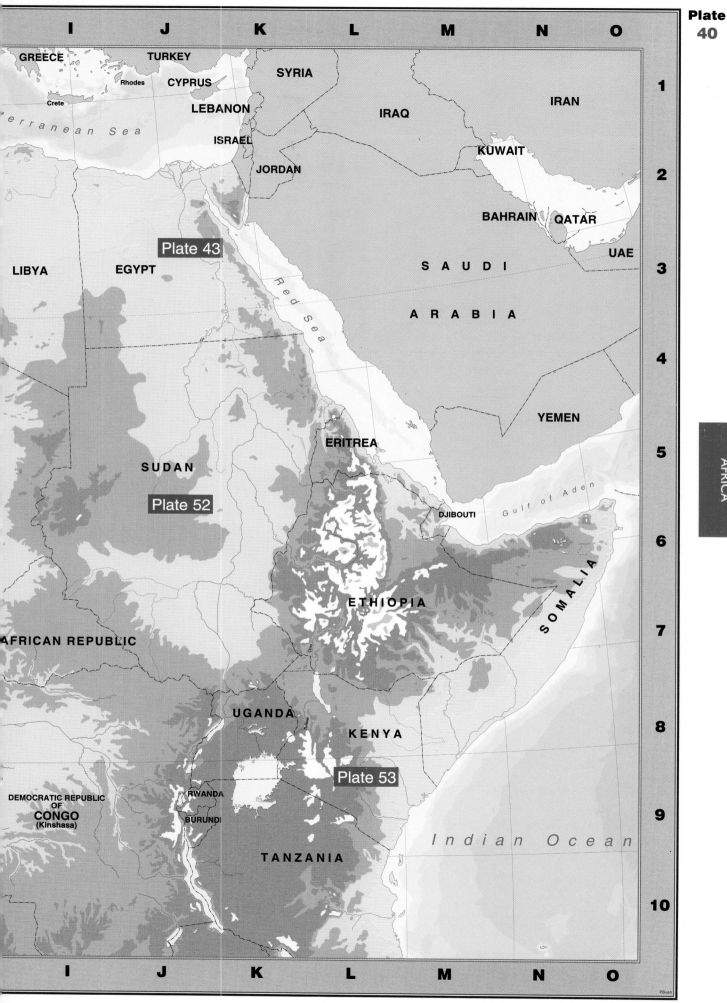

AFRICA

AFRICA

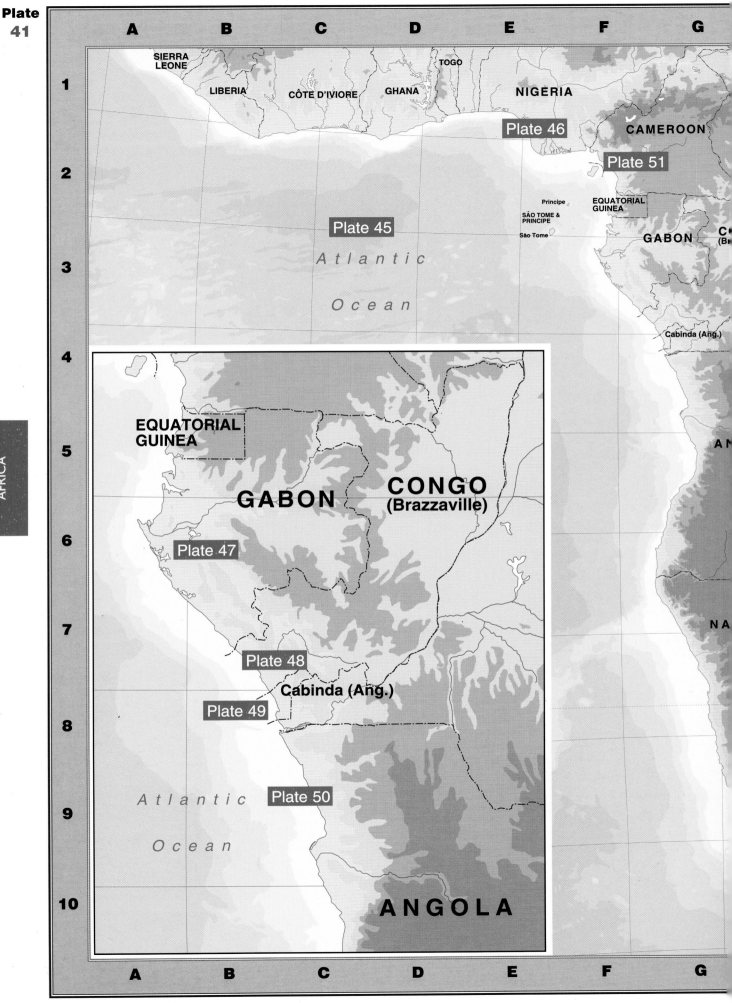

SIERRA LEONE

LIBERIA

CÔTE D'IVIORE

GHANA

TOGO

NIGERIA

Plate 46

Plate 51

CAMEROON

Principe

SÃO TOME & PRINCIPE

São Tome

EQUATORIAL GUINEA

GABON

C (Br

Plate 45

Atlantic

Ocean

Cabinda (Ang.)

AN

NA

EQUATORIAL GUINEA

GABON

CONGO
(Brazzaville)

Plate 47

Plate 48

Cabinda (Ang.)

Plate 49

Plate 50

Atlantic

Ocean

ANGOLA

Scale: 1:20,000,000

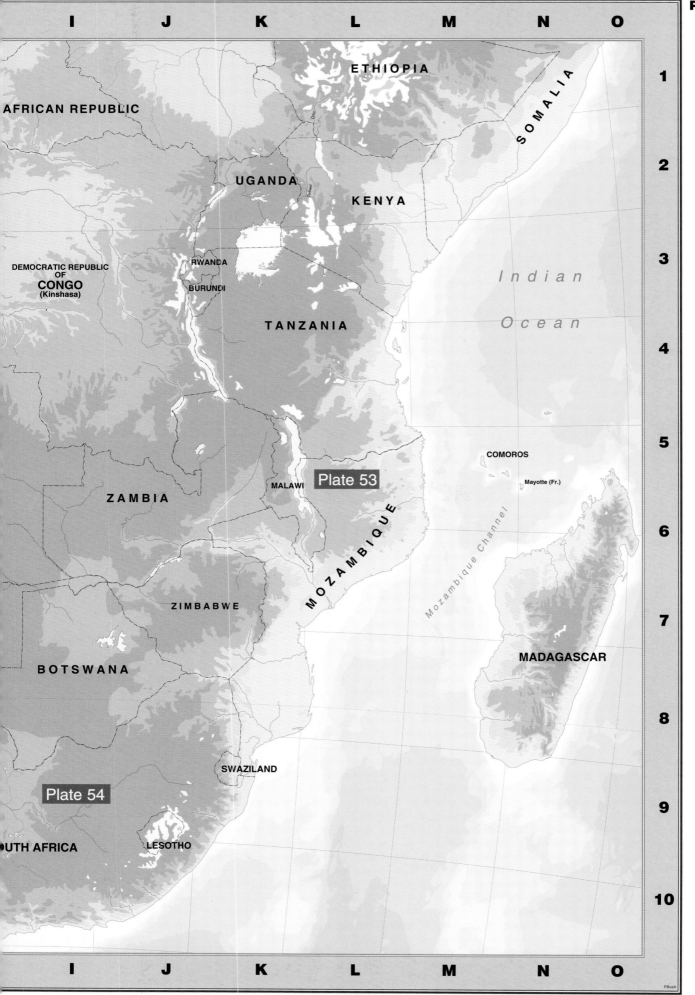

AFRICA

Plate 42

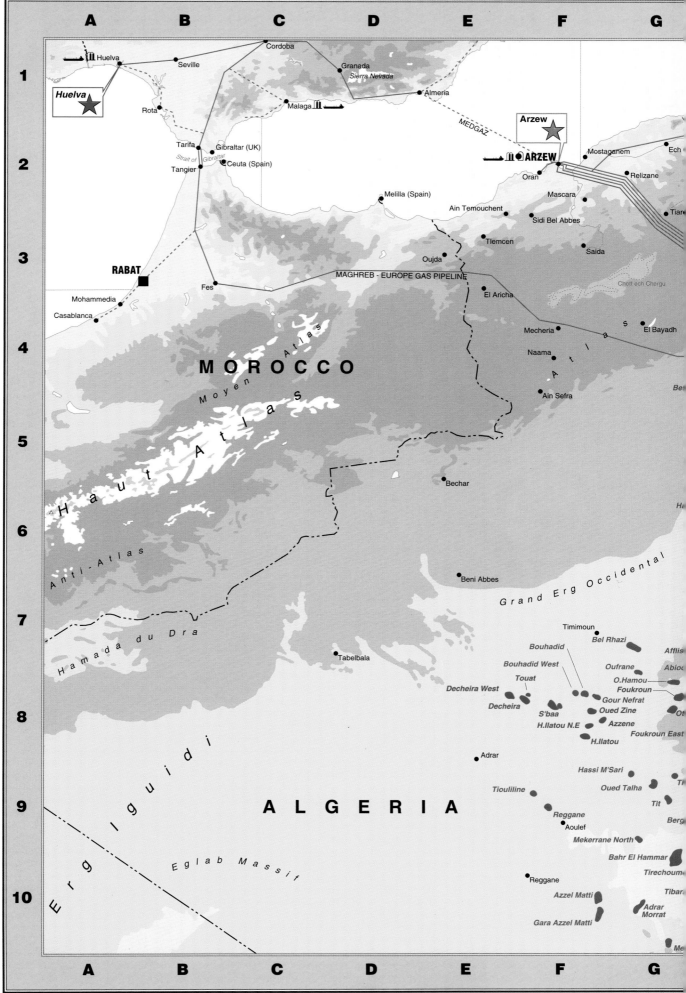

Scale: 1:5,580,000

Huelva

Arzew

MEDGAZ

Cordoba
Seville
Granada
Sierra Nevada
Almeria
Malaga
Rota
Tarifa
Gibraltar (UK)
Strait of Gibraltar
Ceuta (Spain)
Tangier
Melilla (Spain)

Mostaganem
Ech
ARZEW
Relizane
Oran
Mascara
Ain Temouchent
Tiare
Sidi Bel Abbes
Tlemcen
Saida
Oujda
Chott ech Chergu
MAGHREB - EUROPE GAS PIPELINE
El Aricha

RABAT
Fes
Mohammedia
Casablanca

El Bayadh
Mecheria
Naama
A t l a s
Ain Sefra

M O R O C C O
Moyen Atlas
Atlas

H a u t   A t l a s

Anti-Atlas

Bechar

Beni Abbes

Grand Erg Occidental

Hamada du Dra

Timimoun
Bel Rhazi
Bouhadid
Afflis
Bouhadid West
Oufrane
Abiou
Touat
O.Hamou
Foukroun
Decheira West
Gour Nefrat
Decheira
S'baa
Oued Zine
Ot
H.Ilatou N.E
Azzene
Foukroun East
H.Ilatou

Tabelbala

Adrar

Hassi M'Sari
Tiouliline
Oued Talha
Ti
Reggane
Tit
Aoulef
Berg
Mekerrane North

A L G E R I A

Eglab Massif

Bahr El Hammar
Tirechoum
Reggane
Tibar
Azzel Matti
Adrar Morrat
Gara Azzel Matti
Me

E r g   I g u i d i

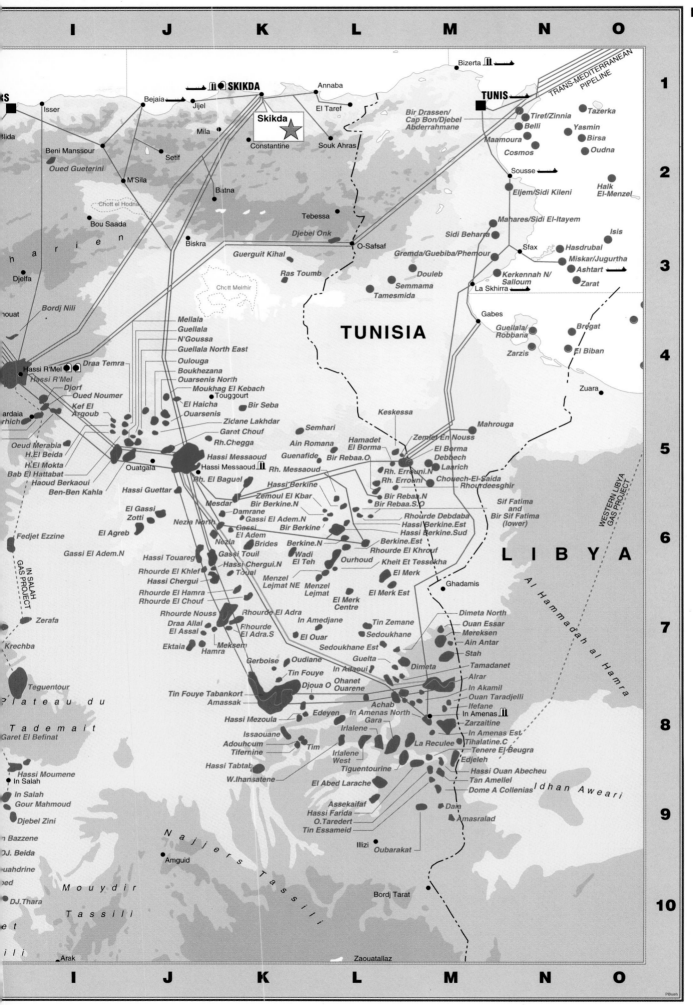

TRANS-MEDITERRANEAN PIPELINE

Bizerta

SKIKDA

Annaba

TUNIS

Bejaia
Jijel
El Taref

Isser
RS

Mila
Skikda

Constantine
Souk Ahras

Bir Drassen/
Cap Bon/Djebel
Abderrahmane

Tiref/Zinnia
Tazerka

lida

Beni Manssour
Setif

Belli
Yasmin
Birsa

Oued Gueterini

Maamoura
Cosmos

Oudna

M'Sila
Batna

Sousse
Eljem/Sidi Kileni

Halk
El-Menzel

Chott el Hodna

Bou Saada

Tebessa

Djebel Onk

Mahares/Sidi El-Itayem

Isis

Biskra
O-Safsaf
Sidi Beharra

Sfax
Hasdrubal

harien

Guerguit Kihal
Gremda/Guebiba/Phemour

Miskar/Jugurtha
Ashtart

Djelfa

Ras Toumb
Douleb

Kerkennah N/
Salloum
Zarat

Chott Melrhir

Semmama
Tamesmida

La Skhirra

houat

Bordj Nili

TUNISIA

Gabes

Bregat

Mellala
Guellala
N'Goussa
Guellala North East

Guellala/
Robbana

El Biban

ardaia

Hassi R'Mel
Draa Temra

Oulouga
Boukhezana
Ouarsenis North

Zarzis

rhich

Hassi R'Mel
Djorf
Oued Noumer

Moukhag El Kebach
Touggourt
Bir Seba

Keskessa

Zuara

Kef El
Argoub
El Haicha
Ouarsenis

Mahrouga

Oeud Merabia
H.El Beida
H.El Mokta
Bab El Hattabat

Ziclane Lakhdar
Garet Chouf
Rh.Chegga

Semhari
Ain Romana
Guenafide

Hamadet
El Borma
Bir Rebaa.O

Zemlet En Nouss
El Borma
Debbech
Laarich

Ouatgala
Hassi Messaoud
Hassi Messaoud
Rh. Messaoud

Rh. Errouni.N
Rh. Errouni

Chouech-El-Saida
Rhourdeesghir

Haoud Berkaoui
Ben-Ben Kahla
Hassi Guettar
Rh. El Baguel
Hassi Berkine

Bir Rebaa.N
Bir Rebaa.S.O

Sif Fatima
and
Bir Sif Fatima
(lower)

El Gassi
Zotti
Mesdar
Damrane
Zemoul El Kbar
Bir Berkine.N

Rhourde Debdaba
Hassi Berkine.Est
Hassi Berkine.Sud

El Agreb
Nezla North
Gassi El Adem.N
Gassi
El Adem
Bir Berkine
Berkine.N

Berkine.Est

Fedjet Ezzine
Gassi El Adem.N
Nezla
Brides

Rhourde El Khrouf

Hassi Touareg
Gassi Touil
Wadi
El Teh
Ourhoud
Kheit Et Tessekha

IN SALAH
GAS PROJECT
Rhourde El Khlef
Hassi Chergui.N
Toual
El Merk

Menzel
Lejmat NE
Menzel
Lejmat
El Merk Est
Ghadamis

L I B Y A

Zerafa
Hassi Chergui
Rhourde El Hamra
Rhourde El Chouf

El Merk
Centre

Al Hammadah al Hamra

Rhourde Nouss
Rhourde El Adra
In Amedjane
Tin Zemane

Dimeta North
Ouan Essar
Mereksen

Krechba
Draa Allal
El Assal
Rhourde
El Adra.S
El Ouar
Sedoukhane
Sedoukhane Est

Ain Antar
Stah

WESTERN-LIBYA
GAS PROJECT

Ektaia
Meksem
Hamra
Guelta
Dimeta
Tamadanet

Gerboise
Oudiane
In Adaoui
Alrar

Teguentour
Tin Fouye
Djoua O
Ohanet
Ouarene
In Akamil
Ouan Taradjelli

Plateau du

Tin Fouye Tabankort
Amassak
Ilefane

Hassi Mezoula
Edeyen
In Amenas North
Gara
Achab
In Amenas

Tademait

Zarzaitine
In Amenas Est

Garet El Befinat
Issaouane
Adouhcum
Tifernine
Tim
Irlalene
La Reculee
Tihalatine.C
Tenere El Beugra

Hassi Moumene
In Salah
Hassi Tabtab
Irlalene
West
Tiguentourine
Edjeleh

In Salah
Gour Mahmoud
W.Ihansatene
El Abed Larache
Hassi Ouan Abecheu
Tan Amellel
Dome A Collenias

Idhan Aweari

Djebel Zini
Assekaifaf
Hassi Farida
O.Taredert
Tin Essameid
Daia
Amasralad

Bazzene
DJ. Beida

N a j j e r s
T a s s i l i

Illizi
Oubarakat

uahdrine
ed

Amguid

M o u y d i r

T a s s i l i

DJ.Thara

Bordj Tarat

li

Arak
Zaouatallaz

AFRICA

Plate
43

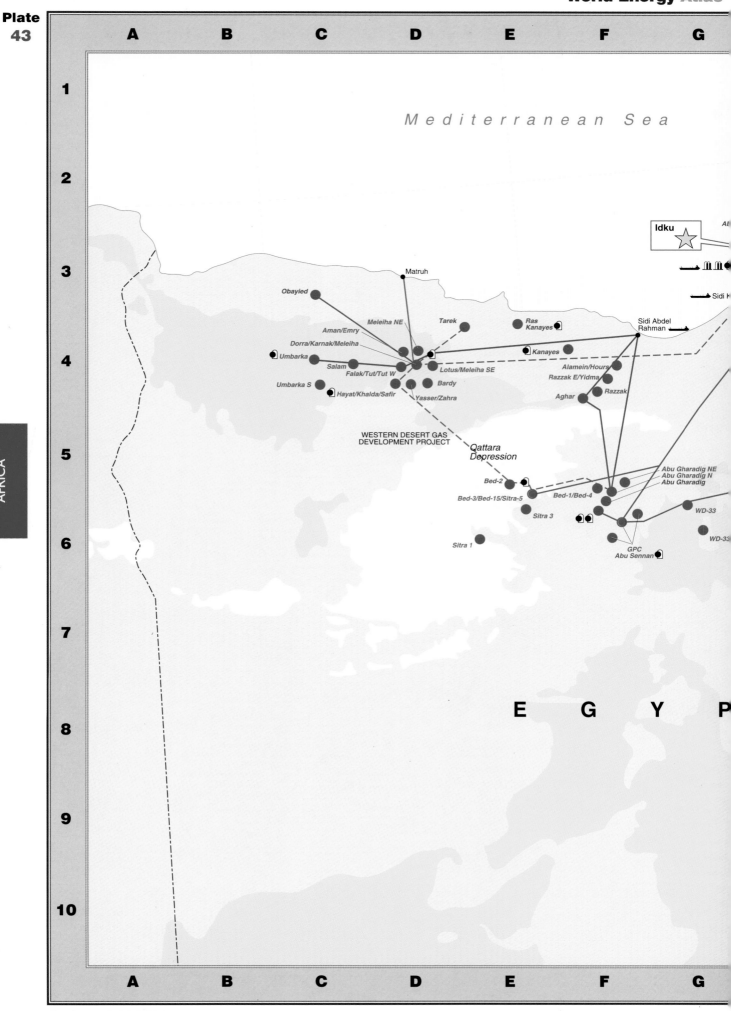

AFRICA

Scale: 1:3,000,000

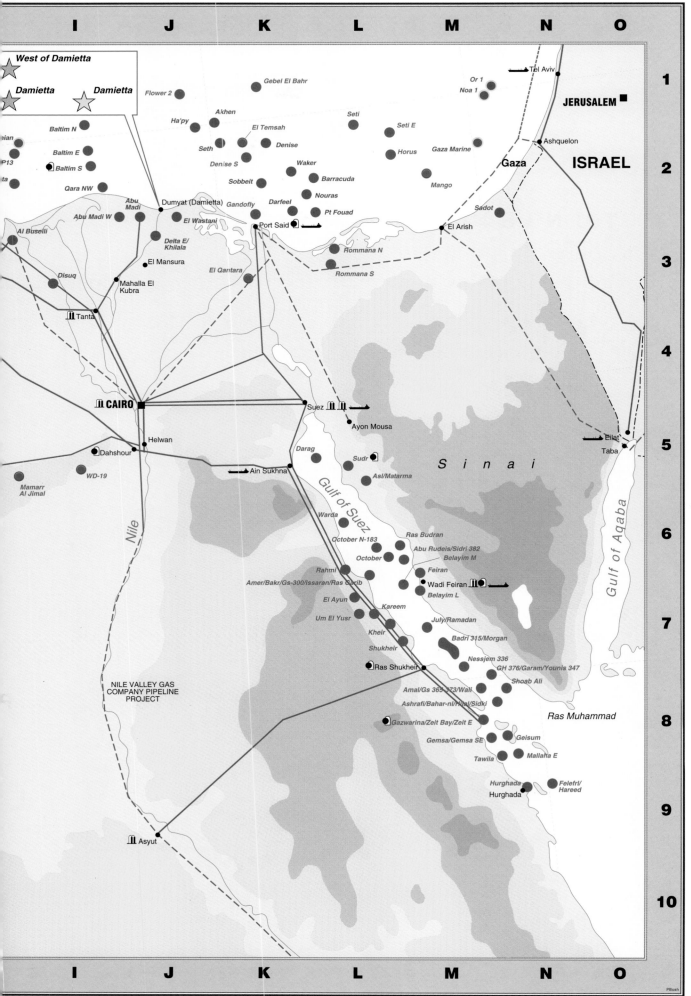

West of Damietta

Damietta   Damietta

Flower 2
Gebel El Bahr
Or 1
Noa 1
→ Tel Aviv

JERUSALEM

Baltim N
Ha'py
Akhen
Seti
Ashquelon
Seti E
P13
Baltim E
El Temsah
Denise
Horus
Gaza Marine
Gaza
ISRAEL
Baltim S
Seth
Denise S
Waker
Qara NW
Abu Madi
Dumyat (Damietta)
Gandofly
Sobbeit
Barracuda
Mango
Abu Madi W
El Wastani
Darfeel
Nouras
Sadot
Al Buselli
Delta E/
Khilala
Port Said
Pt Fouad
El Arish
El Mansura
Disuq
El Qantara
Rommana N
Mahalla El
Kubra
Rommana S
Tanta

CAIRO

Helwan
Suez
Dahshour
Ayon Mousa
Sinai
WD-19
Mamarr
Al Jimal
Darag
Sudr
Eilat
Taba

AFRICA

Ain Sukhna
Asl/Matarma
Warda
Ras Budran
October N-183
Abu Rudeis/Sidri 382
Belayim M
October
Feiran
Rahmi
Wadi Feiran
Amer/Bakr/Gs-300/Issaran/Ras Garib
Belayim L
El Ayun
Kareem
Um El Yusr
July/Ramadan
Kheir
Badri 315/Morgan
Shukheir
Nessjem 336
Ras Shukheir
GH 376/Garam/Younis 347
Amal/Gs 365-373/Wali
Shoab Ali
NILE VALLEY GAS
COMPANY PIPELINE
PROJECT
Ashrafi/Bahar-nl/Hilal/Sidki
Ras Muhammad
Gazwarina/Zeit Bay/Zeit E
Gemsa/Gemsa SE
Geisum
Tawila
Mallaha E
Hurghada
Felefrl/
Hareed
Hurghada

Asyut

Gulf of Suez

Gulf of Aqaba

Nile

Plate 44

AFRICA

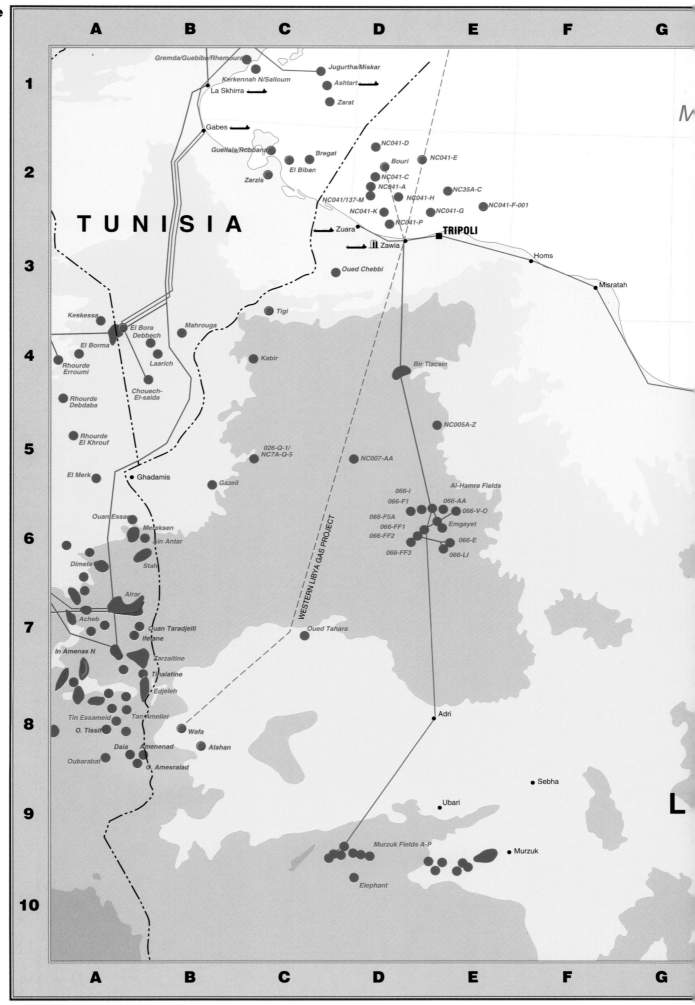

Scale: 1:4,630,000

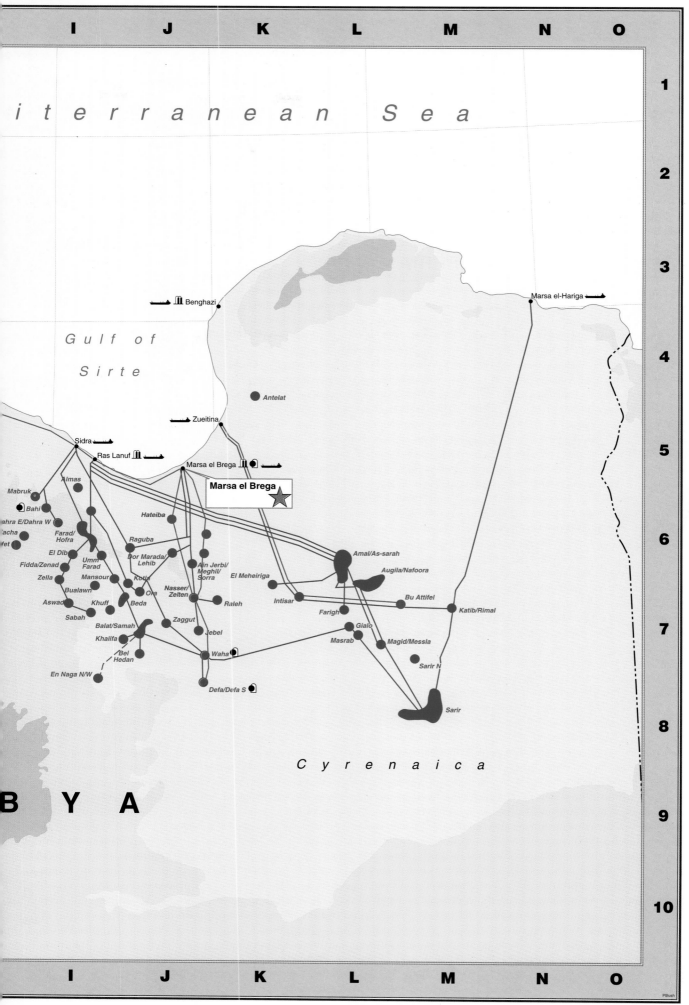

Mediterranean Sea

Gulf of
Sirte

Benghazi

Marsa el-Hariga

Antelat

Zueitina

Sidra

Ras Lanuf

Marsa el Brega

Marsa el Brega

Almas

Mabruk

Bahi

ahra E/Dahra W

acha

fet

Hateiba

Farad/
Hofra

Raguba

El Dib

Dor Marada/
Lehib

Ain Jerbi/
Meghil/
Sorra

El Meheiriga

Amal/As-sarah

Augila/Nafoora

Fidda/Zenad

Umm
Farad

Kotla

Bu Attifel

Zella

Mansour

Ora

Nasser/
Zelten

Intisar

Farigh

Katib/Rimal

Bualawn

Khuff

Beda

Raleh

Aswad

Sabah

Zaggut

Gialo

Balat/Samah

Masrab

Magid/Messla

Khalifa

Jebel

Bel
Hedan

Waha

Sarir N

En Naga N/W

Defa/Defa S

Sarir

Cyrenaica

BYA

Plate 45

AFRICA

Scale: 1:10,000,000

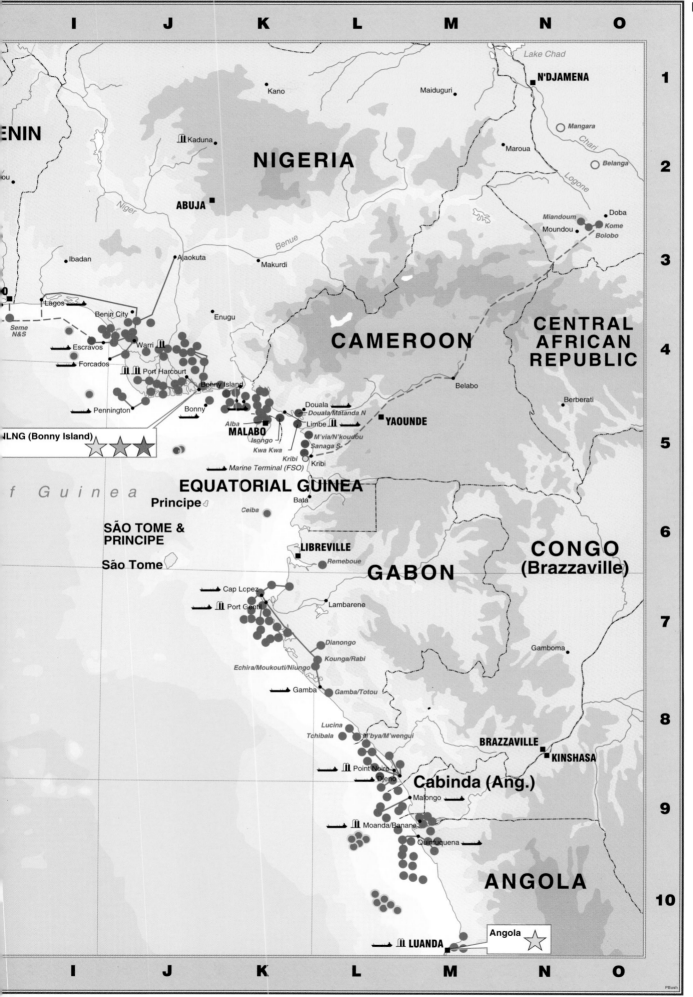

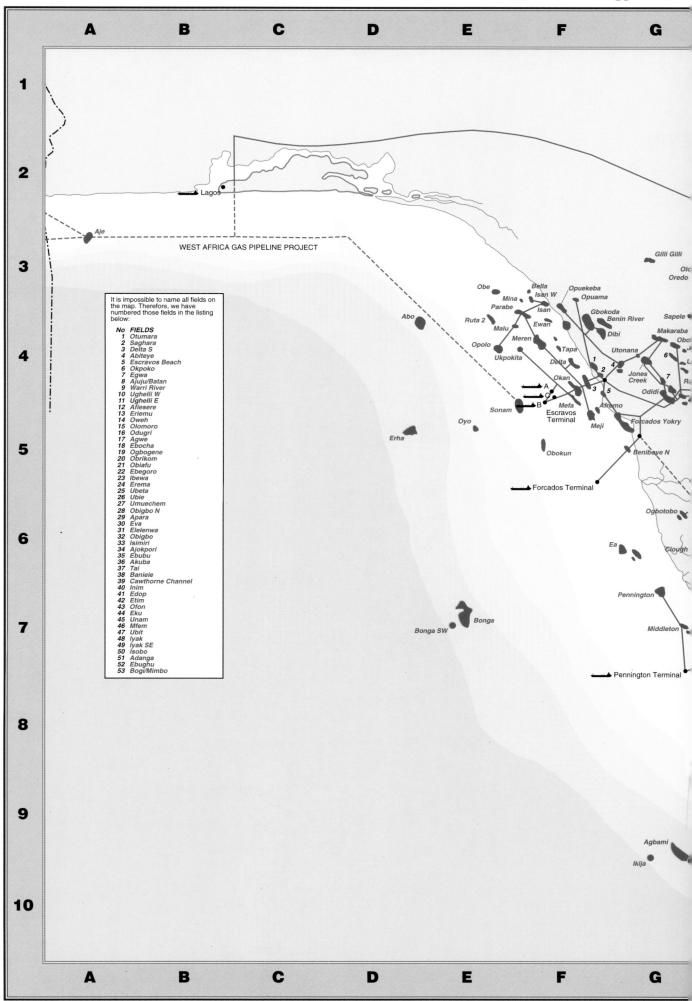

AFRICA

A   B   C   D   E   F   G

1

2

→ Lagos

Aje

WEST AFRICA GAS PIPELINE PROJECT

3

It is impossible to name all fields on
the map. Therefore, we have
numbered those fields in the listing
below:

No	FIELDS
1	Otumara
2	Saghara
3	Delta S
4	Abiteye
5	Escravos Beach
6	Okpoko
7	Egwa
8	Ajuju/Batan
9	Warri River
10	Ughelli W
11	Ughelli E
12	Afiesere
13	Eriemu
14	Oweh
15	Olomoro
16	Odugri
17	Agwe
18	Ebocha
19	Ogbogene
20	Obrikom
21	Obiafu
22	Ebegoro
23	Ibewa
24	Erema
25	Ubeta
26	Ubie
27	Umuechem
28	Obigbo N
29	Apara
30	Eva
31	Elelenwa
32	Obigbo
33	Isimiri
34	Ajokpori
35	Ebubu
36	Akuba
37	Tai
38	Baniele
39	Cawthorne Channel
40	Inim
41	Edop
42	Etim
43	Ofon
44	Eku
45	Unam
46	Mfem
47	Ubit
48	Iyak
49	Iyak SE
50	Isobo
51	Adanga
52	Ebughu
53	Bogi/Mimbo

Gilli Gilli

Old
Oredo

Obe

Bella
Isan W

Opuekeba

Opuama

Mina
Parabe

Isan

Gbokoda

Benin River

Sapele

Ruta 2

Malu

Ewan

Dibi

Makaraba

Obo

Abo

Opolo

Meren

Tapa

Utonana

6

Ukpokita

Delta

1   4

Jones
Creek

7

R

A

2

C

Okan

3   5

Odidi

B

Sonam

Mefa
Escravos
Terminal

Afremo

Oyo

Meji

Forcados Yokry

Erha

Obokun

Benibeye N

→ Forcados Terminal

Ogbotobo

4

Ea

Clough

5

Pennington

6

Bonga

Middleton

Bonga SW

7

→ Pennington Terminal

8

9

Agbami

Ikija

10

A   B   C   D   E   F   G

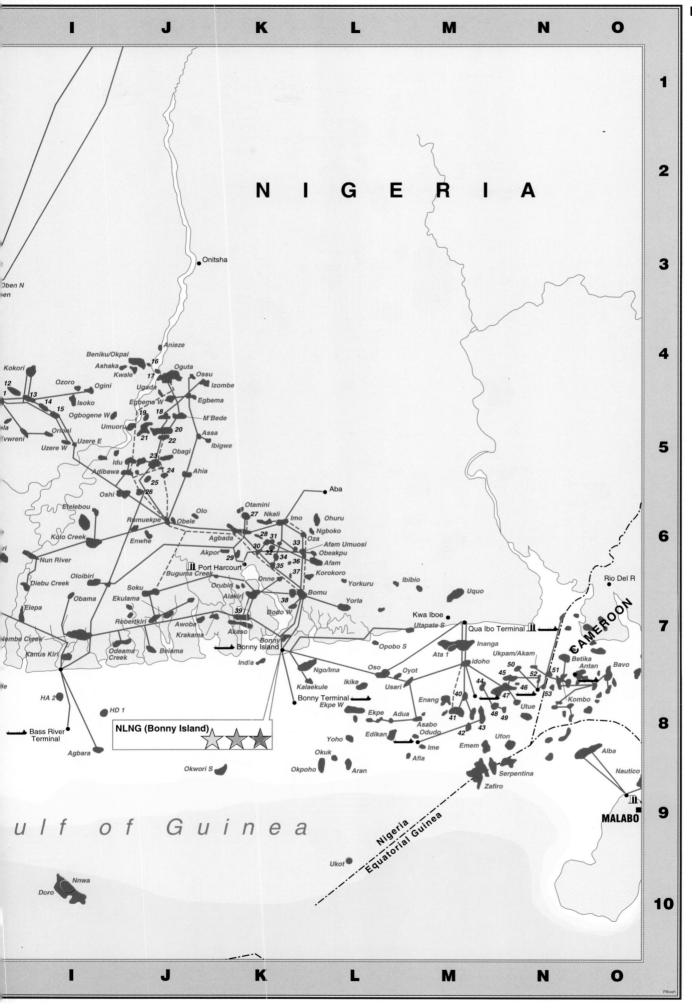

NLNG (Bonny Island) ★ ★ ★

AFRICA

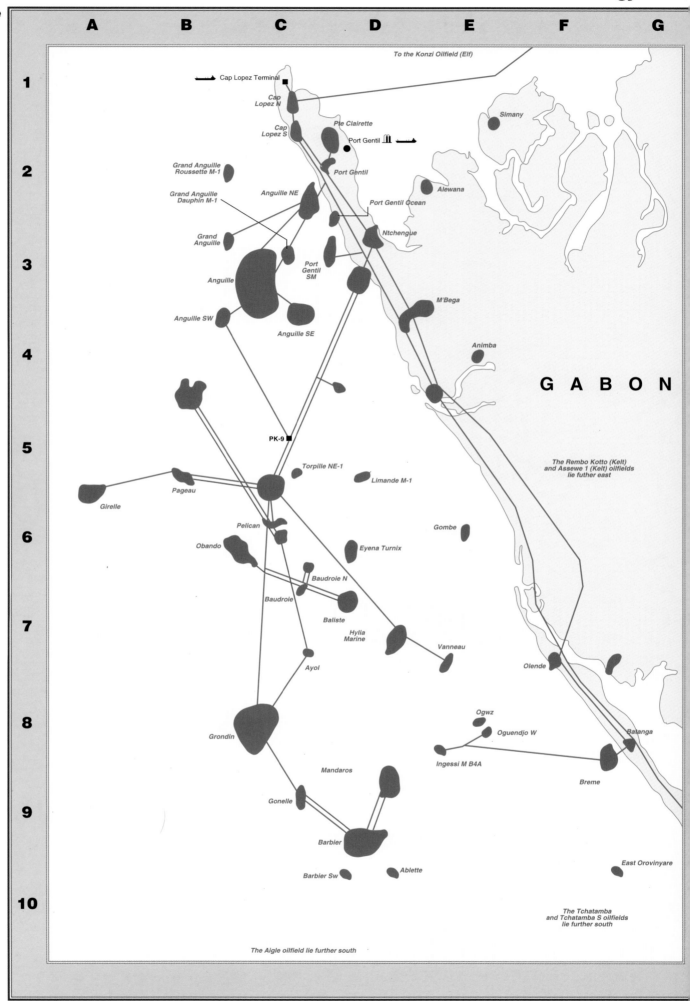

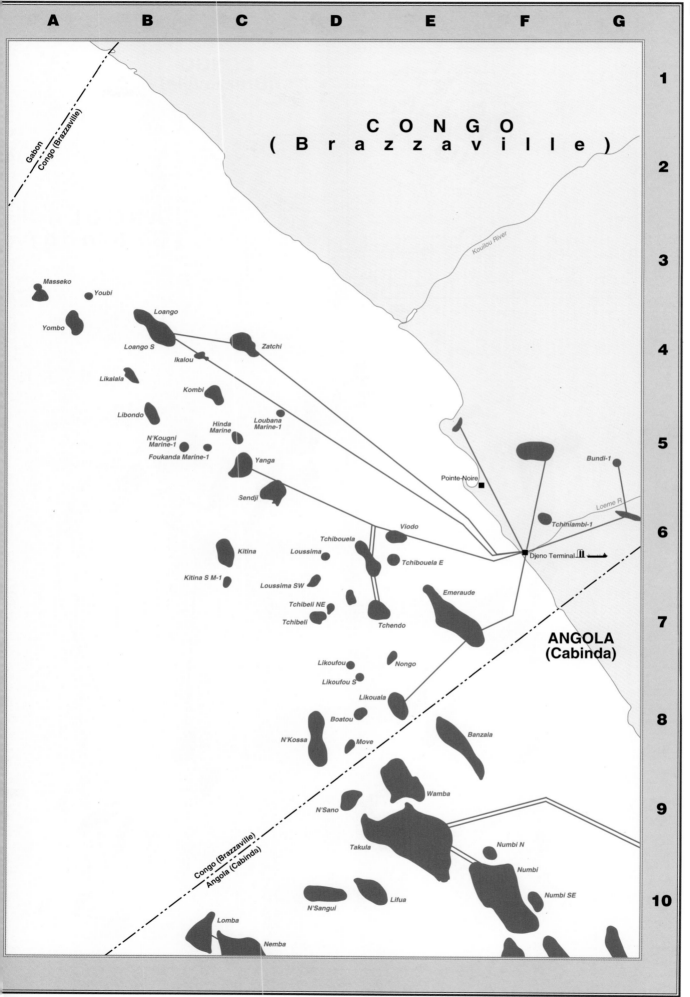

CONGO (Brazzaville)

Gabon
Congo (Brazzaville)

Kouilou River

Masseko
Youbi
Yombo
Loango
Loango S
Ikalou
Zatchi
Likalala
Kombi
Libondo
Hinda Marine
Loubana Marine-1
N'Kougni Marine-1
Foukanda Marine-1
Yanga
Sendji
Pointe-Noire
Bundi-1
Loeme R
Tchiniambi-1
Viodo
Tchibouela
Kitina
Loussima
Tchibouela E
Kitina S M-1
Loussima SW
Emeraude
Tchibeli NE
Tchibeli
Tchendo
Djeno Terminal

ANGOLA
(Cabinda)

Likoufou
Nongo
Likoufou S
Likouala
Boatou
N'Kossa
Move
Banzala
Wamba
N'Sano
N'Sangui
Takula
Numbi N
Numbi
Numbi SE
Lifua
Lomba
Nemba

Congo (Brazzaville)
Angola (Cabinda)

AFRICA

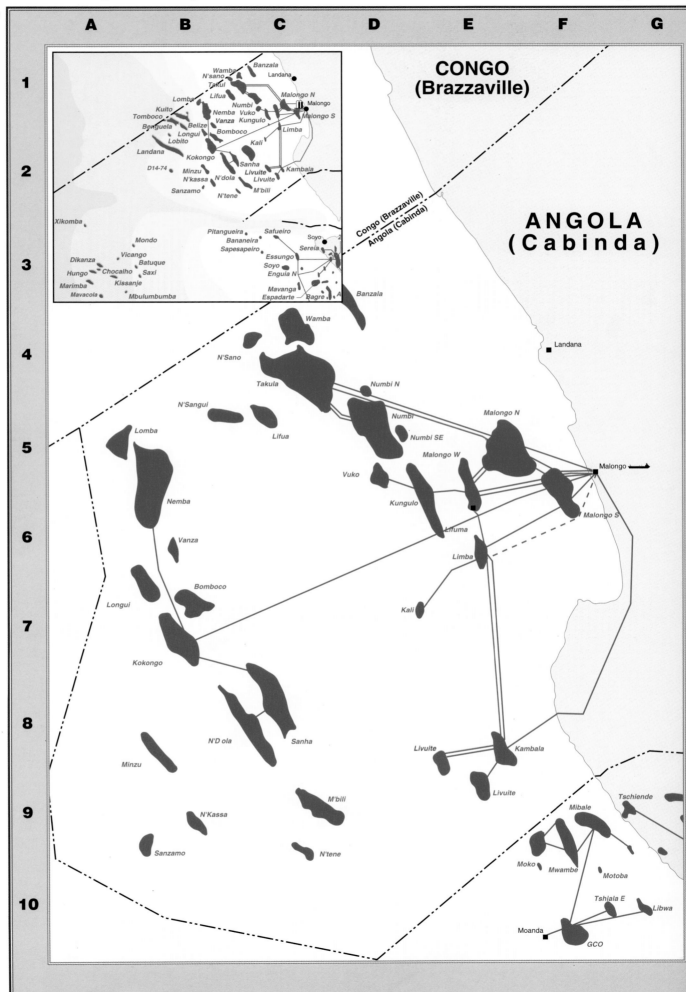

CONGO
(Brazzaville)

ANGOLA
(Cabinda)

Scale: 1:525,000

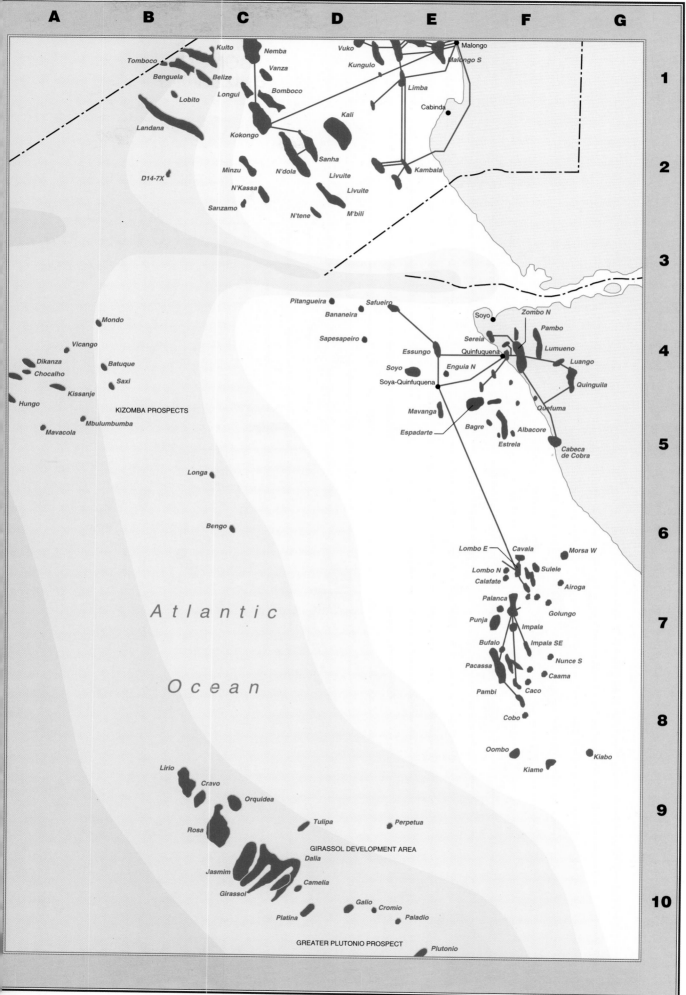

Scale: 1:1,630,000

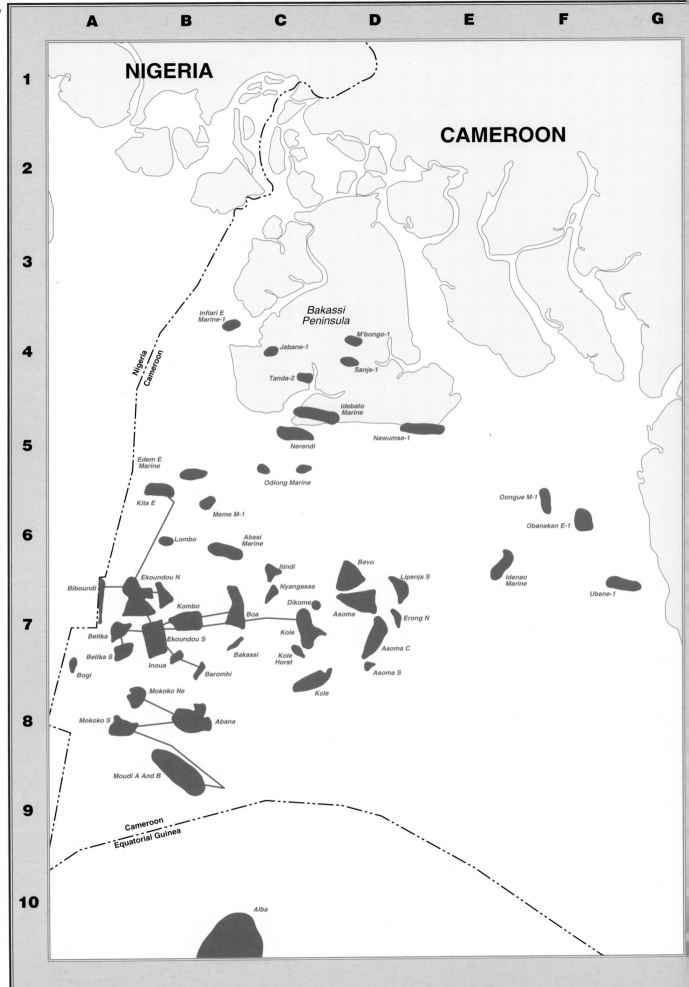

NIGERIA

CAMEROON

Nigeria
Cameroon

Infiari E
Marine-1

M'bongo-1

Jabane-1

Sanje-1

Tanda-2

Bakassi
Peninsula

Idebato
Marine

Nawumse-1

Nerendi

Edem E
Marine

Odiong Marine

Oongue M-1

Kita E

Meme M-1

Obanekan E-1

Lombo

Abasi
Marine

Bavo

Itindi

Lipenja S

Idenao
Marine

Ekoundou N

Nyangassa

Dikome

Ubene-1

Biboundi

Asoma

Erong N

Kombo

Boa

Betika

Ekoundou S

Kole

Betika S

Bakassi

Kole
Horst

Asoma C

Inoua

Barombi

Bogi

Asoma S

Kole

Mokoko Ne

Mokoko S

Abana

Moudi A And B

Cameroon
Equatorial Guinea

Alba

AFRICA

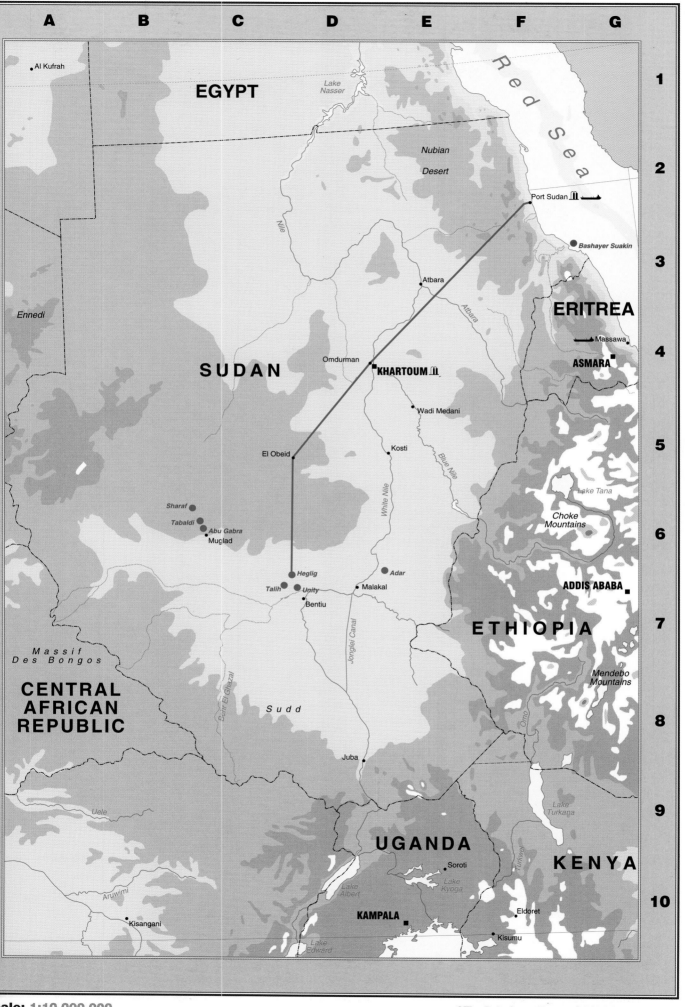

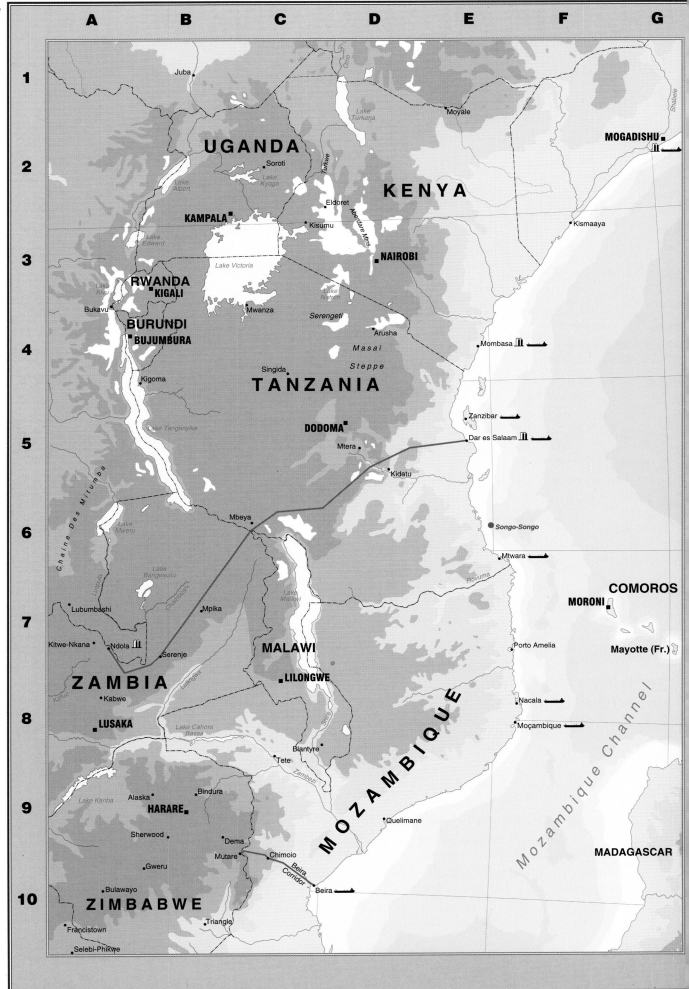

AFRICA

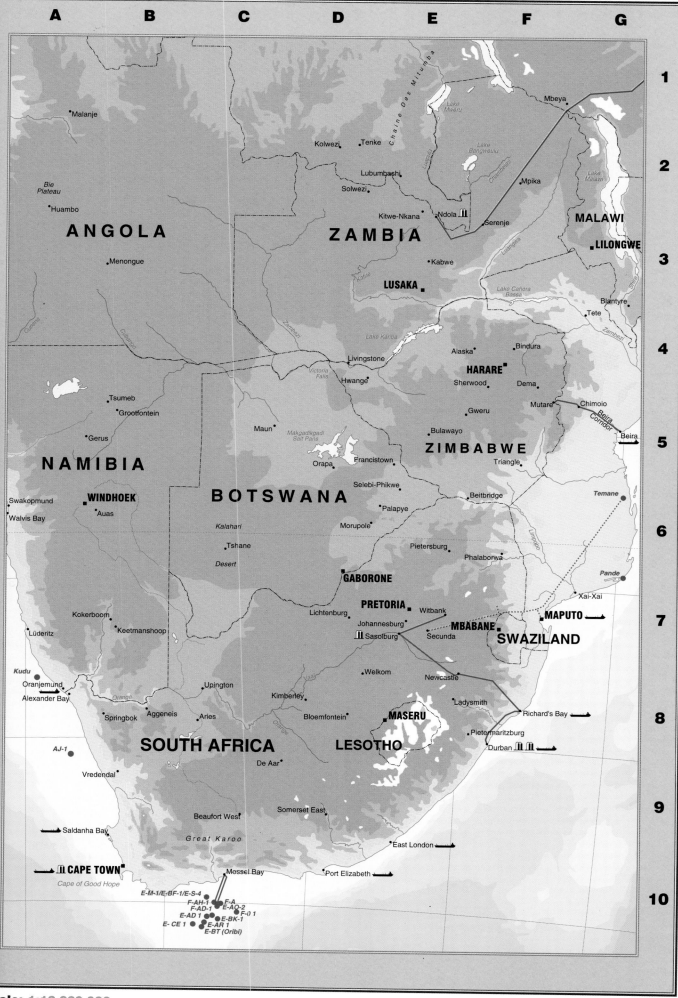

A B C D E F G

1
2
3
4
5
6
7
8
9
10

AFRICA

•Malanje

*Bie
Plateau*
•Huambo

ANGOLA

•Menongue

Kolwezi   •Tenke

Lubumbashi•
Solwezi•   Kitwe-Nkana•

ZAMBIA

•Kabwe

LUSAKA
•

Chaine Des Mitumba

*Lake
Mweru*

*Lake
Bangweulu*

Ndola▥

Mpika•

Serenje•

*Lake
Cahora
Bassa*

Mbeya•

MALAWI

LILONGWE

*Lake
Malawi*

Blantyre•

Tete•

•Tsumeb
•Grootfontein

•Gerus

NAMIBIA

Livingstone•

*Victoria
Falls*

Hwange•

Maun•

*Makgadikgadi
Salt Pans*

Lake Kariba

Alaska•   Bindura•

HARARE•
Sherwood•   Dema•

•Gweru

Bulawayo•

ZIMBABWE

Triangle•

Mutare• Chimoio•

*Beira
Corridor*

Beira•

Swakopmund•
Walvis Bay•

WINDHOEK
•Auas

Orapa• Francistown•

Selebi-Phikwe•

BOTSWANA

Kalahari

•Tshane

Desert

Morupole•

Palapye•

Beitbridge•

Pietersburg•

Temane•

Phalaborwa•

Limpopo

Pande•

Xai-Xai•

Kudu
Oranjemund•

Kokerboom•
•Lüderitz   Keetmanshoop•

Alexander Bay•

Springbok• Aggeneis• Aries•

AJ-1•

Vredendal•

Upington•

Kimberley•

Orange

Bloemfontein•

GABORONE

Lichtenburg•

PRETORIA•
Johannesburg•

▥Sasolburg•

Witbank•

Secunda•

Vaal
Welkom•

MASERU

LESOTHO

Newcastle•

MBABANE•

SWAZILAND

MAPUTO

Ladysmith•

Pietermaritzburg•

Durban▥▥

SOUTH AFRICA

De Aar•

Somerset East•

Beaufort West•

Great Karoo

→Saldanha Bay•

▥**CAPE TOWN**•

Cape of Good Hope

Mossel Bay•

E-M-1/E-BF-1/E-S-4
F-AH-1• •F-A
F-AD-1• •E-AO-2
E-AD 1•   •F-0 1
E- CE 1• •E-BK-1
•E-AR 1
E-BT (Oribi)

Richard's Bay→

East London→

Port Elizabeth→

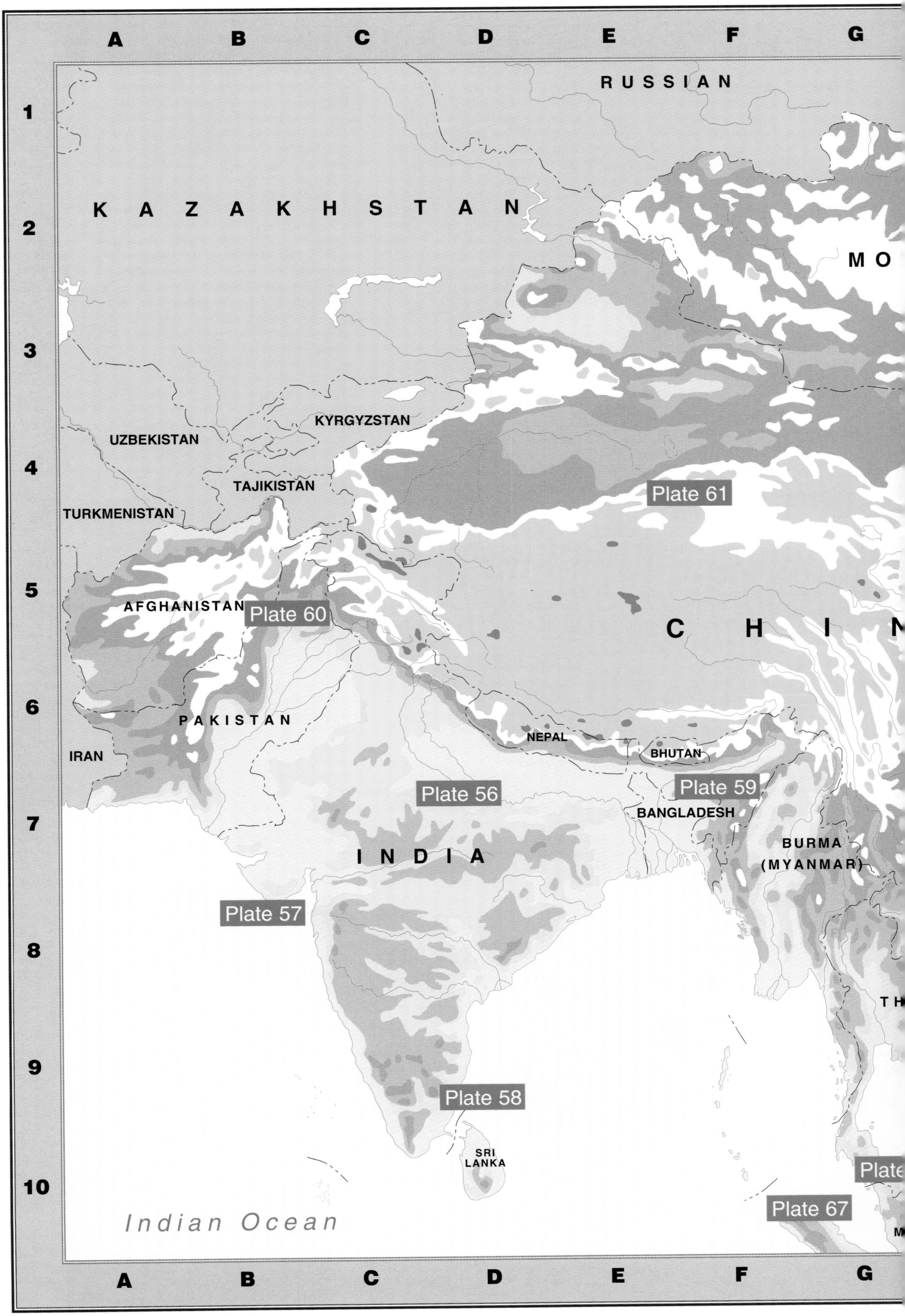

A B C D E F G

1
2
3
4
5
6
7
8
9
10

RUSSIAN

K A Z A K H S T A N

M O

UZBEKISTAN

KYRGYZSTAN

TAJIKISTAN

TURKMENISTAN

Plate 61

C H I N

AFGHANISTAN Plate 60

PAKISTAN

IRAN

NEPAL

BHUTAN

Plate 56

Plate 59

BANGLADESH

I N D I A

BURMA
(MYANMAR)

Plate 57

T H

Plate 58

Plate 59

Plate 67

SRI
LANKA

Plate

Indian Ocean

M

A B C D E F G

ASIA

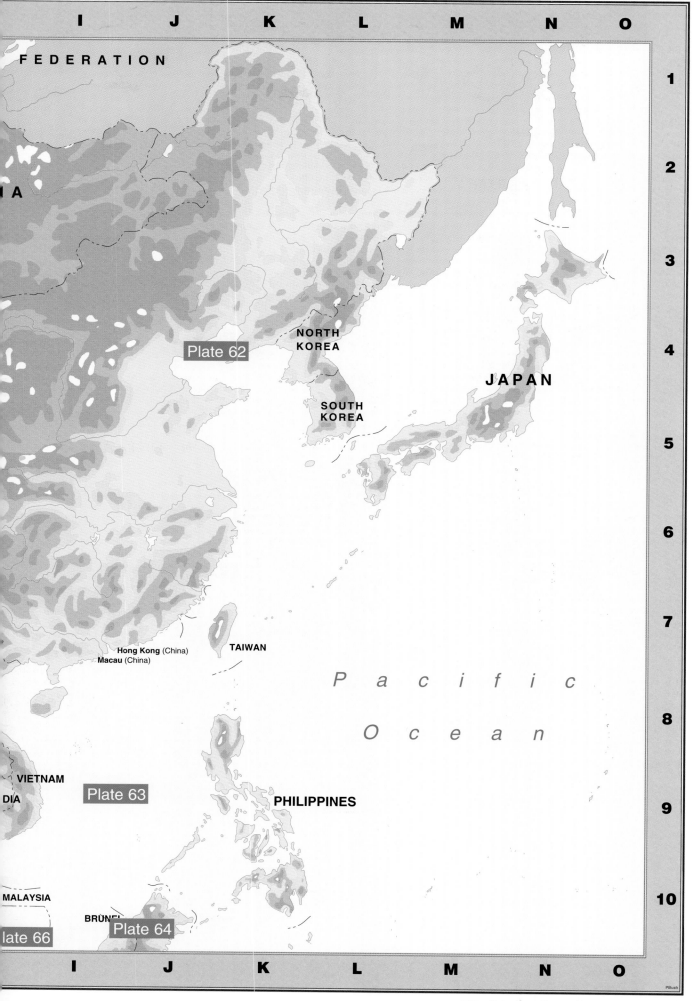

I J K L M N O

1

2

3

4

5

6

7

8

9

10

FEDERATION

A

NORTH
KOREA

Plate 62

SOUTH
KOREA

JAPAN

Pacific

Ocean

Hong Kong (China)
Macau (China)

TAIWAN

VIETNAM

DIA

Plate 63

PHILIPPINES

MALAYSIA

BRUNEI

late 66

Plate 64

ASIA

I J K L M N O

Plate 56

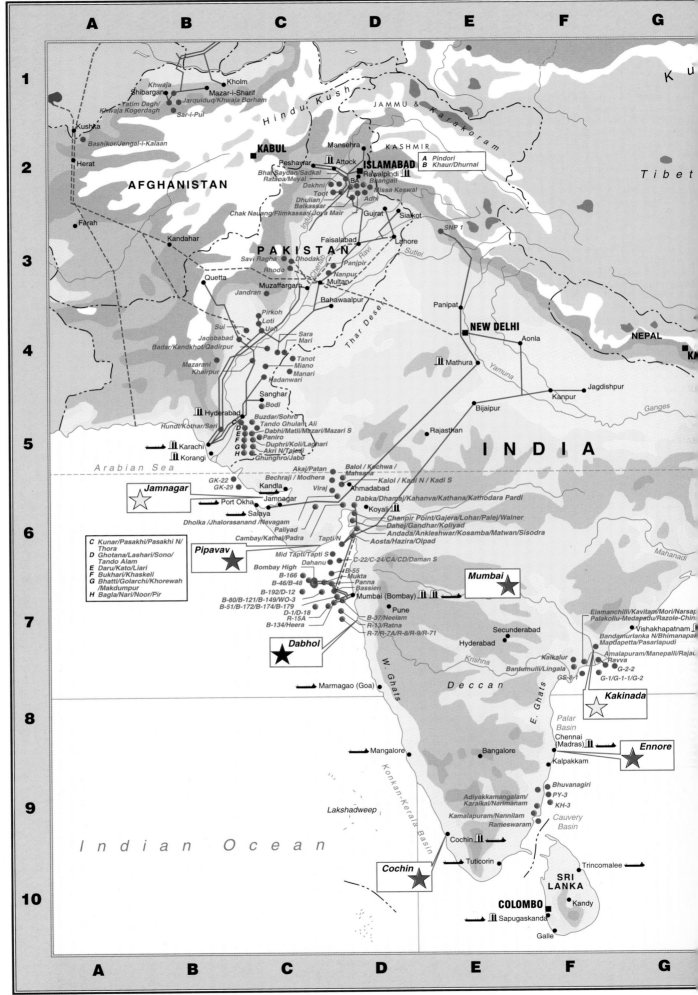

ASIA

I J K L M N O

1 2 3 4 5 6 7 8 9 10

ASIA

Qaidam
Basin

Shaan-Gan-Ning
Dongfanghong
Wuqi
Qingjian
Maline
Panlong
Yongping
Chenghua/Huachi
Yanchang
Xiashiwan/
Yan'an
Golmud
Zhilijo
Changqing/Qinyang/Quzi
Lanzhou
Xi'an
Huang He

CHINA

Qamdo
Zhongba
Nanchong
Yingshan
Chengdu
Sichuan
Nanchong
Jiannan
Lhasa
Penglaizhen
Loutusi/Lungtusi
Hechuan
Tsangpo
Weiyuan
Chongqing
Ziging/Zilinjing
Huangkuan Shan/Shiyougou
Shengdeng-Shan
Luzhou
Yankaosi
Naxi
Changyuanba
Chunxiao
Guiyang

THIMPHU
BHUTAN
Digboi/Kusijian
Digboi
Ravug
Dikom/Nahorkatiya/
Raighati/Tinali/Zaloni
Tharsang
Bongalgaon
Guwahati
Assam
Bogapani/Jorajan/Tarajan/Tipling
Lakwa/Moran/Napuma/Sonari
olla/Champang/Uriamghat
Khogharat
Nagaland
Charalai/Demulgaan/Geleki/Naharhabi/Namti/Rudrasagar
Borsilla
Jamaipur
Masimpur
Myitkyina
Arangsupur/Badarpur
Panchgram
Qili
BANGLADESH
Banshkondi
Kunming
Agartala/Rokhia
Gojalia
DHAKA
Tiandong
Xi

BURMA
(MYANMAR)
Chittagong
Mandalay
Letpando
Ayadaw/Pagan/Tuywintanaung/Yenangyat
Maoming
Ngahaingdain
Chauk/Lanywa
HANOI
Weizhou
Zhanjiang
Chauk
Yenangyat
Sittwe
Mann
Kyundaw
Fang
Haikou
(Akyab)
Htaukshabin/Shwelinban
Malun
Wan
Jinfeng
Yenanima
Ledaung
Mae Soon/San-Sae
Hainan Is
Allanmyo
Pyaye
Pyalo
Chiang Mai
Sanya
Kyaukpyu/Yenandaung
Prome
Prome
LAOS
Vinh
Myanaung/Inbyin/Shwepyitha
Yacheng
Kyontani
VIENTIANE

YANGON (RANGOON)
Syriam
Bung Muang/
Bung Ye
Phu Horm
Dong Mun
Savannakhet
Mae Sot
Wat Tean
Nam Phong
Hue
Kyaiklat/Payagon
Pratutao
Sirikit
Chonnabot
Da Nang
Wichian Buri

3CA/MOC
Yadana (3DA)
THAILAND
Tha Luang
Ayutthaya
Kaeng Khoi
VIETNAM
Sawng
Rat Buri
BANGKOK
Bang Chak
Sri Racha
Yetagun
Mab Ta Phud/
Sattahip
Rayong
CAMBODIA
Andaman Is. (India)
Andaman Sea
Gulf
of
Thailand
PHNOM PENH
Kompong Som
Ho Chi Minh City
Ba Ria
Ruby
Nang Nuan
Tantawan
Vung Tau
Rang Dong
Kaphong/Platong/Surat
Bach Ho
Nicobar Is. (India)
Pladang/Platong S
Rong
Baanpot/Dara/Erawan
Trat
Pakarang/Satun
Con Son Basin
Arun
Khanom
Funan/Jakrawan
Pailin
Dai Hung
Bongkot
Thailand-Malaysia
Joint Development
Area
Lan Do
Songkhla
Pilona
Bunga Pakma/Bunga Orkid
Lan Tay
Penang
Bunga Raya
Damar
Bundi/Bundi S
MALAYSIA
Kangar
Bintang/Lawit
Likut N/Penara
Bedong
Abu Kecil/Bubu
Tujoh
Chermingat/Langat/Peta Kiri/Sertudon

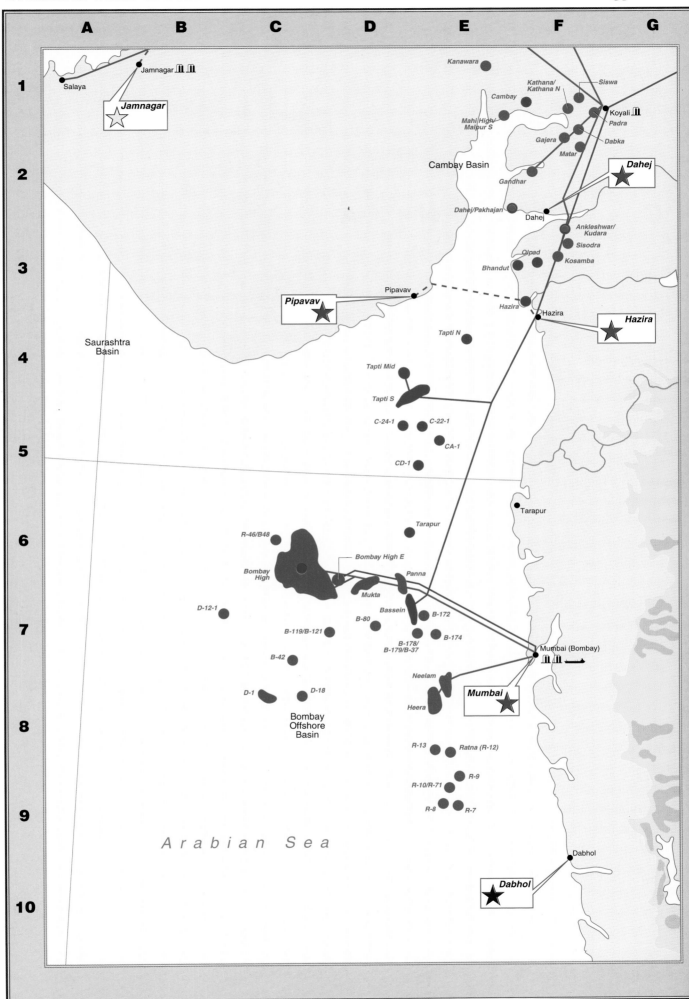

Salaya
Jamnagar
Jamnagar
Kanawara
Kathana/
Kathana N
Siswa
Cambay
Koyali
Padra
Mahi High/
Malpur S
Gajera
Dabka
Matar
Dahej
Cambay Basin
Gandhar
Dahej/Pakhajan
Dahej
Ankleshwar/
Kudara
Sisodra
Olpad
Kosamba
Bhandut
Pipavav
Pipavav
Hazira
Hazira
Hazira
Saurashtra
Basin
Tapti N
Tapti Mid
Tapti S
C-24-1
C-22-1
CA-1
CD-1
Tarapur
Tarapur
R-46/B48
Bombay High E
Bombay
High
Panna
Mukta
D-12-1
Bassein
B-80
B-172
B-119/B-121
B-174
B-178/
B-179/B-37
B-42
Mumbai (Bombay)
D-1
D-18
Neelam
Mumbai
Bombay
Offshore
Basin
Heera
R-13
Ratna (R-12)
R-10/R-71
R-9
R-8
R-7
Arabian Sea
Dabhol
Dabhol

ASIA

Scale: 1:2,500,000

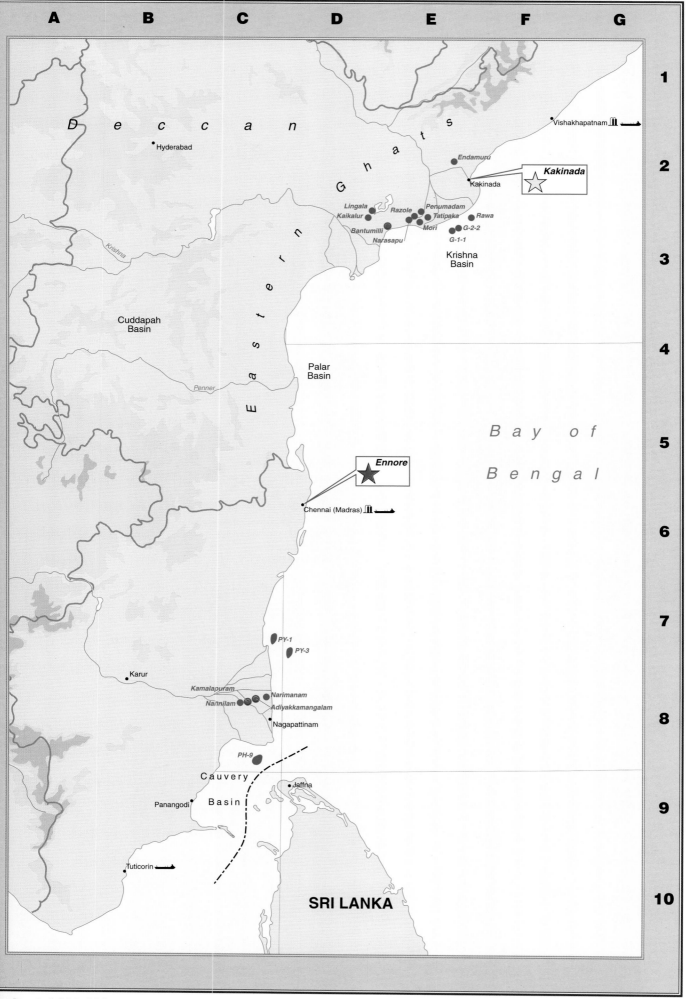

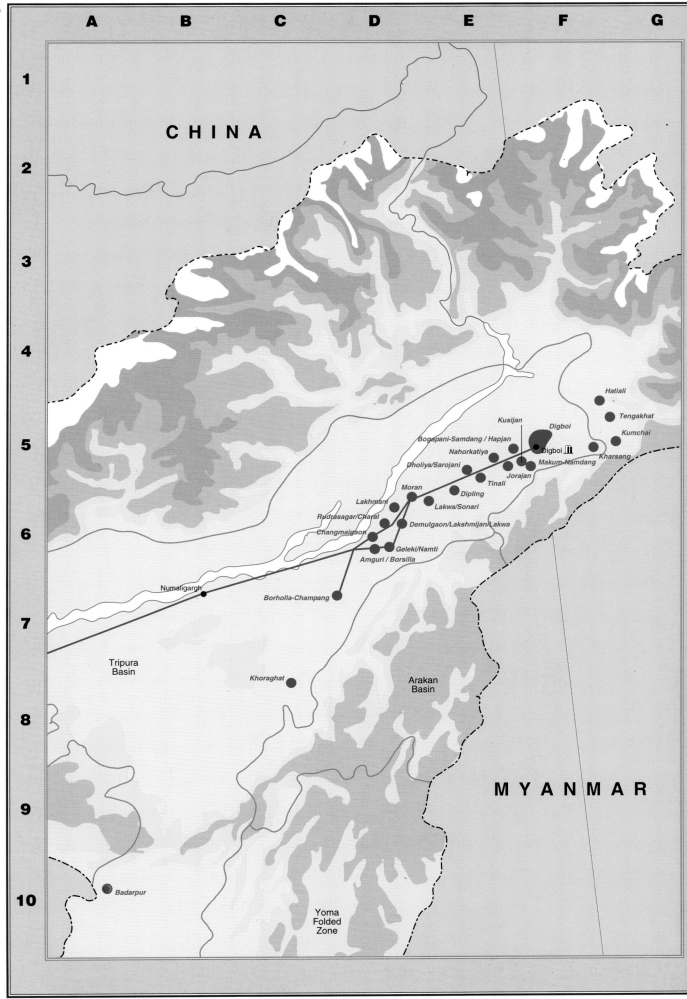

A

B

C

D

E

F

G

1

2

3

4

5

6

7

8

9

10

C H I N A

M Y A N M A R

Hatiali

Tengakhat

Kusijan

Digboi

Kumchai

Bogapani-Samdang / Hapjan

Nahorkatiya

Digboi

Kharsang

Dholiya/Sarojani

Makum-Namdang

Jorajan

Tinali

Moran

Dipling

Lakhmani

Lakwa/Sonari

Rudrasagar/Charal

Demulgaon/Lakshmijan/Lakwa

Changmaigaon

Geleki/Namti

Amguri / Borsilla

Numaligargh

Borholla-Champang

Tripura
Basin

Khoraghat

Arakan
Basin

Badarpur

Yoma
Folded
Zone

Scale: 1:2,480,000

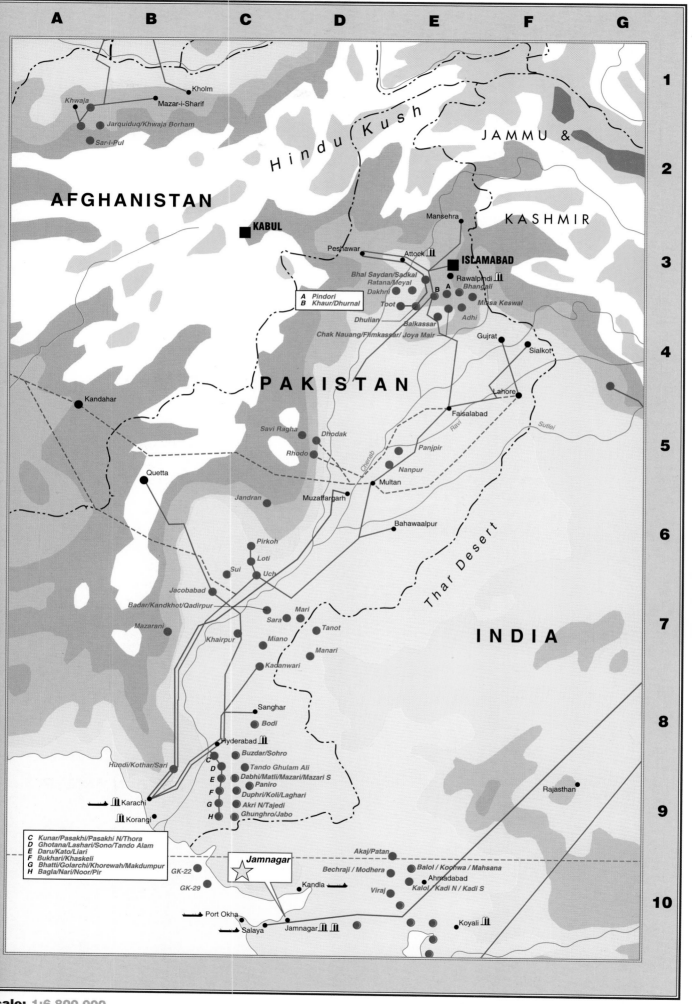

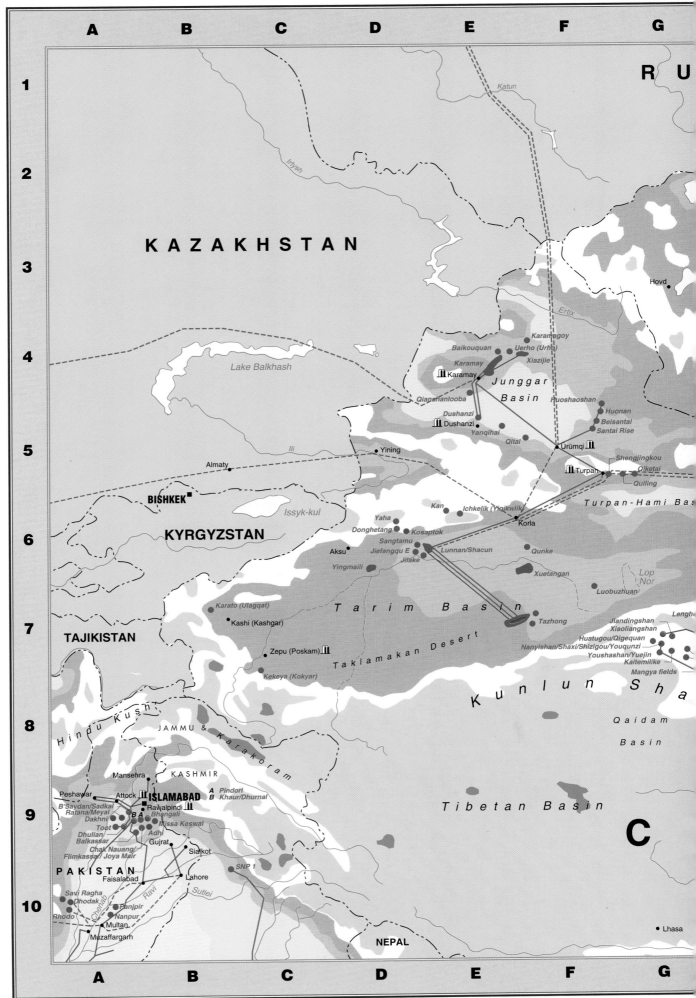

ASIA

R U

KAZAKHSTAN

Lake Balkhash

Almaty

BISHKEK

KYRGYZSTAN

Issyk-kul

TAJIKISTAN

Hindu Kush

JAMMU &

Karakoram

KASHMIR

Mansehra

Peshawar
Attock
ISLAMABAD
B'Saydan/Sadkal
Ratana/Meyal
Dakhni
Toot
Rawalpindi
Bhangali
A
B A
Missa Keswal
Dhulian/
Balkassar
Adhi
Chak Nauang/
Flimkassar/ Joya Mair
Gujrat
Sialkot
A Pindori
B Khaur/Dhurnal

PAKISTAN
Faisalabad
Lahore
SNP 1

Savi Ragha
Dhodak
Rhodo
Panjpir
Nanpur
Multan
Muzaffargarh

NEPAL

Lhasa

Katun

Hovd

Ertix

Irtysh

Ili

Yining

Karamgoy
Baikouquan
Uerho (Urho)
Karamay
Xiazijie
Karamay
Junggar
Basin
Qiapghanlooba
Huoshaoshan
Huonan
Dushanzi
Beisantal
Dushanzi
Santai Rise
Yanqihai
Qitai
Urümqi
Shengjingkou
Turpan
Qiketai
Quiling
Turpan-Hami Bas

Kan
Ichkelik (Yiqikwlik)
Yaha
Korla
Donghetang
Kosaptok
Sangtamu
Aksu
Jiefangqu E
Lunnan/Shacun
Yingmaili
Jilake
Qunke
Xuetangan
Lop
Nor
Luobuzhuan

T a r i m   B a s i n

Karato (Ulagqat)
Kashi (Kashgar)
Tazhong
Jiandingshan
Xiaoliangshan
Huatugou/Qigequan
Nanyishan/Shaxi/Shizigou/Youqunzi
Youshashan/Yuejin
Kaitemilike
Mangya fields
Lengh

Zepu (Poskam)
T a k l a m a k a n   D e s e r t

Kekeya (Kokyar)

K u n l u n   S h a

Qaidam
Basin

Tibetan Basin

C

Ertix

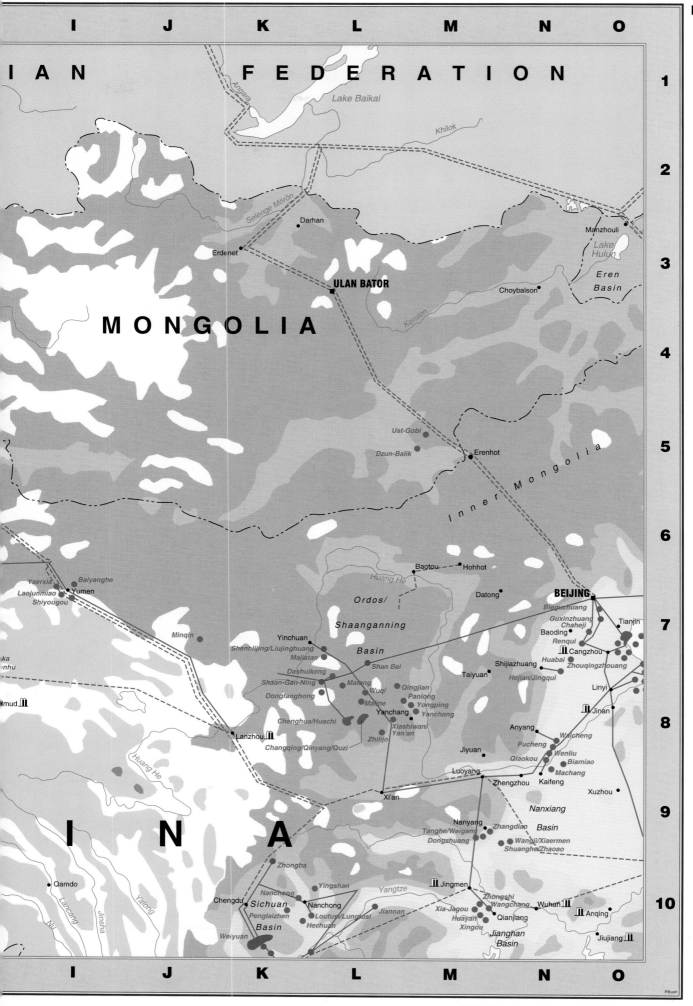

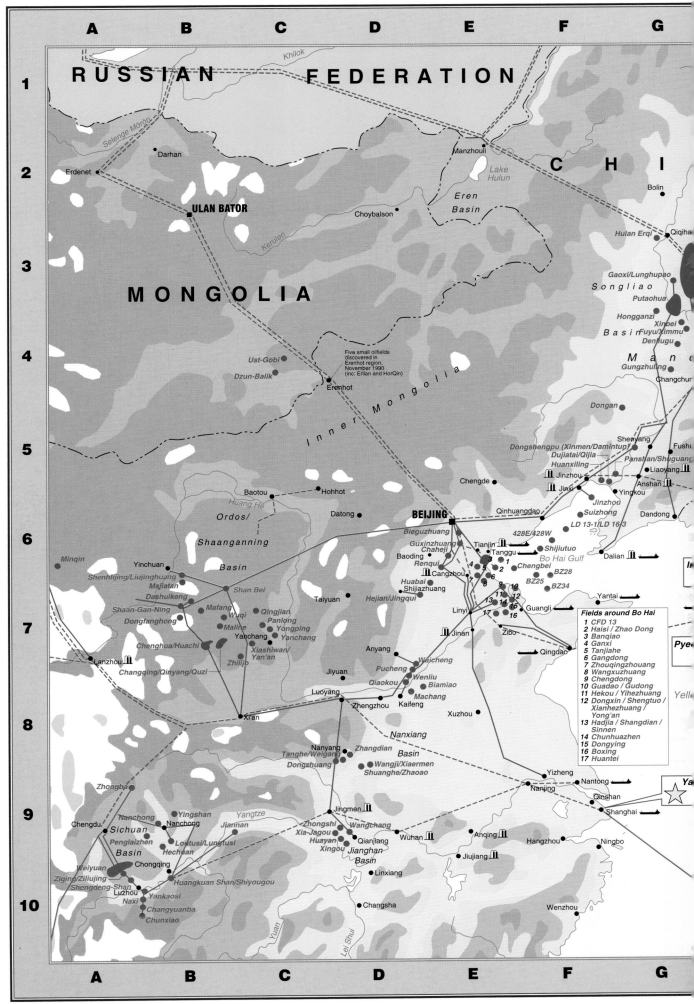

RUSSIAN   FEDERATION

Khilok

Darhan

Manzhouli

CHI

Erdenet

Lake Hulun

Bolin

Selenge Mörön

Eren Basin

Choybalsan

ULAN BATOR

Hulan Erqi   Qiqiha

Kerulen

MONGOLIA

Gaoxi/Lunghupao

Songliao

Putaohua

Hongganzi   *Xinbei*

Basin *Fuyu/Ximmu*

Denglugu

Ust-Gobi

Five small oilfields
discovered in
Erenhot region,
November 1990
(inc: Erlian and HorQin)

Man

Dzun-Balik

Gungzhuling

Inner Mongolia

Dongan

Changchur

Erenhot

Dongshengpu (Xinmen/Damintun)

Shenyang   Fushu

Dujiatai/Qijia

Huanxiling   *Panshan/Shiguang*

Baotou   Hohhot

Chengde

Jinzhou

Jinxi   Liaoyang

Yingkou   Anshan

Huang He

Jinzhou

Datong

BEIJING

Qinhuangdao

Suizhong

Dandong

Ordos/

Bieguzhuang

LD 13-1/LD 16-3

Shaanganning

Guxinzhuang

428E/428W

Chaheji

Tianjin

Dalian

Basin

Tanggu

Shijiutuo

Renqui

Bo Hai Gulf

Minqin

Baoding

4

Chengbei

BZ28

Yinchuan

Cangzhou

3   1

5   2

BZ25   BZ34

Shenhlijing/Liujinghuang

Huabai

7   6

Majiatan

Shijiazhuang

8   9   10

Shan Bei

Taiyuan

Hejian/Jingqui

11   12

Yantai

Dashuikeng

13   14   15

Shaan-Gan-Ning

Mafang   *Qingjian*

Linyi

16

Dongfanghong   *Wuqi*   *Panlong*

17

Guangli

Maline   *Yongping*

Yanchang   *Yanchang*

Zibo

Chenghua/Huachi   *Xiashiwan/*

Yan'an

Lanzhou

Zhilijo

Jinan

Changqing/Qinyang/Quzi

Anyang

Weicheng

Qingdao

Jiyuan

Pucheng

Wenliu

Qiaokou   *Biamiao*

Luoyang

Machang

Zhengzhou

Kaifeng

Xuzhou

Xi'an

Nanxiang

Nanyang

Zhangdian

Basin

Tanghe/Weigang

Wangji/Xiaermen

Yizheng

Dongzhuang

Shuanghe/Zhaoao

Nanjing

Nantong

Zhongba

Yangtze

Jingmen

Qinshan

Ya

Nanchong   *Yingshan*

Shanghai

Chengdu   Nanchong

Jiannan

Zhongshi   *Wangchang*

Sichuan   *Loutusi/Lungtusi*

Xia-Jagou

Wuhan

Anqing

Hangzhou

Ningbo

Penglaizhen   *Hechuan*

Huayan   Qianjiang

Basin   Chongqing   *Xingou*   *Jianghan*

Weiyuan   *Basin*

Jiujiang

Ziging/Ziliujing   *Huangkuan Shan/Shiyougou*

Linxiang

Shengdeng-Shan

Luzhou

Yankaosi

Naxi   *Changyuanba*

Changsha

Wenzhou

Chunxiao

Yuan

Lei Shui

Fields around Bo Hai

1 CFD 13
2 Haisi / Zhao Dong
3 Banqiao
4 Ganxi
5 Tanjiahe
6 Gangdong
7 Zhouqingzhouang
8 Wangxuzhuang
9 Chengdong
10 Guadao / Gudong
11 Hekou / Yihezhuang
12 Dongxin / Shengtuo /
   Xianhezhuang /
   Yong'an
13 Hadjia / Shangdian /
   Sinnen
14 Chunhuazhen
15 Dongying
16 Boxing
17 Huantei

ASIA

In

Pye

Yelle

JAPAN LNG IMPORT TERMINALS

Higashi-Niigata ⭐

Kawagoe ⭐

Senboku I
Senboku II ⭐

Himeji
Himeji II ⭐

Tobata ⭐

Fukuoka ⭐

Shin Oita ⭐

Kagoshima ⭐

⭐ Midorihama

⭐ Shin-Minato

⭐ Sodeshi / Shimizu

⭐ Sodegaura

TOKYO

⭐ Futtsu, Higashi-Ohgishima,
Negishi, Ohgishima

⭐ Chita (Kyodo)
Chita

⭐ Yokkaichi
Yokkaichi (Kawagoe)

⭐ Bingo

⭐ Hatsukaichi

⭐ Yanai

Adnikan

Yilan

Lake Xinghai
(Khanka)

Mudanjiang

Ussuri

Hunchun

Vladivostok

Nakhodka

Tumen Delta

Unggi

Teshio fields

Hokkaido

Sapporo

Shiratsukari fields

Muroran

Tomakomai

Oshamanbe

Yufutsu

Hakodate

JAPAN

Sea of Japan

Akita fields

Funakawa

Tsuchizaki

Yamagata fields

Amarume

Atsuni

Iwanfune-Oki
Aga-Oki/Agaoki-Kita

Niigata

Yamagata

Sendai

Ofunato

Niigata fields

Iwaki

Toyama

Onahama

TOKYO

Himeji

Honshu

Kashima Port

Chiba

Chiba fields

Shimizu

Sagara/Shimizu/Yaizu

Kawasaki

SOUTH
KOREA

Mizushima

Ulsan

Dolorae

Onsan

Pusan

Iwakuni/

Yamaguchi

Marifu

Kobe

Sakaide

Matsuyama

Yokkaichi

Chita /Aichi

Osaka

/Senboku

/Sakai

Yokohama /Negishi

Sodegaura /Futtsu

B **A**

Oita

Owase

Shimotsu

Kainan /Wakayama

Sasebo

Kashima

Nagasaki

Kyushu

Imabari

Kagoshima

Kiire

Miyazaki

Yanai

Kudamatsu

Tokuyama

Pacific Ocean

Okinawa

A Shimonoseki /Ube
B Kitakyushu/Kanmon
/Kokura /Moji
/Tobata /Wakamatsu
/Yahata

I J K L M N O

ASIA

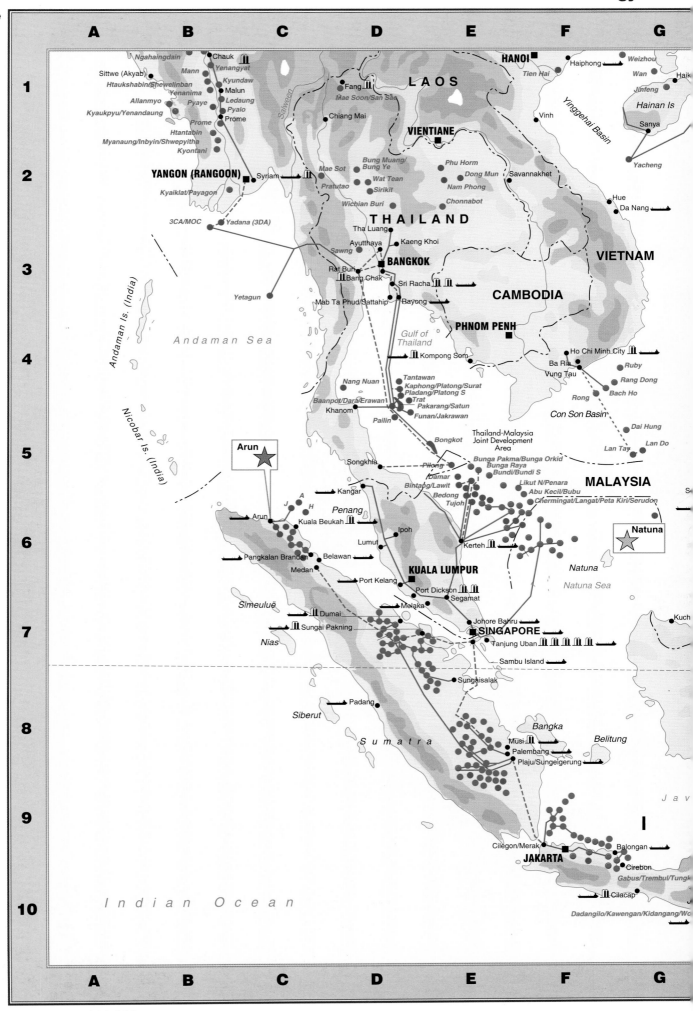

A B C D E F G

1 2 3 4 5 6 7 8 9 10

Ngahaingdain
Chauk
Yenangyat
Sittwe (Akyab)
Mann
Htaukshabin/Shewelinban
Kyundaw
Yenanima
Malun
Allanmyo
Ledaung
Pyaye
Pyalo
Kyaukpyu/Yenandaung
Prome
Htantabin
Myanaung/Inbyin/Shwepyitha
Kyontani

YANGON (RANGOON)
Syriam

Kyaiklat/Payagon

3CA/MOC
Yadana (3DA)

Yetagun

Andaman Is. (India)

Andaman Sea

Nicobar Is. (India)

Arun

L A O S

HANOI
Haiphong
Weizhou
Wan
Tien Hai
Jinfeng
Hainan Is
Vinh
Sanya
Yacheng

Fang
Mae Soon/San Sao
Chiang Mai
VIENTIANE

Bung Muang/
Bung Ye
Phu Horm
Dong Mun
Savannakhet
Nam Phong
Chonnabot
Hue
Da Nang

Mae Sot
Wat Tean
Pratutao
Sirikit
Wichian Buri

T H A I L A N D
Tha Luang
Ayutthaya
Kaeng Khoi
Sawng
BANGKOK
VIETNAM
Rat Buri
Bang Chak
Sri Racha
Mab Ta Phud/Sattahip
Bayong
CAMBODIA

Gulf of
Thailand
PHNOM PENH

Kompong Som
Ho Chi Minh City
Ba Ria
Ruby
Vung Tau
Rang Dong
Rong
Bach Ho
Con Son Basin

Yinggehai Basin

Nang Nuan
Tantawan
Kaphong/Platong/Surat
Pladang/Platong S
Baanpot/Dara/Erawan
Trat
Pakarang/Satun
Khanom
Funan/Jakrawan
Pailin
Dai Hung
Bongkot
Thailand-Malaysia
Joint Development
Area
Lan Do
Lan Tay
Songkhla
Pilong
Bunga Pakma/Bunga Orkid
Bunga Raya
Damar
Bundi/Bundi S
Bintang/Lawit
Likut N/Penara
MALAYSIA
Kangar
Bedong
Abu Kecil/Bubu
Tujoh
Chermingat/Langat/Peta Kiri/Serudon
A
Penang
H
J
Kuala Beukah
Natuna
Arun
Ipoh
Kerteh
Natuna
Lumut
Natuna Sea
Pangkalan Brandan
Belawan
Medan
KUALA LUMPUR
Port Kelang
Port Dickson
Kuch
Simeuluë
Melaka
Segamat
Dumai
Johore Bahru
SINGAPORE
Sungai Pakning
Tanjung Uban
Nias
Sambu Island
Sungaisalak

Padang
Siberut
Bangka
Belitung
S u m a t r a
Musi
Palembang
Plaju/Sungeigerung
J a v
Cilegon/Merak
Balongan
JAKARTA
Cirebon
Gabus/Trembul/Tungk
Cilacap

I n d i a n   O c e a n
Dadangilo/Kawengan/Kidangang/Wo

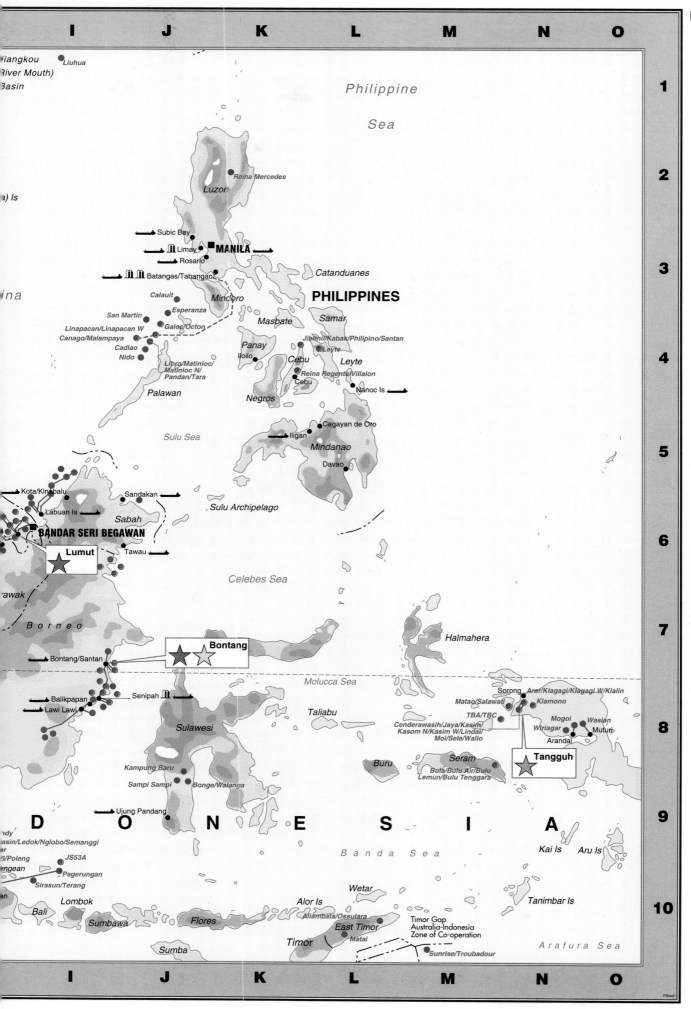

I J K L M N O

1

Philippine

Sea

• *Liuhua*
iangkou
River Mouth)
Basin

a) Is

2

• *Reina Mercedes*
Luzon

PHILIPPINES

→ Subic Bay
Limay
→ Rosario
Batangas/Tabangao
Catanduanes
3

Calauit
Esperanza
Mindoro
San Martin
Linapacan/Linapacan W
Galoc/Octon
Canago/Malampaya
Cadlao
Nido
Libro/Matinloc/
Matinloc N/
Pandan/Tara
Masbate
Samar
Panay
Iloilo
Cebu
Jibinil/Kabak/Philipino/Santan
Leyte
Reina Regente/Villalon
Cebu
Leyte
4

ina

Palawan
Negros
Nanoc Is →

Sulu Sea
Cagayan de Oro
→ Iligan
Mindanao
Davao
5

Kota/Kinabalu
Sandakan →
Sulu Archipelago

Sabah
Labuan Is
BANDAR SERI BEGAWAN

Lumut ★
Tawau →
6

Halmahera
Celebes Sea

rawak
Borneo
7

Bontang ★☆
→ Bontang/Santan
Sorong Arar/Klagagi/Klagagi W/Klalin
Matao/Salawati Klamono
Mogoi Wasian
TBA/TBC
Cenderawasih/Jaya/Kasim/ Wiriagar Muturi
Kasom N/Kasim W/Lindai/ Arandai
Moi/Sele/Walio
→ Balikpapan
Senipah
→ Lawi Lawi
Sulawesi
Taliabu
Buru
Seram
Buta/Bulu Air/Bulu
Lemun/Bulu Tenggara
Tangguh ★
8

Kampung Baru
Sampi Sampi Bonge/Walanga
D O N E S I A
→ Ujung Pandang
9

Banda Sea
Kai Is *Aru Is*

ndy
asin/Ledok/Nglobo/Semanggi
/Poleng JS53A
ungean Pagerungan
Sirasun/Terang
Lombok
Bali
Sumbawa *Flores*
Wetar
Alor Is
Aliambata/Ossulara
East Timor
Matai
Timor Gap
Australia-Indonesia
Zone of Co-operation
Tanimbar Is
10

Sumba
Timor
Sunrise/Troubadour
Arafura Sea

I J K L M N O

PBush

ASIA

Plate
64

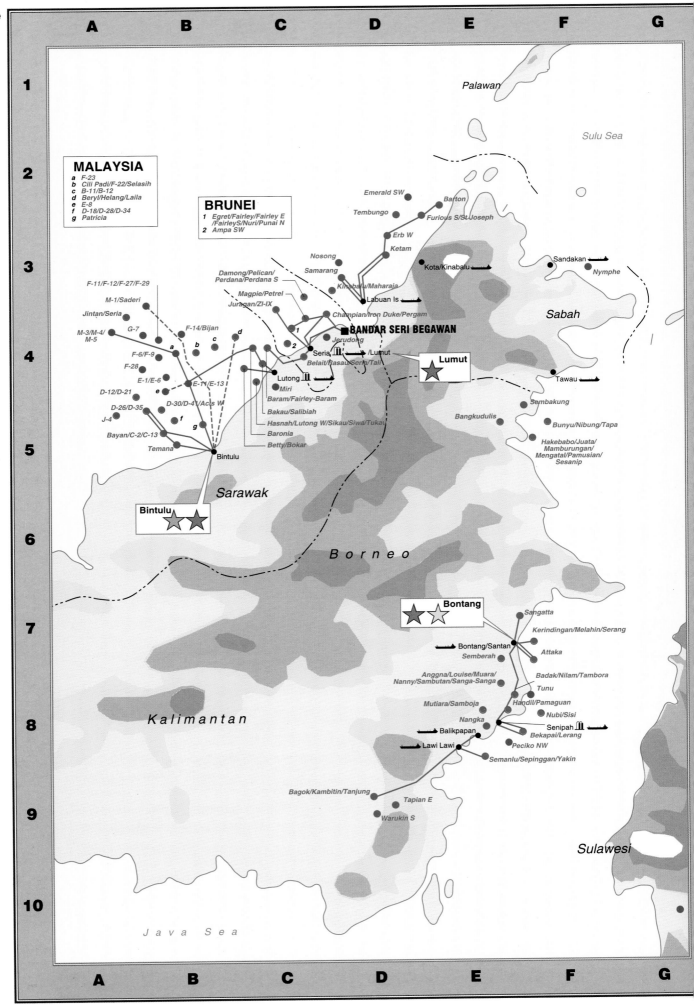

MALAYSIA
a F-23
b Cili Padi/F-22/Selasih
c B-11/B-12
d Beryl/Helang/Laila
e E-8
f D-18/D-28/D-34
g Patricia

BRUNEI
1 Egret/Fairley/Fairley E
/FairleyS/Nuri/Punai N
2 Ampa SW

Palawan

Sulu Sea

Emerald SW
Tembungo
Barton
Furious S/St.Joseph
Erb W
Ketam
Nosong
Kota/Kinabalu
Sandakan
Samarang
Nymphe
Damong/Pelican/
Perdana/Perdana S
Kinabalu/Maharaja
Sabah
F-11/F-12/F-27/F-29
Magpie/Petrel
Labuan Is
M-1/Saderi
Juragan/ZI-IX
Jintan/Seria
Champian/Iron Duke/Pergam
M-3/M-4/
M-5
G-7
F-14/Bijan
d
BANDAR SERI BEGAWAN
a
b
c
Jerudong
F-6/F-9
1
/Lumut
Lumut
2
Seria
F-28
Belait/Rasau/Serta/Tali
Tawau
E-1/E-6
E-11/E-13
Lutong
D-12/D-21
e
Miri
Sembakung
D-30/D-41/Acis W
Baram/Fairley-Baram
D-26/D-35
f
Bakau/Salibiah
Bangkudulis
Bunyu/Nibung/Tapa
J-4
g
Hasnah/Lutong W/Sikau/Siwa/Tukau
Hakebabo/Juata/
Bayan/C-2/C-13
Baronia
Mamburungan/
Temana
Betty/Bokar
Mengatal/Pamusian/
Bintulu
Sesanip

Sarawak

Bintulu

B o r n e o

Bontang
Sangatta
Kerindingan/Melahin/Serang
Bontang/Santan
Attaka
Semberah
Anggna/Louise/Muara/
Badak/Nilam/Tambora
Nanny/Sambutan/Sanga-Sanga
Tunu
Mutiara/Samboja
Handil/Pamaguan
Nubi/Sisi
Kalimantan
Nangka
Senipah
Balikpapan
Bekapai/Lerang
Lawi Lawi
Peciko NW
Semanlu/Sepinggan/Yakin

Bagok/Kambitin/Tanjung
Tapian E
Warukin S

Sulawesi

J a v a   S e a

Scale: 1:6,210,000

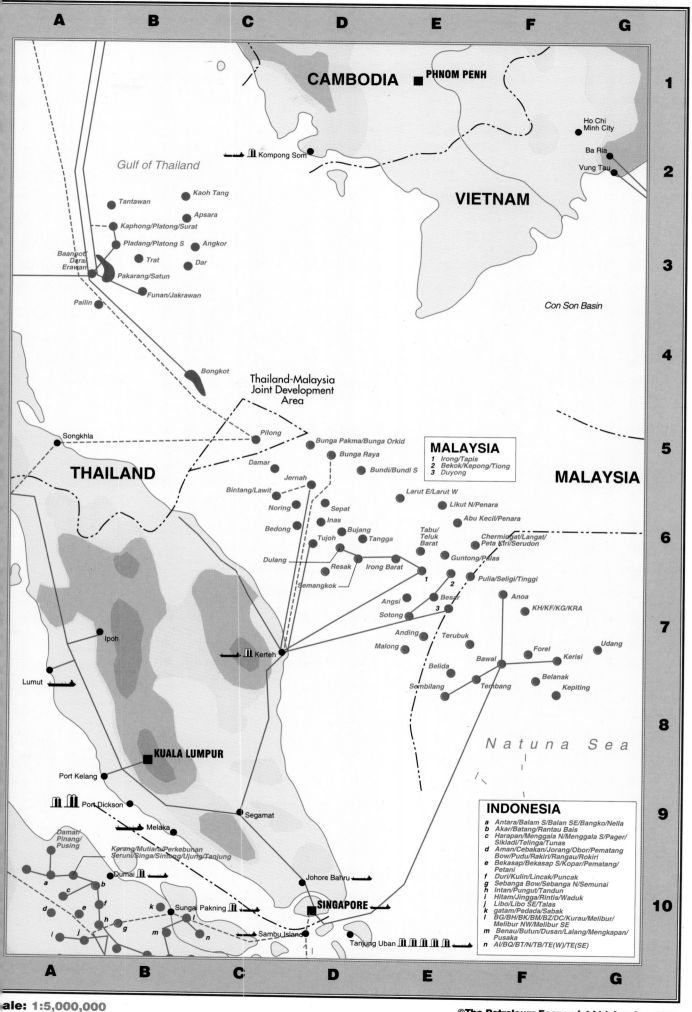

ASIA

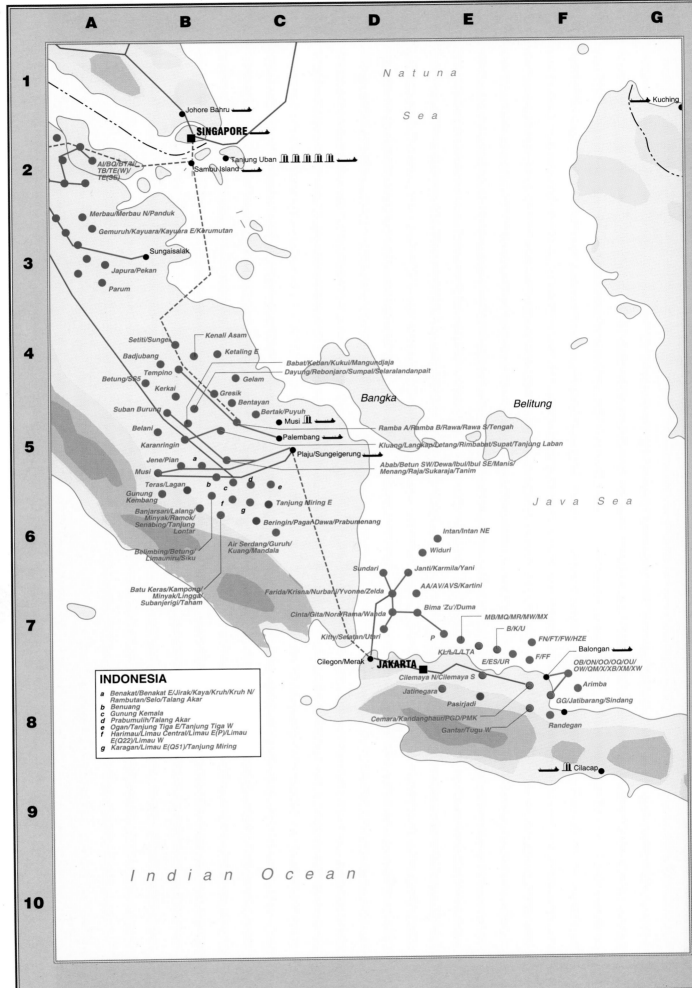

ASIA

INDONESIA

a Benakat/Benakat E/Jirak/Kaya/Kruh/Kruh N/
Rambutan/Selo/Talang Akar
b Benuang
c Gunung Kemala
d Prabumulih/Talang Akar
e Ogan/Tanjung Tiga E/Tanjung Tiga W
f Harimau/Limau Central/Limau E(P)/Limau
E(Q22)/Limau W
g Karagan/Limau E(Q51)/Tanjung Miring

Scale: 1:6,000,000

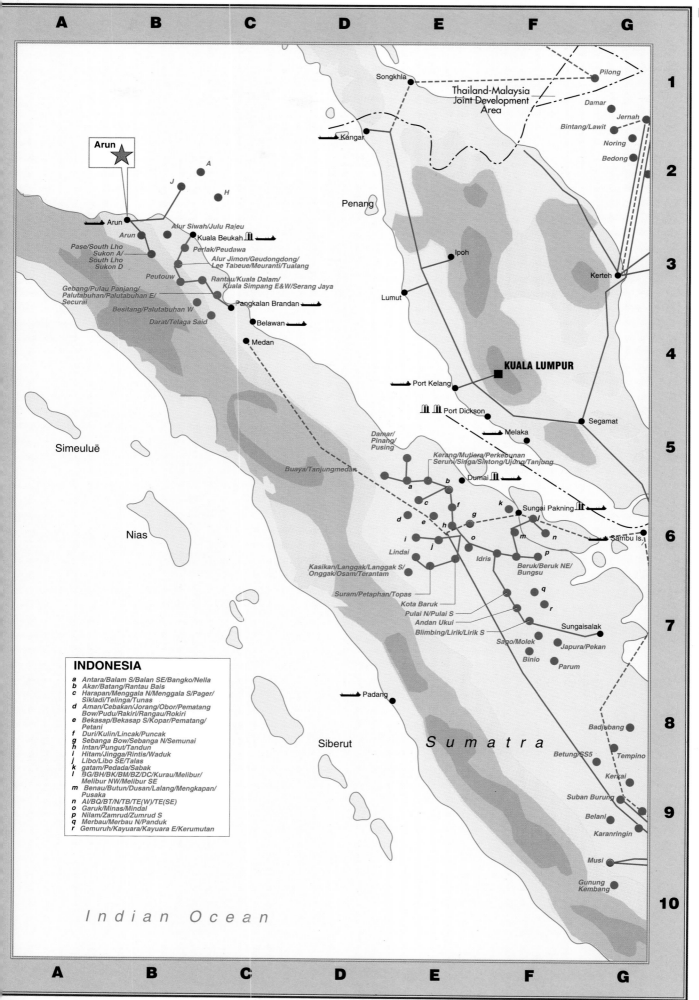

ASIA

INDONESIA

a   Antara/Balam S/Balan SE/Bangko/Nella
b   Akar/Batang/Rantau Bais
c   Harapan/Menggala N/Menggala S/Pager/
     Sikladi/Telinga/Tunas
d   Aman/Cebakan/Jorang/Obor/Pematang
     Bow/Pudu/Rakiri/Rangau/Rokiri
e   Bekasap/Bekasap S/Kopar/Pematang/
     Petani
f   Duri/Kulin/Lincak/Puncak
g   Sebanga Bow/Sebanga N/Semunai
h   Intan/Pungut/Tandun
i   Hitam/Jingga/Rintis/Waduk
j   Libo/Libo SE/Talas
k   gatam/Pedada/Sabak
l   BG/BH/BK/BM/BZ/DC/Kurau/Melibur/
     Melibur NW/Melibur SE
m   Benau/Butun/Dusan/Lalang/Mengkapan/
     Pusaka
n   AI/BQ/BT/N/TB/TE(W)/TE(SE)
o   Garuk/Minas/Mindal
p   Nilam/Zamrud/Zumrud S
q   Merbau/Merbau N/Panduk
r   Gemuruh/Kayuara/Kayuara E/Kerumutan

**Plate
68**

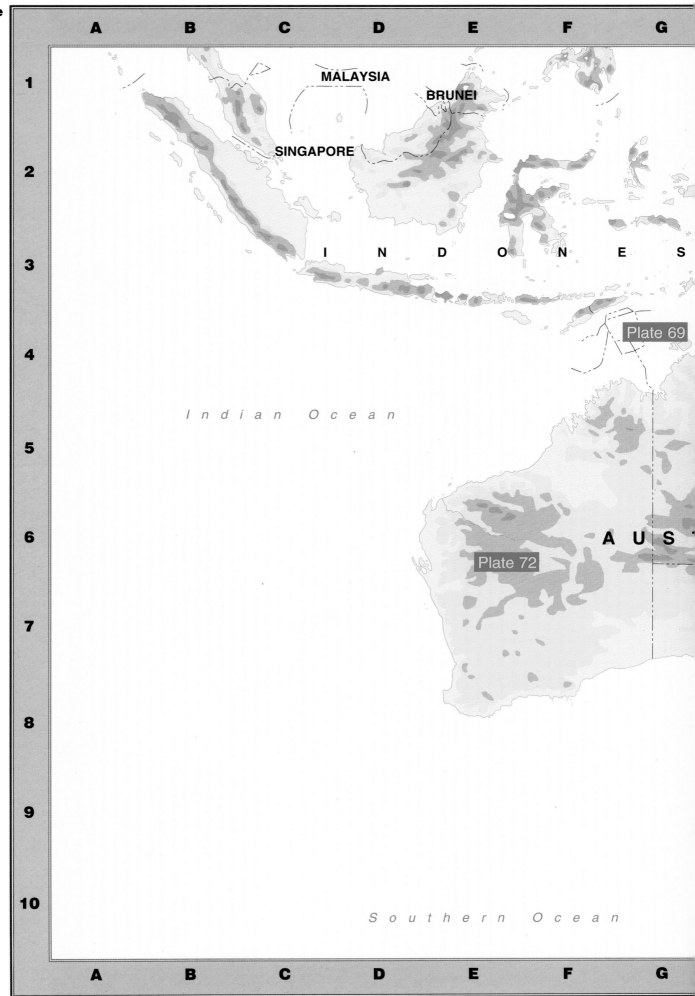

MALAYSIA

BRUNEI

SINGAPORE

I N D O N E S

Plate 69

Indian Ocean

Plate 72

A U S T

Southern Ocean

AUSTRALASIA

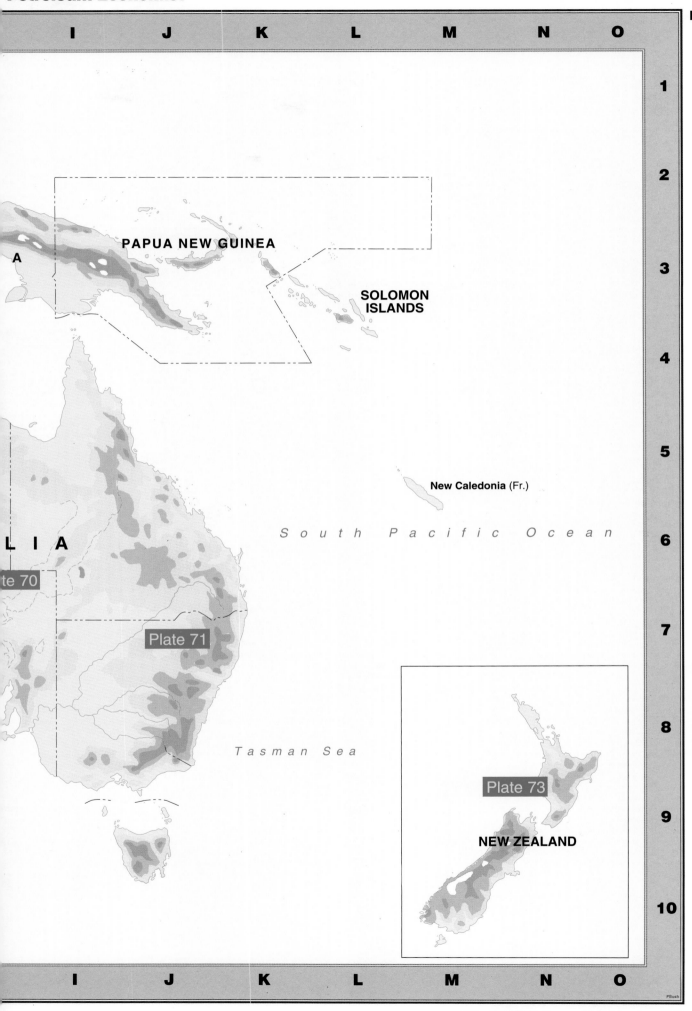

I   J   K   L   M   N   O

1

2

PAPUA NEW GUINEA

A

3

**SOLOMON
ISLANDS**

4

5

New Caledonia (Fr.)

S o u t h   P a c i f i c   O c e a n

6

LIA

te 70

Plate 71

7

T a s m a n   S e a

8

Plate 73

9

NEW ZEALAND

10

I   J   K   L   M   N   O

AUSTRALASIA

PBush

AUSTRALASIA

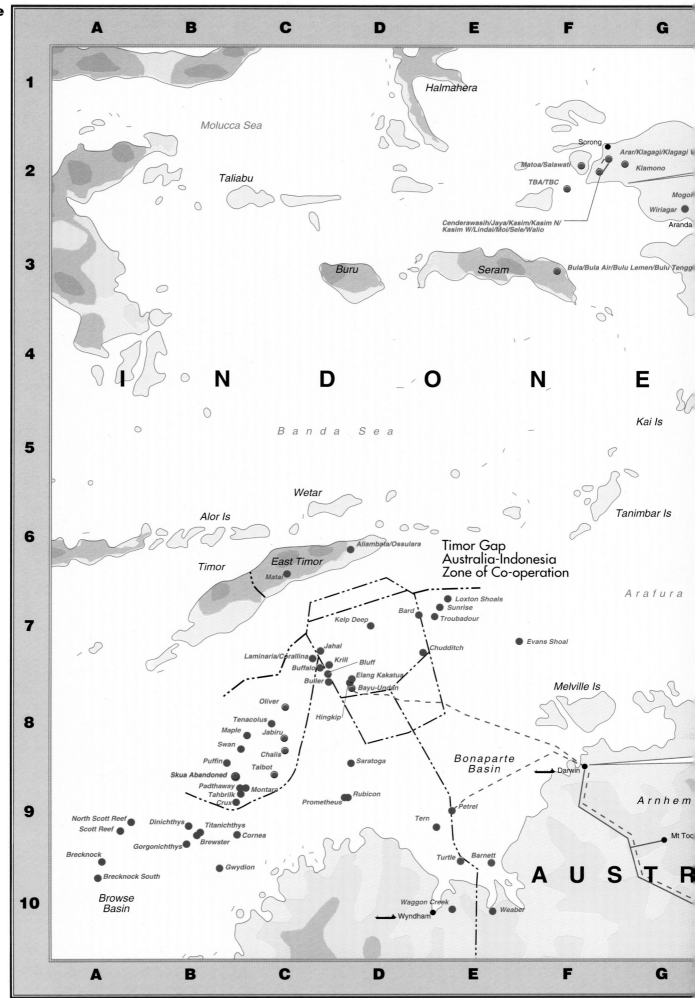

Scale: 1:7,640,000

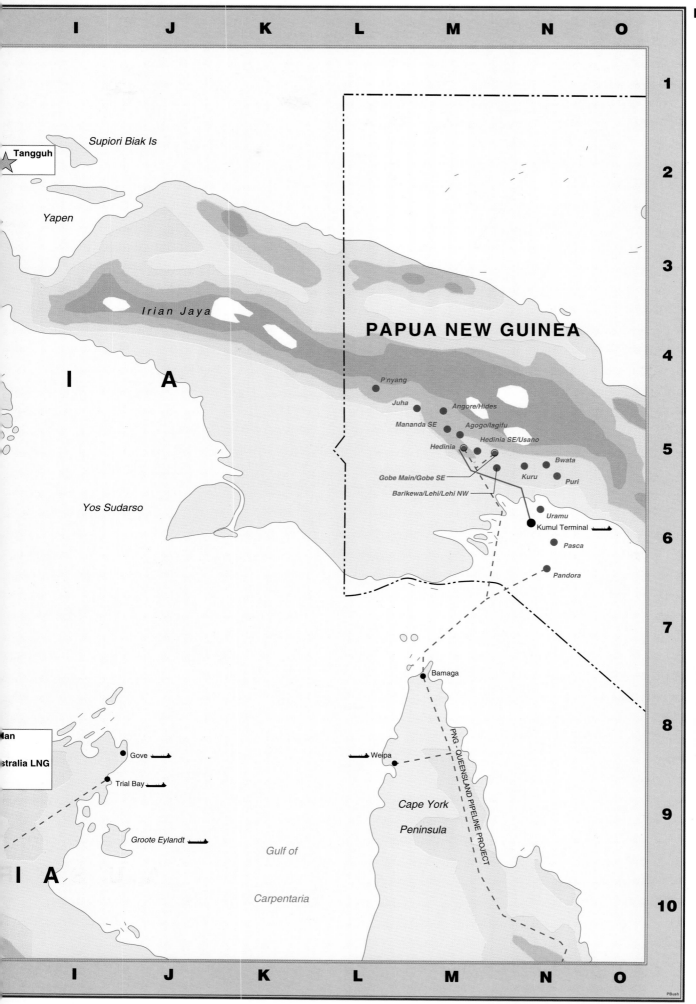

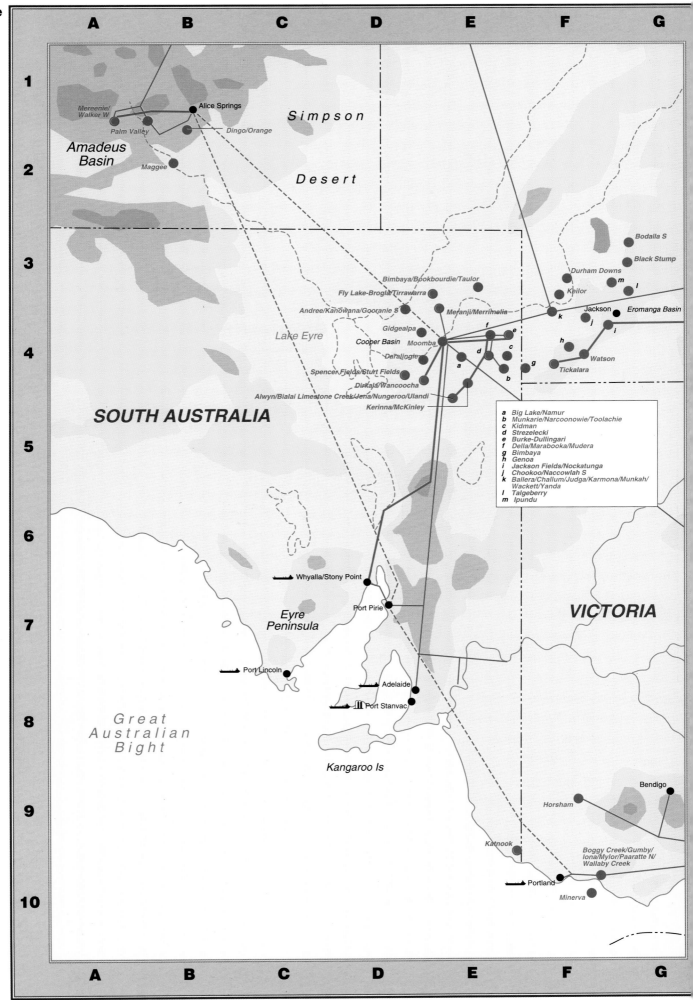

AUSTRALASIA

Scale: 1:7,890,000

A **B** **C** **D** **E** **F** **G**

Simpson

Desert

Alice Springs

Mereenie/
Walker W

Palm Valley

Dingo/Orange

*Amadeus
Basin*

Maggee

Bodalla S

Black Stump

Durham Downs

Keilor

m *l*

Bimbaya/Bookbourdie/Taulor

Fly Lake-Brogla/Tirrawarra

Andree/Kanowana/Gooranie S

Meranji/Merrimelia

Jackson

Eromanga Basin

k

j

i

Gidgealpa

Lake Eyre

f

e

Cooper Basin

Moomba

d

c

h

Deralingie

a

g

Watson

Spencer Fields/Sturt Fields

b

Tickalara

Dirkala/Wancoocha

Alwyn/Bialai Limestone Creek/Jena/Nungeroo/Ulandi

Kerinna/McKinley

a	Big Lake/Namur
b	Munkarie/Narcoonowie/Toolachie
c	Kidman
d	Strezelecki
e	Burke-Dullingari
f	Della/Marabooka/Mudera
g	Bimbaya
h	Genoa
i	Jackson Fields/Nockatunga
j	Chookoo/Naccowlah S
k	Ballera/Challum/Judga/Karmona/Munkah/
	Wackett/Yanda
l	Talgeberry
m	Ipundu

SOUTH AUSTRALIA

Whyalla/Stony Point

Port Pirie

VICTORIA

*Eyre
Peninsula*

*Great
Australian
Bight*

Port Lincoln

Adelaide

Port Stanvac

Kangaroo Is

Bendigo

Horsham

Katnook

*Boggy Creek/Gumby/
Iona/Mylor/Paaratte N/
Wallaby Creek*

Portland

Minerva

A **B** **C** **D** **E** **F** **G**

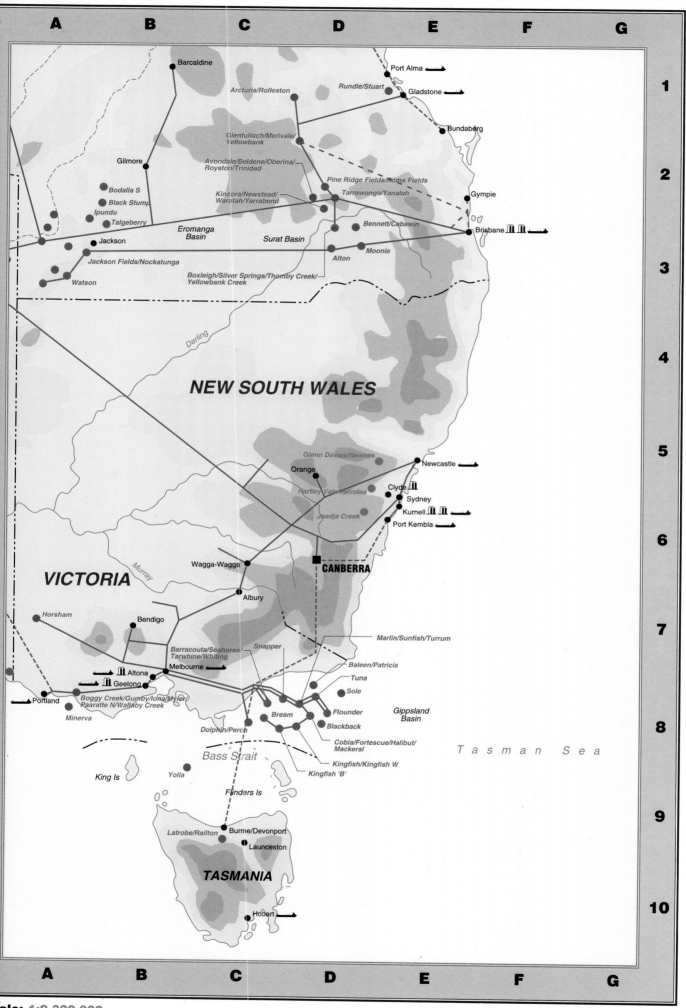

AUSTRALASIA

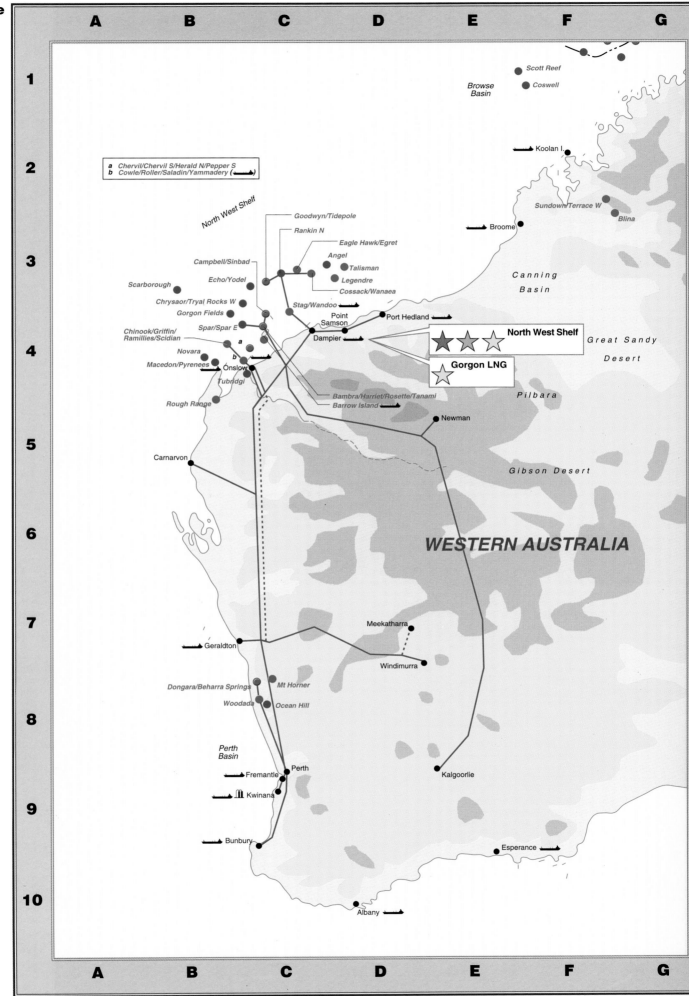

a *Chervil/Chervil S/Herald N/Pepper S*
b *Cowle/Roller/Saladin/Yammadery* (→)

North West Shelf

Goodwyn/Tidepole

Rankin N

Eagle Hawk/Egret

Angel

Campbell/Sinbad

Talisman

Scarborough

Echo/Yodel

Legendre

Cossack/Wanaea

Chrysaor/Tryal Rocks W

Gorgon Fields

Stag/Wandoo

Point
Samson

Port Hedland

*Chinook/Griffin/
Ramillies/Scidian*

Spar/Spar E

Dampier

Canning

Basin

★ ★ ☆ **North West Shelf**

Novara

a

Great Sandy

Desert

Macedon/Pyrenees

Onslow

b

☆ **Gorgon LNG**

Tubridgi

Bambra/Harriet/Rosette/Tanami

Pilbara

Rough Range

Barrow Island

Newman

Carnarvon

Gibson Desert

WESTERN AUSTRALIA

Meekatharra

Geraldton

Windimurra

Dongara/Beharra Springs

Mt Horner

Woodada

Ocean Hill

*Perth
Basin*

Fremantle

Perth

Kwinana

Kalgoorlie

Bunbury

Esperance

10

Albany

Scott Reef

*Browse
Basin*

Coswell

Koolan I.

Sundown/Terrace W

Blina

Broome

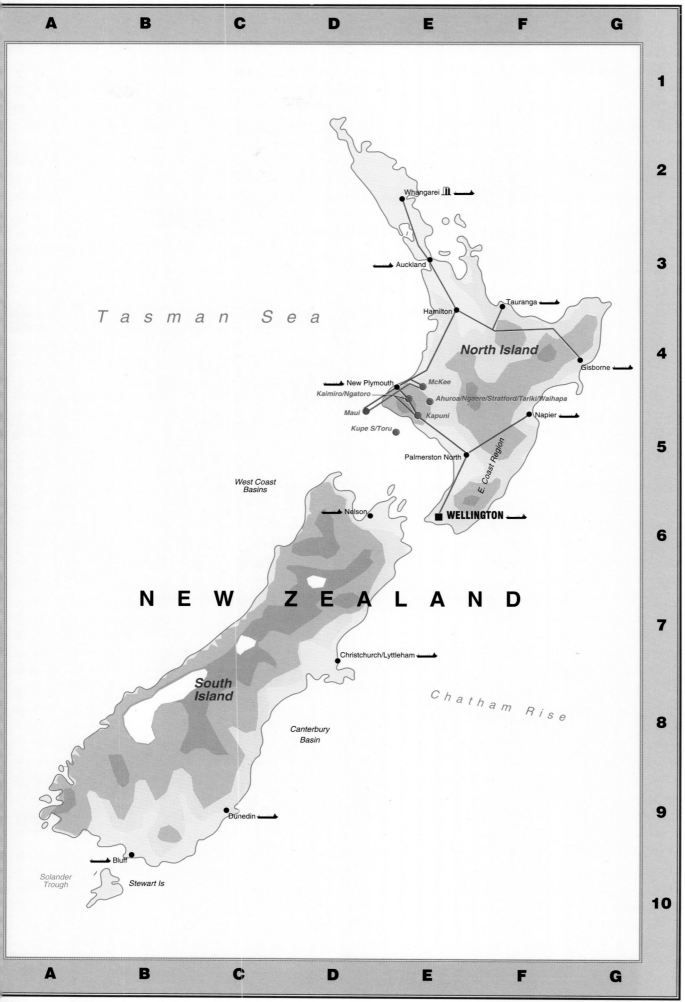

A B C D E F G

1
2
3
4
5
6
7
8
9
10

Whangarei

Auckland

Tasman Sea

Hamilton

Tauranga

North Island

Gisborne

New Plymouth
McKee
Kaimiro/Ngatoro
Ahuroa/Ngaere/Stratford/Tariki/Waihapa
Maui
Kapuni
Napier
Kupe S/Toru

Palmerston North

E. Coast Region

West Coast Basins

Nelson

■ WELLINGTON

N E W   Z E A L A N D

Chatham Rise

Christchurch/Lyttleham

South Island

Canterbury Basin

Dunedin

Bluff

Solander Trough

Stewart Is

Plate
74

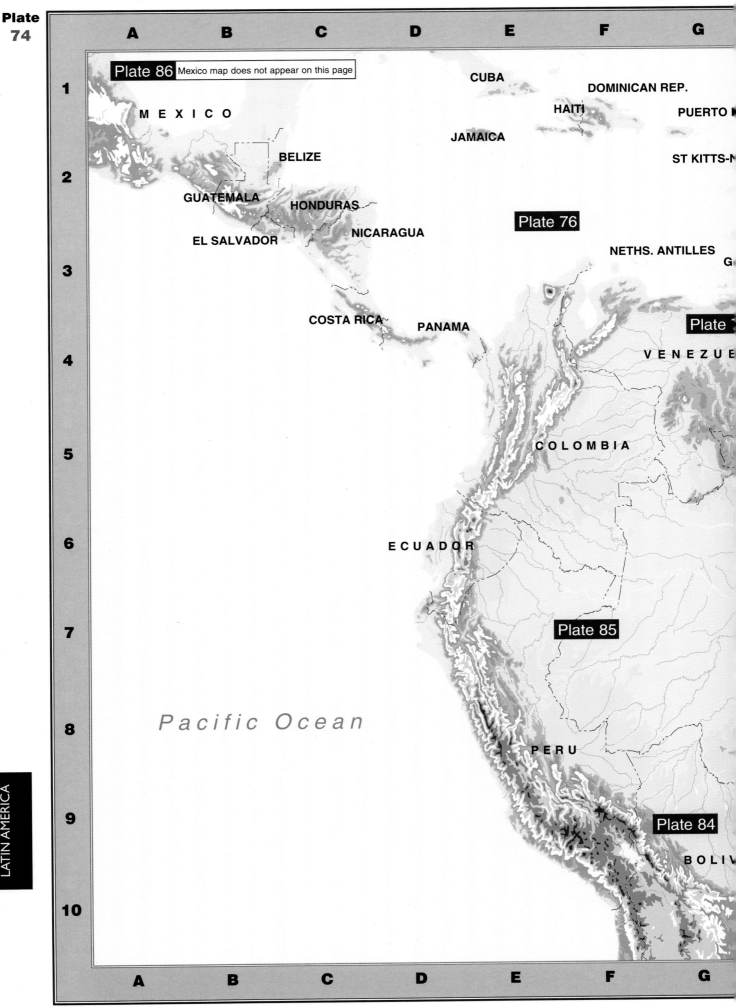

Plate 86 Mexico map does not appear on this page

MEXICO

CUBA

DOMINICAN REP.

HAITI

PUERTO R

JAMAICA

BELIZE

ST KITTS-N

GUATEMALA

HONDURAS

Plate 76

EL SALVADOR

NICARAGUA

NETHS. ANTILLES

G

COSTA RICA

PANAMA

Plate

VENEZUE

COLOMBIA

ECUADOR

Plate 85

Pacific Ocean

PERU

Plate 84

BOLIV

Scale: 1:19,500,000

I   J   K   L   M   N   O

1

2

3

Atlantic Ocean

4

UA & BARBUDA

NICA

BARBADOS

ate 79

DAD & TOBAGO

YANA

FRENCH
GUIANA

SURINAME

5

6

Plate 78

7

B R A Z I L

8

9

Plate 81

10

I   J   K   L   M   N   O

Plate
75

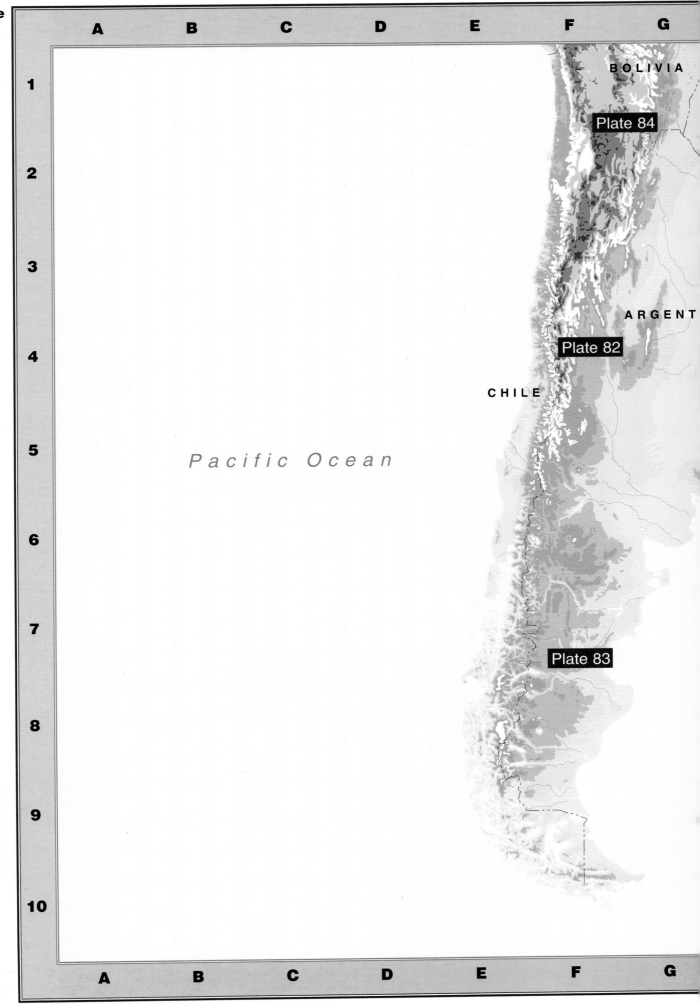

Plate
75

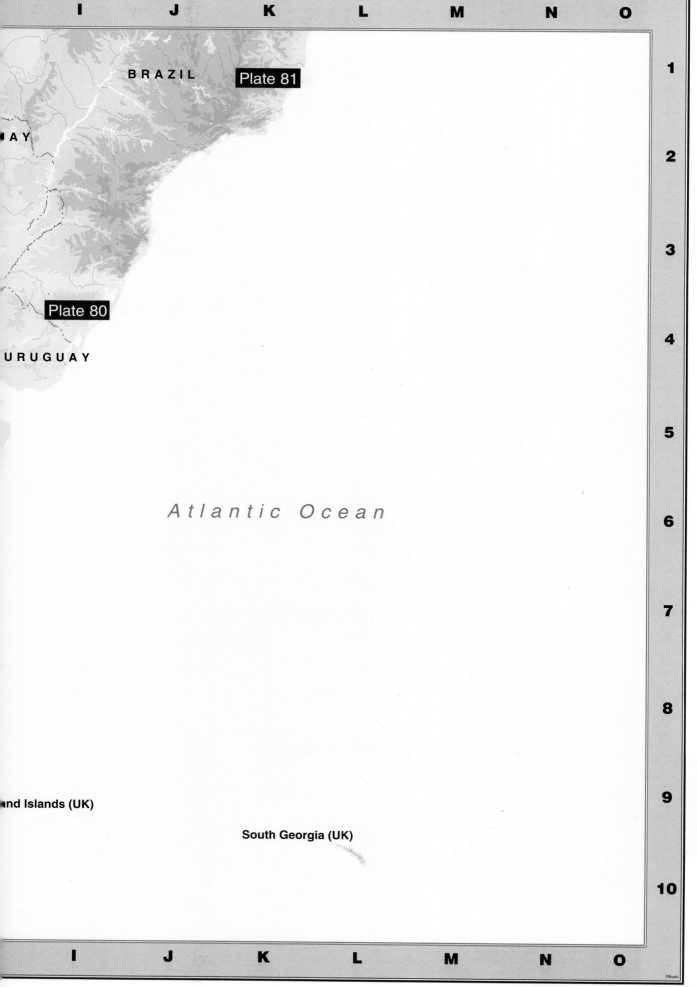

B R A Z I L

Plate 81

Plate 80

U R U G U A Y

Atlantic Ocean

nd Islands (UK)

South Georgia (UK)

LATIN AMERICA

Andros

Gulf of Mexico

Boca Jaruco/Guanabo/Juanita/Via Blanca
HAVANA
Matanzas
Chapelin/Varadero
Camarioca
Bacuranao/Cruz Verde/Santa Maria
Motembo
Jarahueca
Cienfuegos
Cabaiguan
Jatiboni
Cristales
Catalina

Isla de la Juventud

MEXICO

Cayman Is. (UK)

Montego Bay
JAMAICA
Port Kaiser

Belize
BELMOPAN
Xan
Laguna Blanca
Chocop
La Libertad
BELIZE
San Roman Caribe/ W Chinaja
Puerto Barrios
Puerto Castilla
San Diego
Tortugas Wells
Rubelsanto
Puerto Cortes
GUATEMALA
HONDURAS
GUATEMALA
TEGUCIGALPA
Escuintla
Cayos Miskitos
San Jose
SAN SALVADOR
I. de Providencia
Acajutla
EL SALVADOR
Cutuco
NICARAGUA
Corinto
I. de san Andres
MANAGUA
Corn Is.
Lago de Nicaragua
COSTA RICA
Puerto Limon
Puntarenas
Soledad 1
Las Minas
SAN JOSE
Panama Canal
Chiriqui Grande
PANAMA
Puerto Mogos
Puerto Armuelles
Pacific Ocean
PANAMA

Scale: 1:8,438,000

I J K L M N O

Atlantic Ocean

1

San Salvador

Acklins

2

Turks & Caicos Is. (UK)

Great
Inagua

★ *Punta Caucedo*

★ *Andres*

ntilla ➤

3

DOMINICAN REP.

• Guantanamo Bay (US) ➤

Puerto Plata • ➤

HAITI

Licey Medio

★ *Penuelas*

PUERTO RICO

Bonao • ⌂

PORT-AU-PRINCE ➤ ■

⌂ Bayamon

4

GPD 1

**SANTO
DOMINGO** ⌂

La Romana • ➤

SAN JUAN ⌂ ➤

➤ ⌂

Virgin Is. (UK)

Yabucoa ⌂ ➤

➤ Guayama

Virgin Is. (US) ⌂ ➤

ST KITTS-NEVIS

5

ANTIGUA & BARBUDA

➤ Guadeloupe (Fr.)

b b e a n   S e a

DOMINICA

6

⌂ Martinique (Fr.)

➤ **ST LUCIA**

7

NETHS. ANTILLES

⌂ Aruba (Neths.)

Curacao ⌂

➤ **GRENADA**

Chuchupa •

Amuay ⌂ ➤

Bonaire

Ballena •

➤ ⌂ Cardon

Cumarebo •

TRINIDAD & TOBAGO

8

• Santa Marta

Amana

La Vela de Coro

Venezuela LNG
★

**PORT OF
SPAIN** ■

arranquilla ➤

*El Mojan/La Paz/
Mara/Netick*

Maracaibo •

*El Mamon
La Palmas*

Mene de Acosta

El Palito ⌂ ➤

Abundancia

CARACAS

Puerto la Cruz ⌂

Carij/El Totumo
Cabimas

*Los Lanudos
Monte Claro
Quiroz*

Maracay

El Dificil

*La Villa
Alturitas*

Barquisimeto •

Valencia •

⌂ El Chaure

9

Arjona

Garcia

Lama

Bolivar fields

★ ★ ★ *Atlantic LNG*

Tucupita •

Boquete •

Rosario

San Lorenzo •
Poco

Rio de Oro

Buturina

*Bonito/El Cubo/
Las Cruces*

El Toreno •

Caipa/Estero/Maporal/Silvan

Puerto Ordaz •

uore ➤

*Concordia/Tres
Bocas/W Tarra*

Hato Viejo.Palmita/San Silvestre/Sinco

Lebrija

Carbonera/Petrolea

Ciudad Bolivar •

10

na ➤

Tisquirama
Bonanza
Rio Zulia

Cantagalo

Corazon

San Cristobal •

Orinoco Heavy/Extra-Heavy Oil Belt

Yarigui

Aguascleras
La Victoria

Galan/San Silvestre

Bucaramanga • ⌂

V E N E Z U E L A

Penas Blancas

Casabe/Infantas

Cano Limon/Cano Verde/Matanegra/Redondo

Arauca •

I J K L M N O

LATIN AMERICA

Plate
77

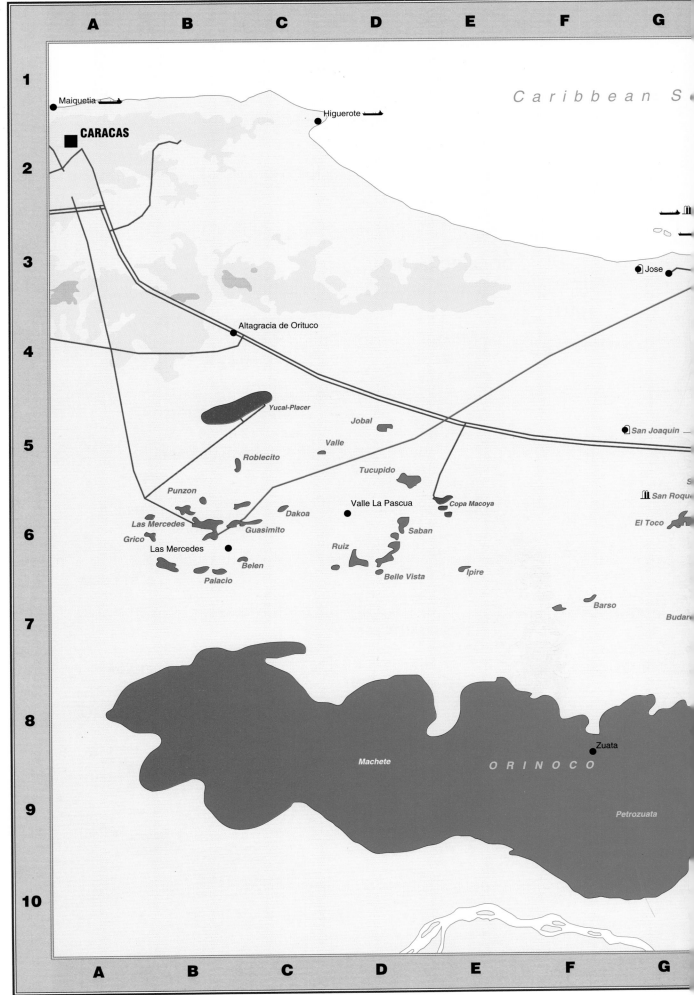

A B C D E F G

1

Maiquetia

Higuerote

Caribbean S

CARACAS

2

3

Jose

Altagracia de Orituco

4

Yucal-Placer

Jobal

San Joaquin

Valle

Roblecito

Tucupido

5

Punzon

Copa Macoya

San Roque

Dakoa

Valle La Pascua

Saban

El Toco

Las Mercedes

Guasimito

Ruiz

Grico

Ipire

Las Mercedes

Belen

Belle Vista

Palacio

Barso

Budare

6

7

8

Machete

O R I N O C O

Zuata

9

Petrozuata

10

A B C D E F G

Scale: 1:1,431,000

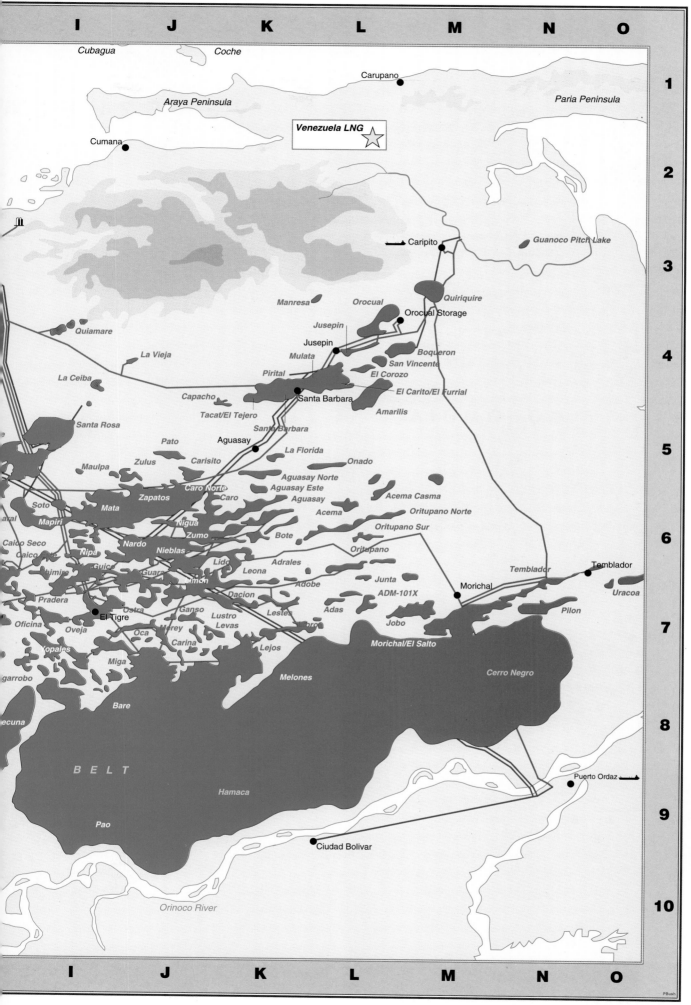

LATIN AMERICA

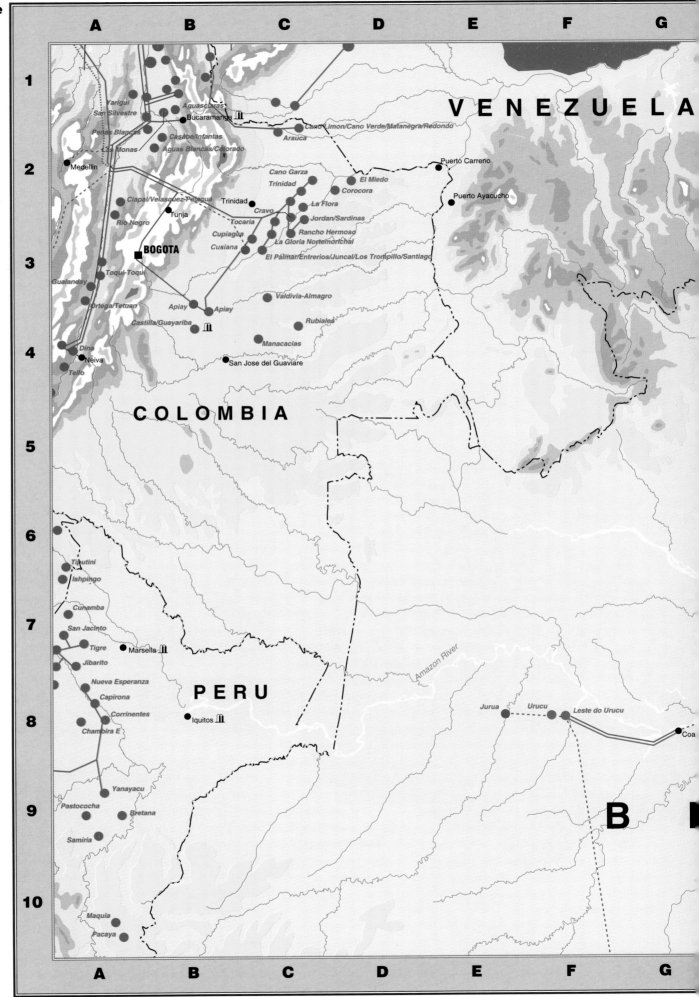

Scale: 1:9,000,000

Atlantic Ocean

GEORGETOWN

GUYANA

PARAMARIBO

Tambaredjo Tout Lui Faut

SURINAME

CAYENNE

FRENCH GUIANA

Pirapema

Mouth of the Amazon

Macapa

Ilha de Marajo

Belem

Amazon River

Manaus

Nova Olinda

BRAZIL

LATIN AMERICA

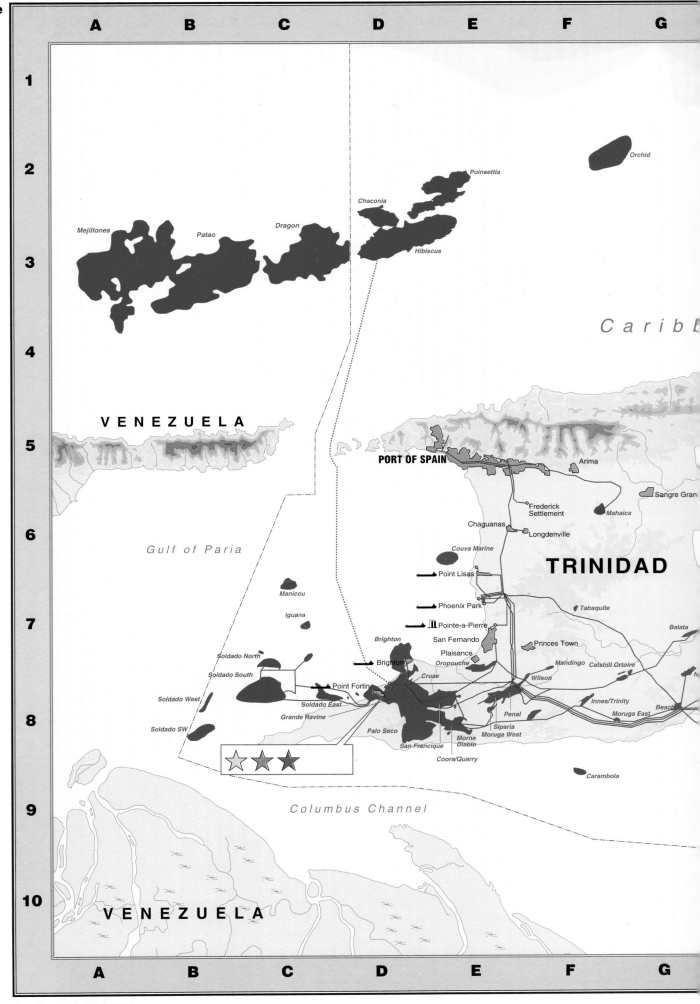

LATIN AMERICA

Scale: 1:1,000,000

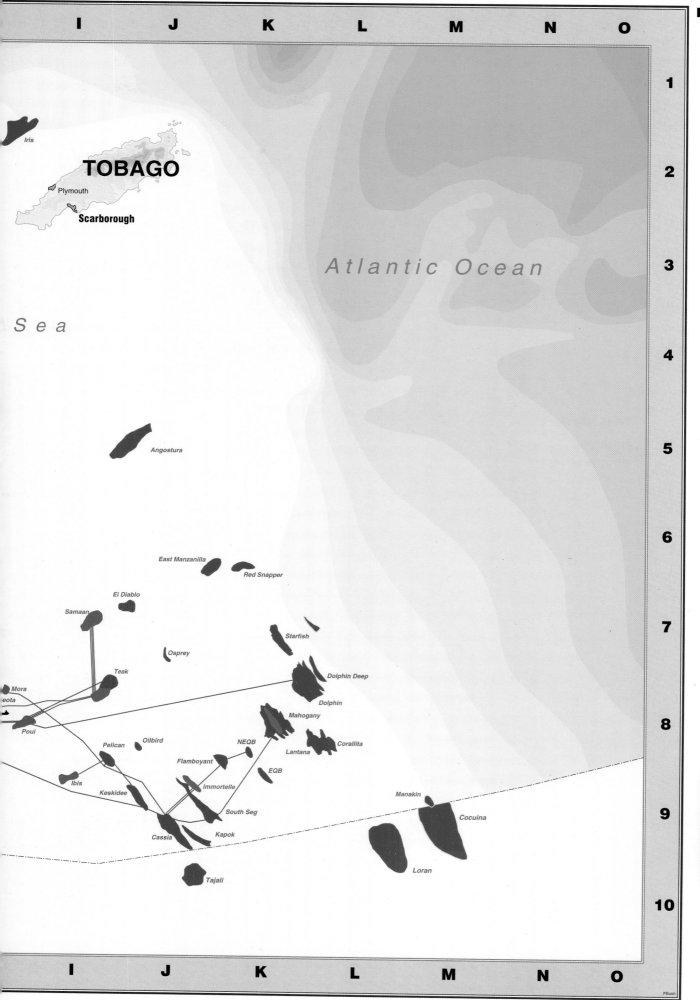

Iris

TOBAGO

Plymouth

Scarborough

Atlantic Ocean

Sea

Angostura

East Manzanilla

Red Snapper

El Diablo

Samaan

Starfish

Osprey

Teak

Dolphin Deep

Mora

eota

Dolphin

Mahogany

Poui

Oilbird

NEQB

Corallita

Pelican

Lantana

Flamboyant

EQB

Ibis

Immortelle

Manakin

Keskidee

Cocuina

South Seg

Cassia

Kapok

Loran

Tajali

LATIN AMERICA

Scale: 1:13,250,000

A B C D E F G

1

Atlantic Ocean

2

Belem

Sao Luis de Maranhao

Xareu

Fortaleza

3

Pescada
Ubarana
Agulha
Canto Amaro
Aratum
Macau
Estreito
Alto Rodrigues

Teresina

Natal

4

Campina Grande
Joao Pessoa

B R A Z I L

Recife
Suape

5

Suape

Coqueiro Seco
Maceio
Cidade SM Dos Campos/Furado
Tabuleiro Do Martins
SM Dos Campos
Pilar

6

Brejo Grande
Sirizinho
Carmopolis
Riachuelo
Aracaju
Camorin
Guaricema
Caioba
Dourado
Imbe/Malombe
Buracica/Panelas/Santana
Aracas
Cassarongongo
Miranga
Candeias/D Joao
Agua Grande/Jacuipe
Mataripe
Aratu
Salvador

7

Jequie

Itabuna

8

Atlantic

Ocean

BRASILIA

9

Sao Mateus
Fazendra Cedro
Cacao
Fazendra Sao Rafael

10

Vitoria

Plate
82

ARGENTINA (Neuquen)
1. El Quemado/El Santiagueno
2. Puesto Morales/Bajo De Los Cajones/Medianera/
   El Medanito
3. Charco Bayo/Piedras Blancas/Bajada Del Palo/
   Borde Montuoso
4. Loma Guadalosa
5. Loma La Lata
6. Rincon Chico
7. La Calera/Tres Picos
8. Meseta Buena Esperanza/Barrosa Norte/
   Sierra Barrosa/Aguada Baguales/Aguada
   Toledo/Barda Gonzales
9. Rio Neuquen
10. Est Fernandez Oro/Rio Negro
11. Centenario/Agua Del Cajon/El Salitral
12. Aguada Anacleto/Las Chivas/Punta Senillo/
    Los Bastos
13. Cerro Iotena/Cerro Granito/Ranquil Co.
14. Cutral-Co/Campamento II/Norte Octogono/
    Guanaco
15. Piedras Negras
16. Meseta Alta
17. Loma Las Yeguas
18. Loma La Lata
19. Aguada Del Los Indios/Puesto Bravo
20. Cerro Moro/Lindero Atravesado
21. Barrosa Oeste
22. Challaco/Puesto Touquet

ARGENTINA (Bolivia Border)
1. Macueta/Acambuco
2. Ipaguazu/Jollin
3. Tonono
4. San Pedro/Yacuy/Lomita
5. Madre Jones/Campo Duran

LATIN AMERICA

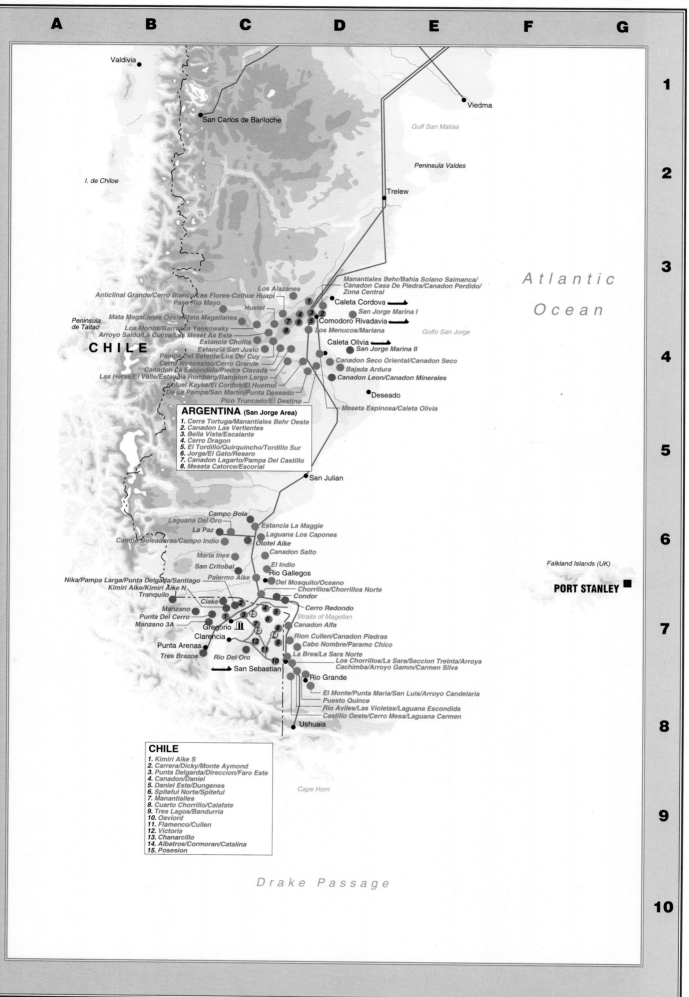

Atlantic

Ocean

Valdivia

San Carlos de Bariloche

Viedma

Gulf San Matias

I. de Chiloe

Peninsula Valdes

Trelew

Los Alazanes

Manantiales Behr/Bahia Solano Salmanca/
Canadon Casa De Piedra/Canadon Perdido/
Zona Central

Anticlinal Grande/Cerro Blanco/Las Flores-Colhue Huapi

Caleta Cordova

Paso Rio Mayo

Huetel

San Jorge Marina I

*Peninsula
de Taitao*

Mata Magallanes Oeste/Mata Magallanes

Comodoro Rivadavia

Los Monos/Barranca Yankowsky

Los Menucos/Mariana

Golfo San Jorge

CHILE

Arroyo Saldo/La Cueva/Las Meset As Este

Estancia Cholita

Caleta Olivia

San Jorge Marina II

Estancia San Justo

Pampa Del Setente/Los Del Cuy

Canadon Seco Oriental/Canadon Seco

Cerro Wenceslao/Cerro Grande

Bajada Ardura

Canadon La Escondida/Piedra Clavada

Canadon Leon/Canadon Minerales

Las Heras/El Valle/Estancia Romberg/Ramblon Largo

Koluel Kayke/El Cordon/El Huemul

Deseado

De La Pampa/San Martin/Punta Deseado

Pico Truncado/El Destino

Meseta Espinosa/Caleta Olivia

ARGENTINA (San Jorge Area)
1. *Cerra Tortuga/Manantiales Behr Oeste*
2. *Canadon Las Vertientes*
3. *Bella Vista/Escalante*
4. *Cerro Dragon*
5. *El Tordillo/Quirquincho/Tordillo Sur*
6. *Jorge/El Gato/Resero*
7. *Canadon Lagarto/Pampa Del Castillo*
8. *Meseta Catorce/Escorial*

San Julian

Campo Bola

Laguana Del Oro

Estancia La Maggie

La Paz

Laguana Los Capones

Campo Boleadoras/Campo Indio

Ototel Aike

Maria Ines

Canadon Salto

San Critobal

El Indio

Palermo Aike

Rio Gallegos

Nika/Pampa Larga/Punta Delgada/Santiago

Del Mosquito/Oceano

Kimiri Aike/Kimiri Aike N

Chorrillos/Chorrillos Norte

Tranquilo

Condor

Ciake

Manzano

Cerro Redondo

Punta Del Cerro

Straits of Magellan

Falkland Islands (UK)

PORT STANLEY ■

Manzano 3A

Gregorio

Canadon Alfa

Clarencia

Rion Cullen/Canadon Piedras

Punta Arenas

Cabo Nombre/Paramo Chico

Tres Brazos

Rio Del Oro

La Brea/La Sara Norte

San Sebastian

Los Chorrillos/La Sara/Seccion Treinta/Arroya
Cachimba/Arroyo Gamm/Carmen Silva

Rio Grande

El Monte/Punta Maria/San Luis/Arroyo Candelaria

Puesto Quince

Rio Aviles/Las Violetas/Laguana Escondida

Castillo Oeste/Cerro Mesa/Laguana Carmen

Ushuaia

CHILE
1. *Kimiri Aike S*
2. *Carrera/Dicky/Monte Aymond*
3. *Punta Delgarda/Direccion/Faro Este*
4. *Canadon/Daniel*
5. *Daniel Este/Dungenes*
6. *Spiteful Norte/Spiteful*
7. *Manantialles*
8. *Cuarto Chorrillo/Calafate*
9. *Tres Lagos/Bandurria*
10. *Oaviord*
11. *Flamenco/Cullen*
12. *Victoria*
13. *Chanarcillo*
14. *Albatros/Cormoran/Catalina*
15. *Posesion*

Cape Horn

Drake Passage

LATIN AMERICA

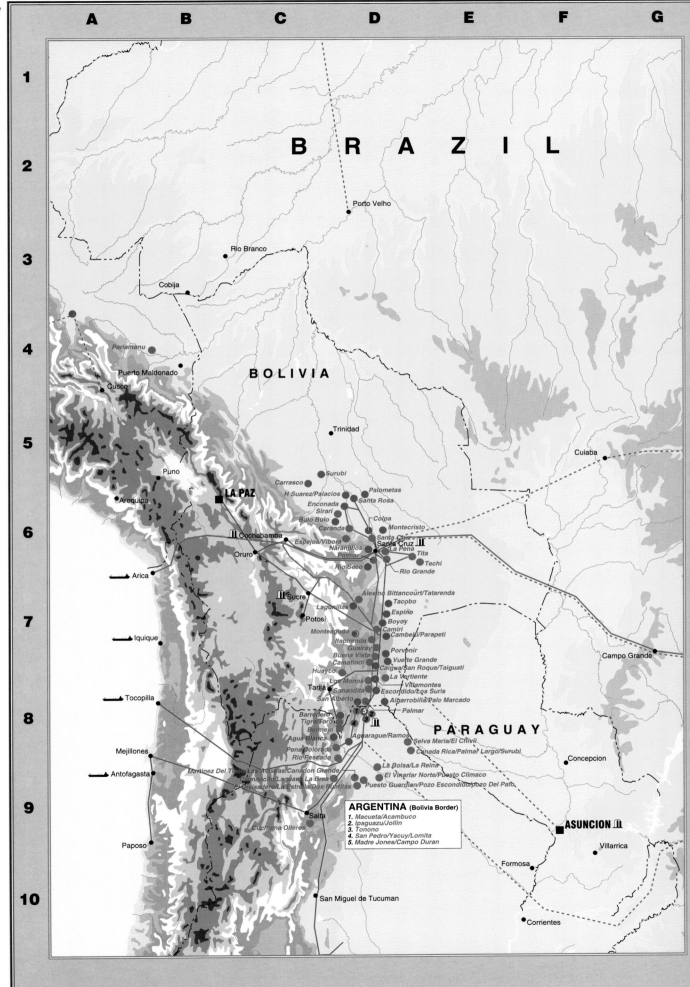

Scale: 1:10,100,000

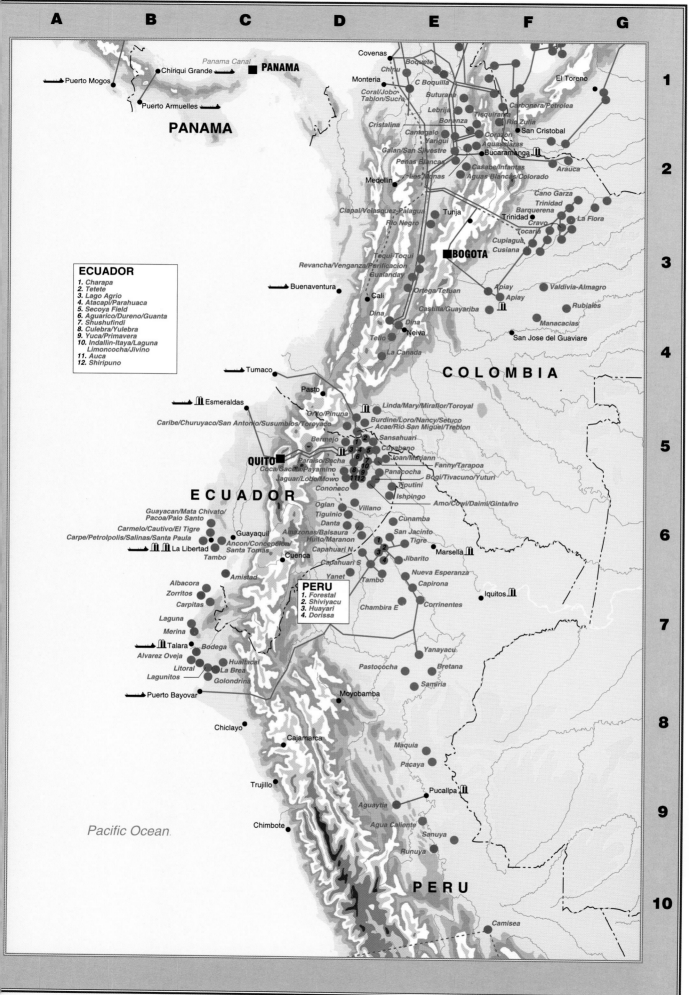

ECUADOR
1. Charapa
2. Tetete
3. Lago Agrio
4. Atacapi/Parahuaca
5. Secoya Field
6. Aguarico/Dureno/Guanta
7. Shushufindi
8. Culebra/Yulebra
9. Yuca/Primavera
10. Indallin-Itaya/Laguna Limoncocha/Jivino
11. Auca
12. Shiripuno

PERU
1. Forestal
2. Shiviyacu
3. Huayari
4. Dorissa

Pacific Ocean

PANAMA

COLOMBIA

ECUADOR

PERU

LATIN AMERICA

ale: 1:9,400,000

©The Petroleum Economist Ltd, London 2001

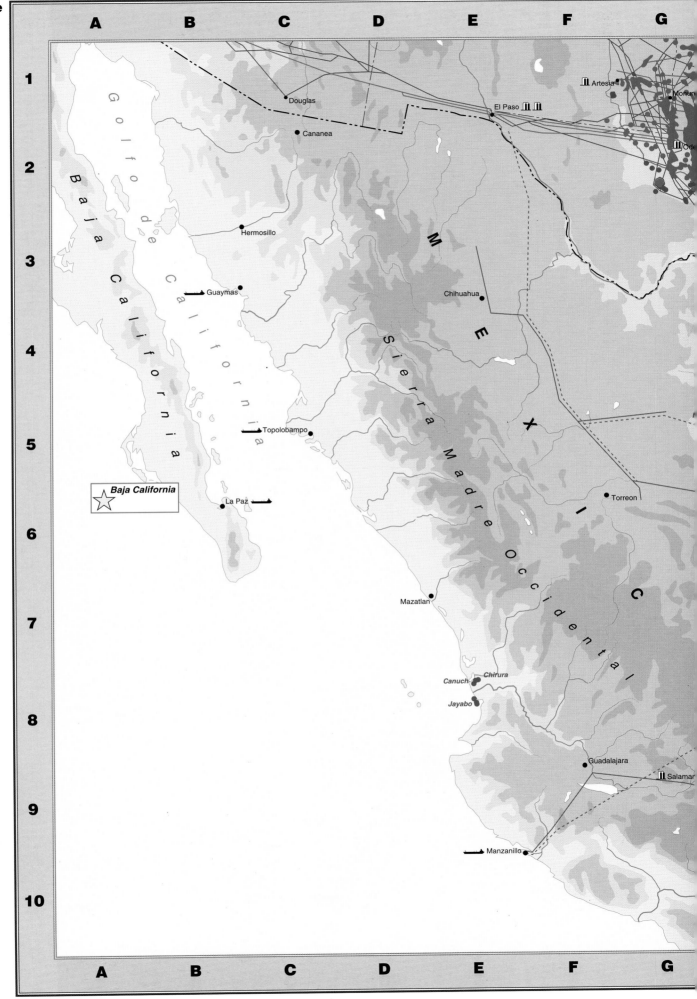

Golfo de California

Baja California

Sierra Madre Occidental

MEXICO

Douglas

Cananea

Hermosillo

Guaymas

Topolobampo

La Paz

Baja California

Chihuahua

Torreon

Mazatlan

Chirura

Canuch

Jayabo

Guadalajara

Salamar

Manzanillo

El Paso

Artesia

Monun

Ode

Scale: 1:7,000,000

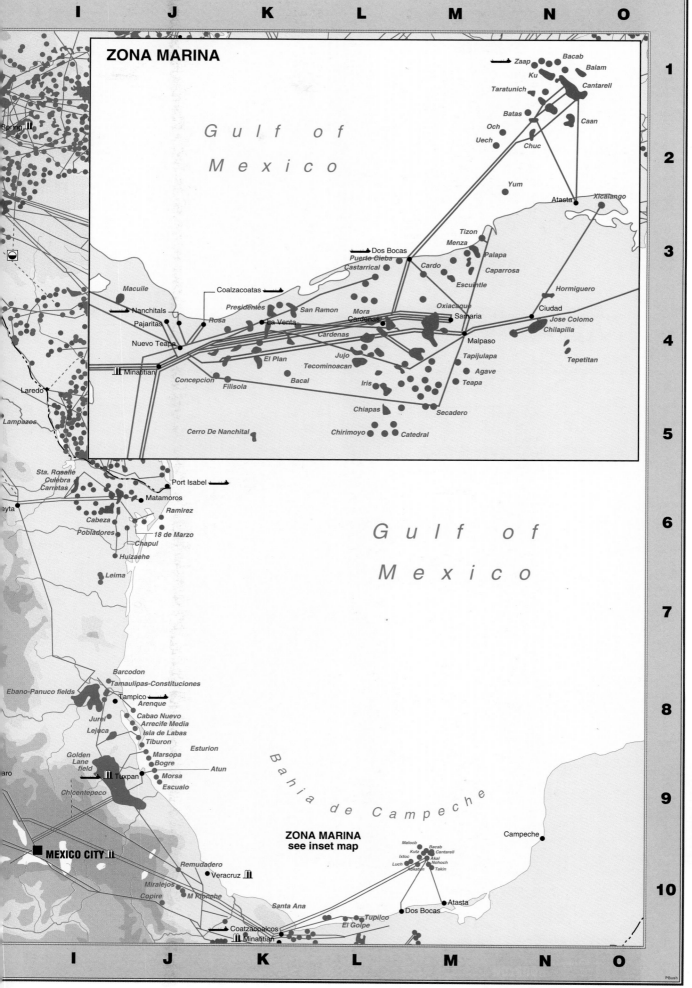

LATIN AMERICA

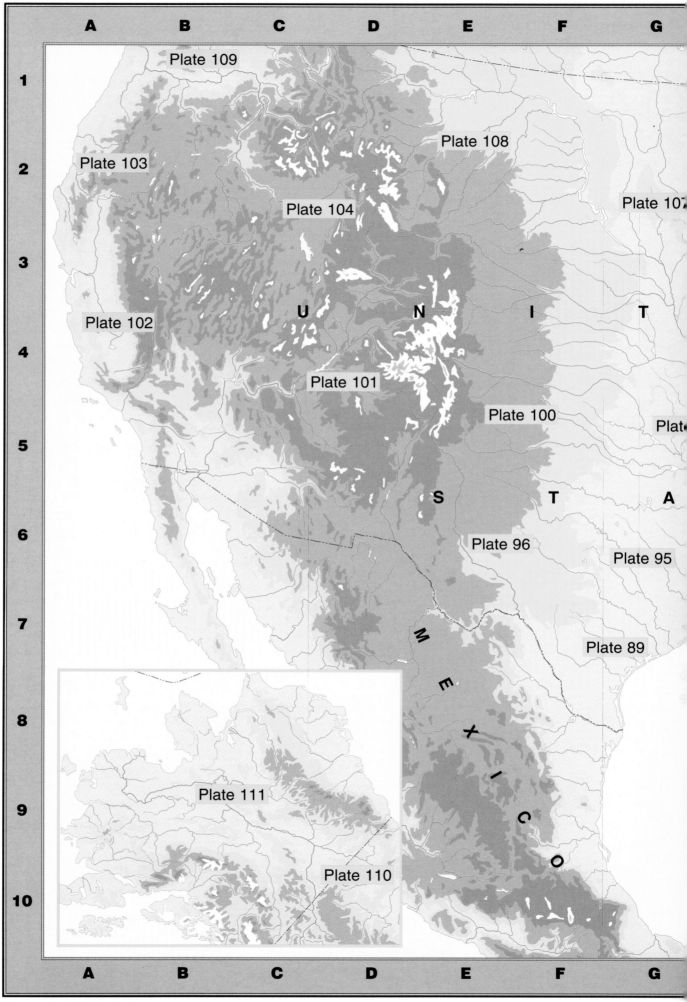

Plate 109

Plate 103

Plate 108

Plate 104

Plate 107

Plate 102

U   N   I   T

Plate 101

Plate 100

Plat

S   T   A

Plate 96

Plate 95

M

Plate 89

E

X

Plate 111

I

C

Plate 110

O

NORTH AMERICA

Scale: 1:13,170,000

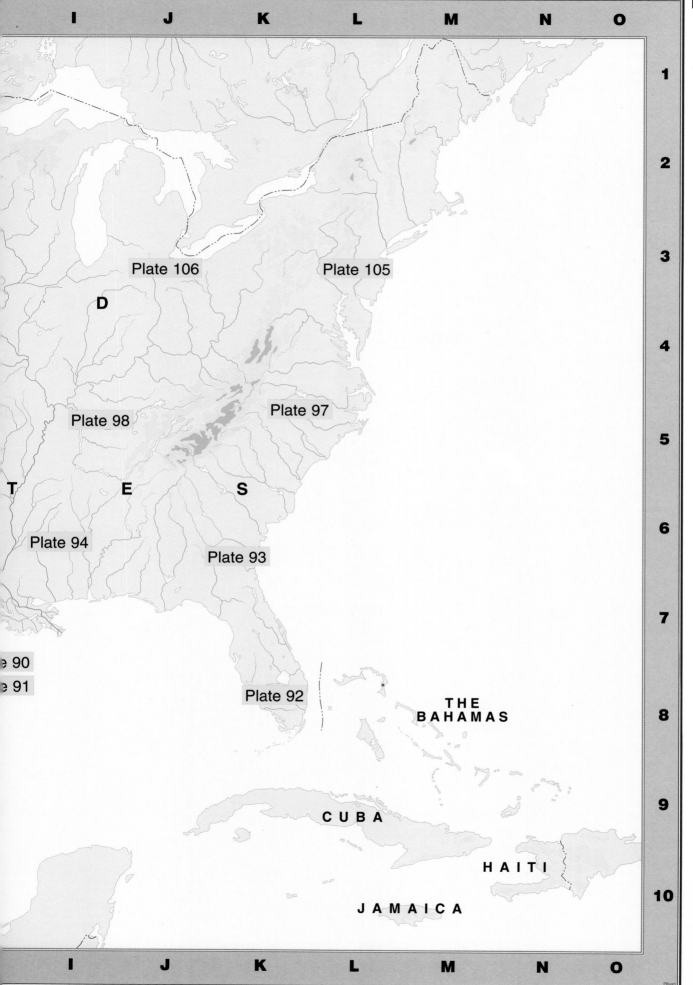

I   J   K   L   M   N   O

1

2

3

Plate 106   Plate 105

D

4

Plate 98   Plate 97

5

T   E   S

6

Plate 94

Plate 93

7

e 90

e 91

Plate 92

THE
BAHAMAS

8

9

CUBA

HAITI

10

JAMAICA

I   J   K   L   M   N   O

NORTH AMERICA

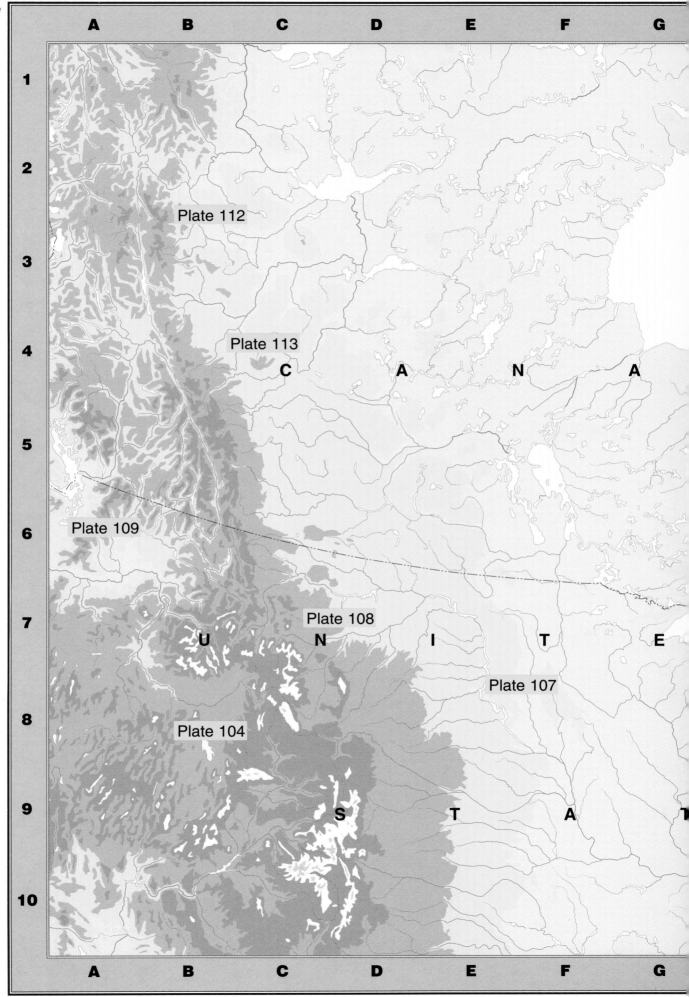

Plate 112

Plate 113

C   A   N   A

Plate 109

Plate 108

U   N   I   T   E

Plate 107

Plate 104

S   T   A   T

NORTH AMERICA

Scale: 1:14,255,000

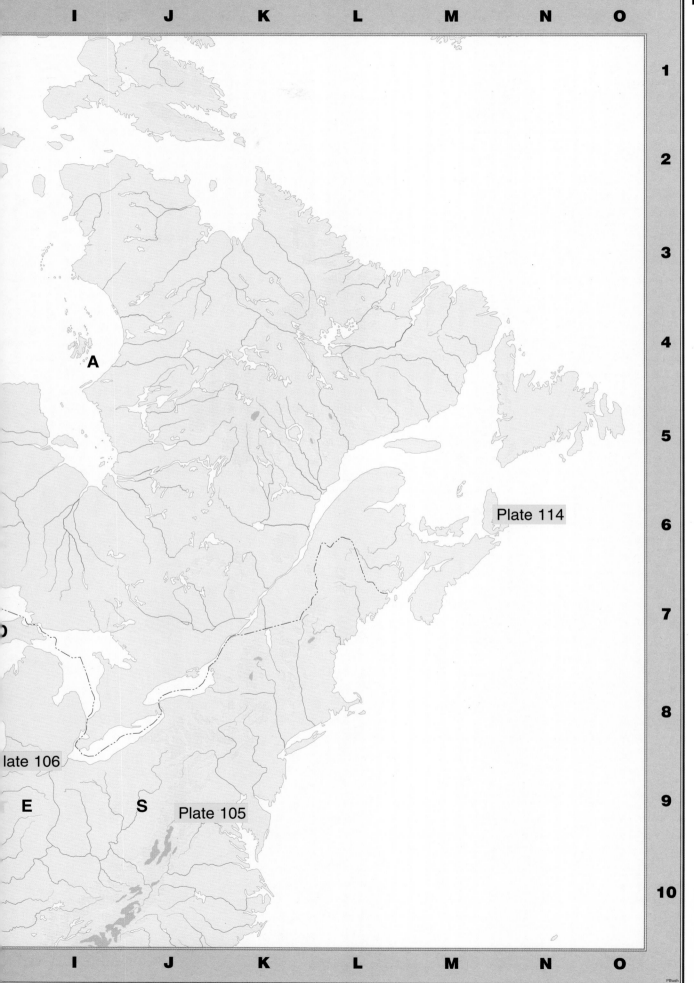

Plate 114

Plate 106

Plate 105

NORTH AMERICA

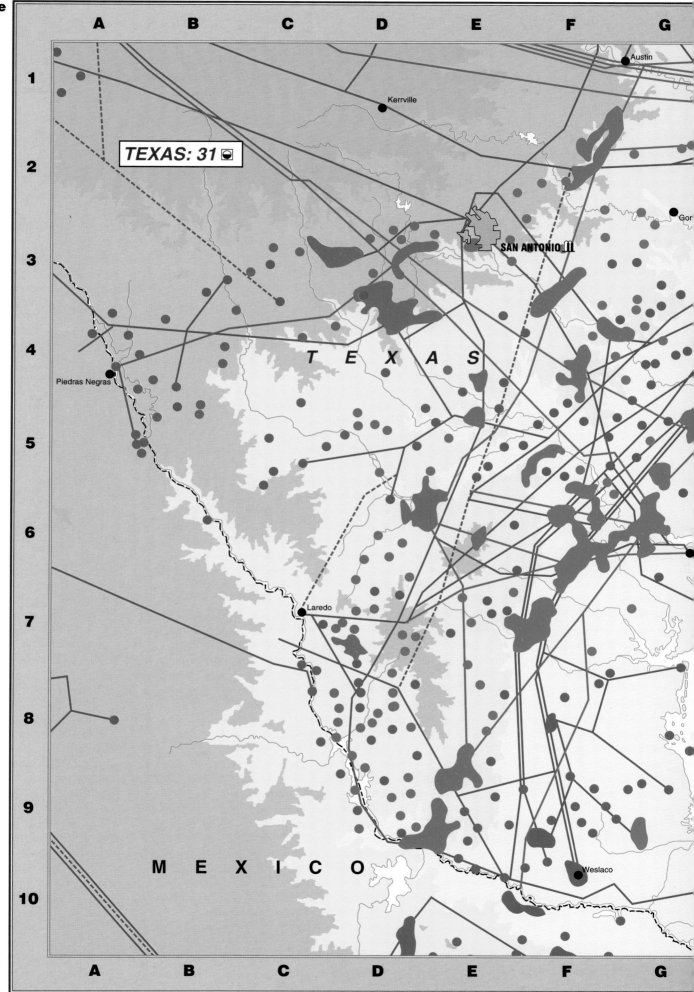

TEXAS: 31

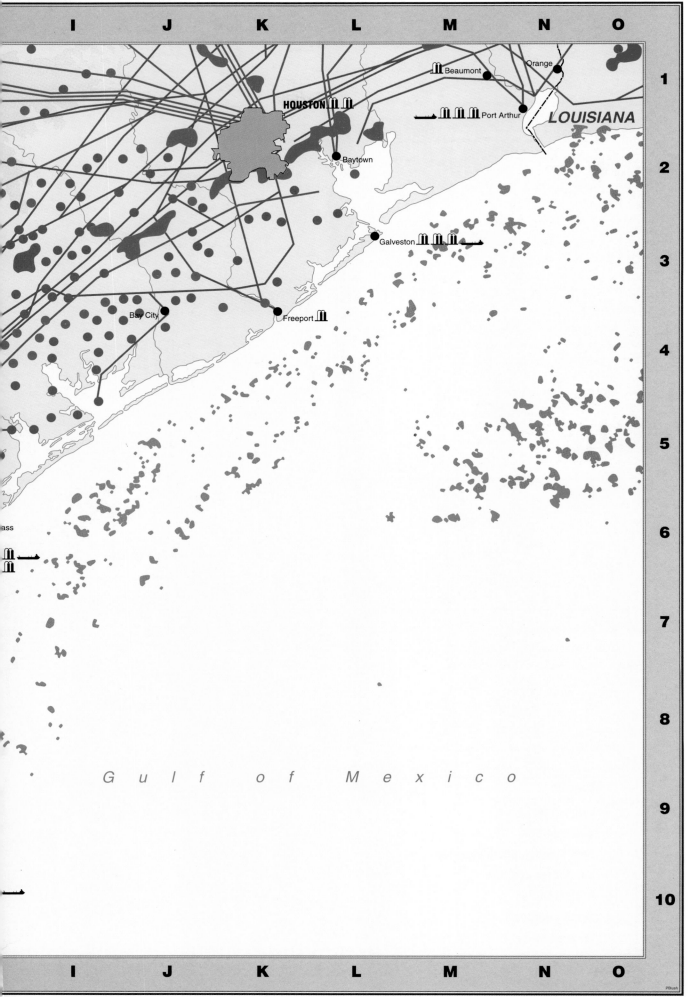

Gulf of Mexico

Beaumont
Orange
Port Arthur
LOUISIANA
HOUSTON
Baytown
Galveston
Bay City
Freeport
ass

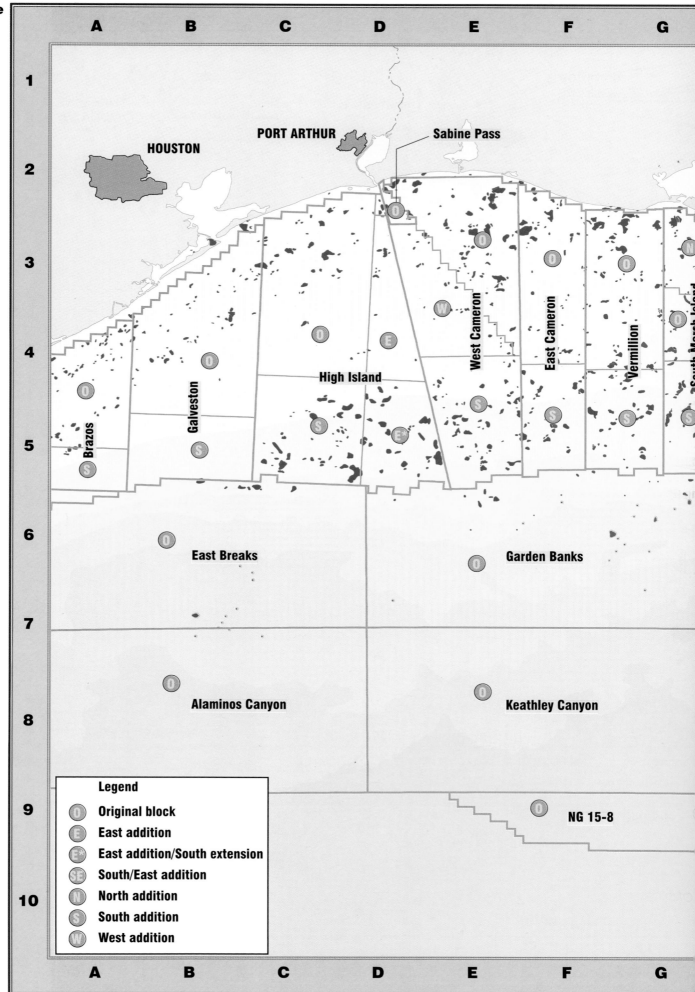

NORTH AMERICA

Scale: 1:2,115,000

PRIMARY BLOCKS IN US GULF OF MEXICO

Plate
90

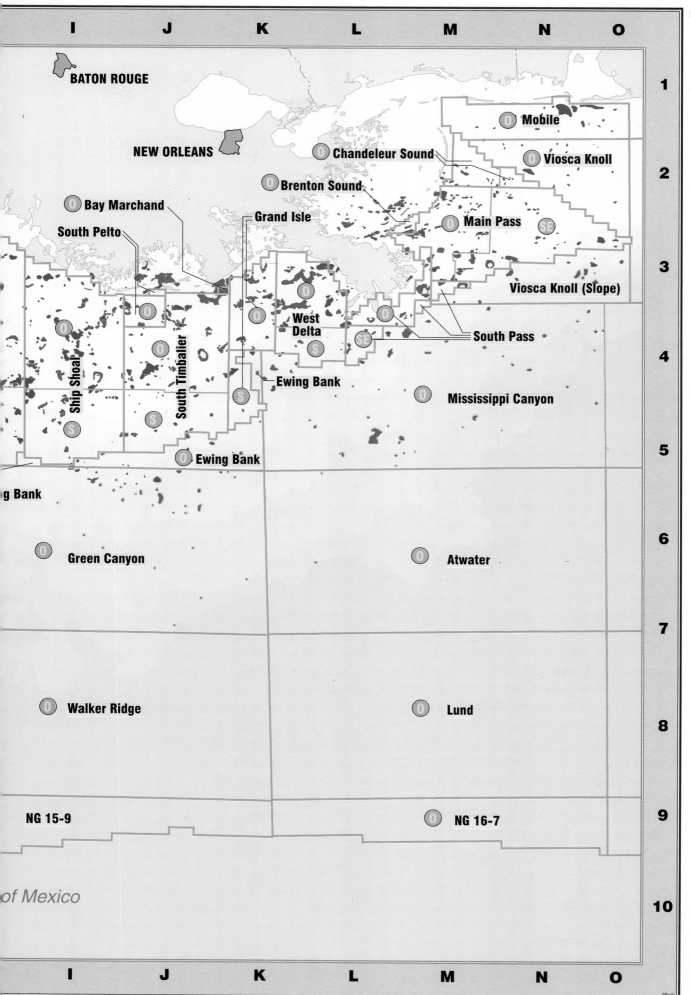

BATON ROUGE

Mobile

NEW ORLEANS

Chandeleur Sound

Viosca Knoll

Brenton Sound

Bay Marchand

Main Pass

South Pelto

Grand Isle

Viosca Knoll (Slope)

West
Delta

South Pass

Ship Shoal

South Timbalier

Ewing Bank

Mississippi Canyon

Ewing Bank

g Bank

Green Canyon

Atwater

Walker Ridge

Lund

NG 15-9

NG 16-7

of Mexico

PBush

LOUISIANA GULF COAST

Plate
91

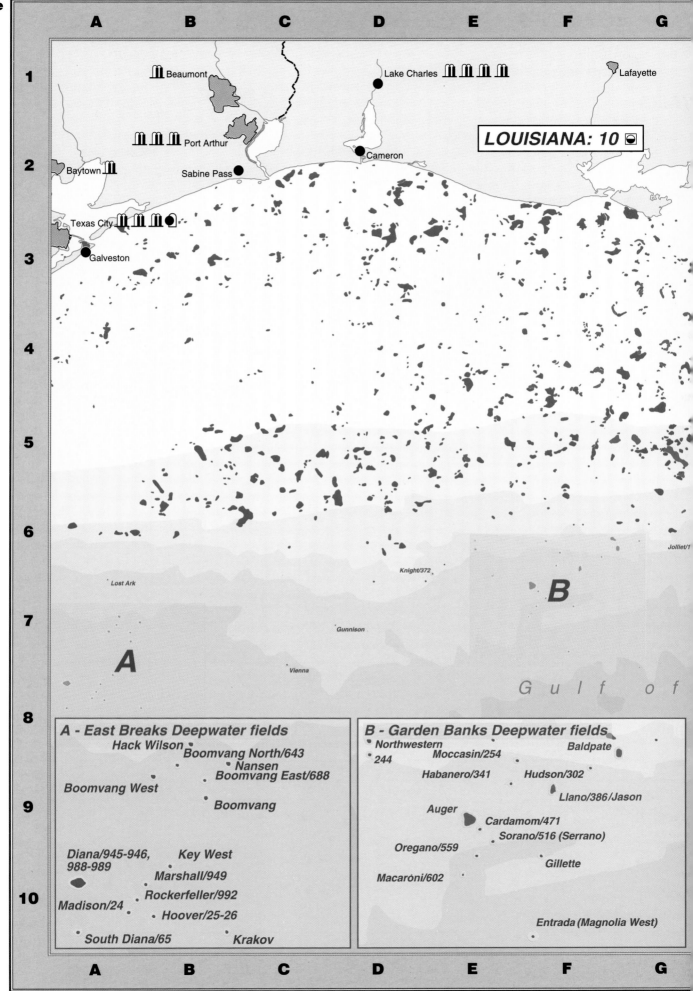

LOUISIANA: 10 ◉

A - East Breaks Deepwater fields

Hack Wilson
Boomvang North/643
Nansen
Boomvang East/688
Boomvang West
Boomvang

Diana/945-946,
988-989
Key West
Marshall/949
Rockerfeller/992
Madison/24
Hoover/25-26
South Diana/65
Krakov

B - Garden Banks Deepwater fields

Northwestern
244
Moccasin/254
Baldpate
Habanero/341
Hudson/302
Llano/386/Jason
Auger
Cardamom/471
Sorano/516 (Serrano)
Oregano/559
Gillette
Macaróni/602
Entrada (Magnolia West)

Beaumont
Lake Charles
Lafayette
Port Arthur
Cameron
Baytown
Sabine Pass
Texas City
Galveston

Knight/372
Lost Ark
B
Jolliet/1
Gunnison
A
Vienna
Gulf of

Scale: 1:1,900,000

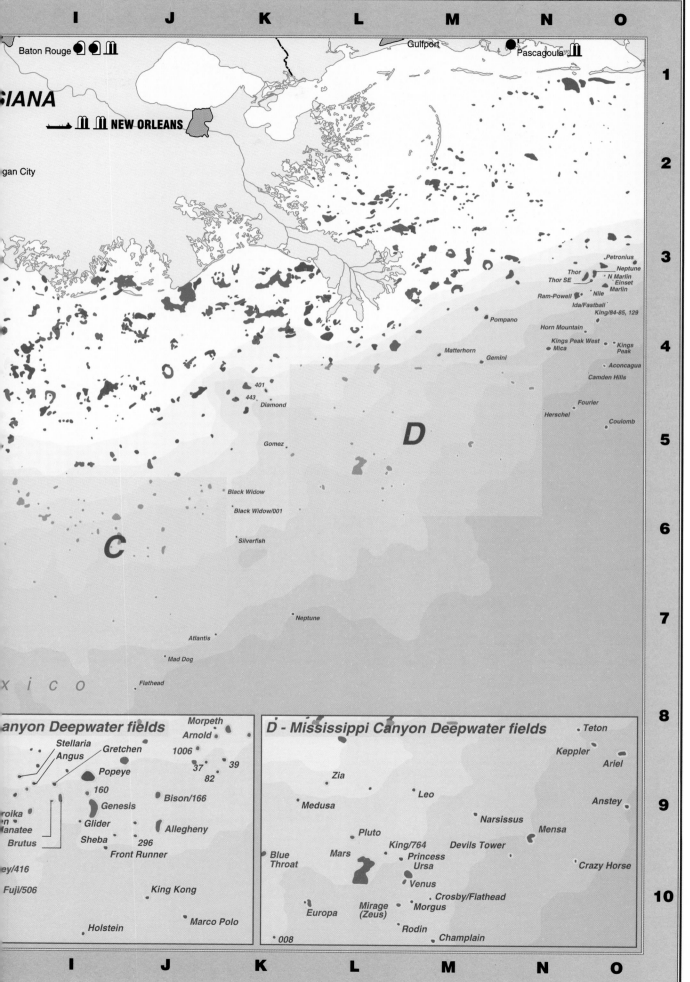

I · J · K · L · M · N · O

Baton Rouge

NEW ORLEANS

Gulfport

Pascagoula

SIANA

gan City

XICO

1

2

3

Petronius
Neptune
Thor
Thor SE
N Marlin
Einset
Marlin
Ram-Powell
Nile
Ida/Fastball
King/84-85, 129

Pompano
Horn Mountain
Kings Peak West
Mica
Kings Peak
Matterhorn
Gemini
Aconcagua
Camden Hills

4

401
443
Diamond
Fourier
Herschel
Coulomb

D

5

Gomez

Black Widow
Black Widow/001

6

Silverfish

C

Neptune

7

Atlantis

Mad Dog

Flathead

8

anyon Deepwater fields

Morpeth
Arnold
Stellaria
Gretchen
1006
Angus
37   39
Popeye
82
160
Bison/166
Genesis
roika
n
Glider
Allegheny
anatee
Brutus
Sheba   296
Front Runner
ey/416
Fuji/506
King Kong
Holstein
Marco Polo

D - Mississippi Canyon Deepwater fields

Teton
Keppler
Ariel
Zia
Leo
Medusa
Anstey
Narsissus
Mensa
Pluto
Devils Tower
King/764
Mars
Princess
Ursa
Crazy Horse
Blue
Throat
Venus
Crosby/Flathead
Europa
Mirage
(Zeus)
Morgus
Rodin
008
Champlain

9

10

PBush

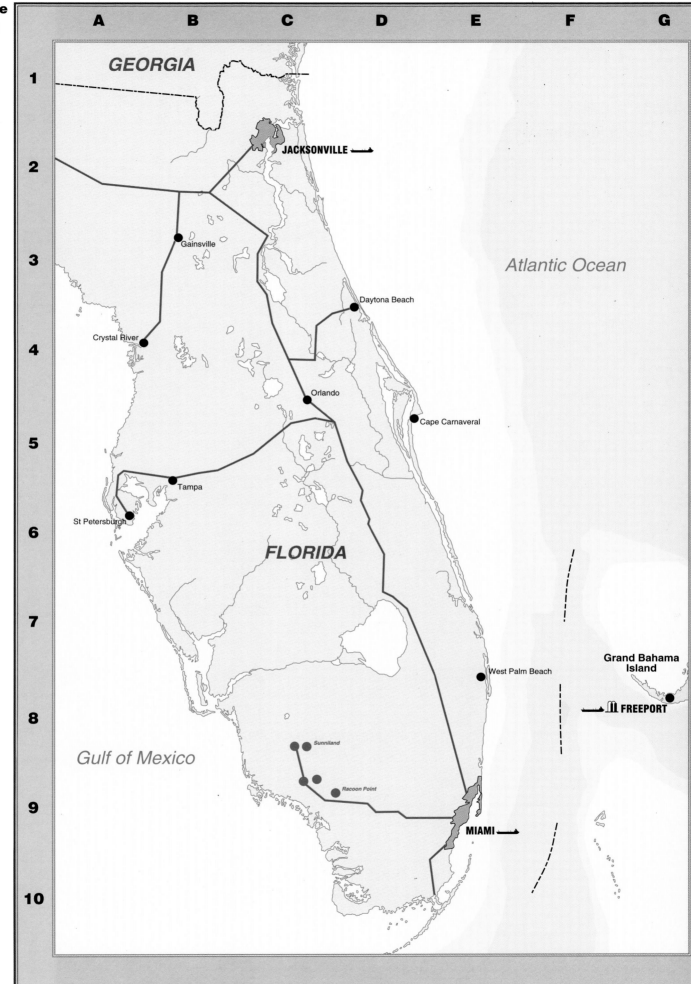

GEORGIA

JACKSONVILLE ➜

Atlantic Ocean

● Gainsville

● Daytona Beach

Crystal River ●

Orlando ●

● Cape Carnaveral

Tampa ●

St Petersburgh ●

FLORIDA

Gulf of Mexico

● West Palm Beach

**Grand Bahama
Island**

➜ 🏭 **FREEPORT**

Sunniland

Racoon Point

MIAMI ➜

GEORGIA AND NORTHERN FLORIDA

Plate
93

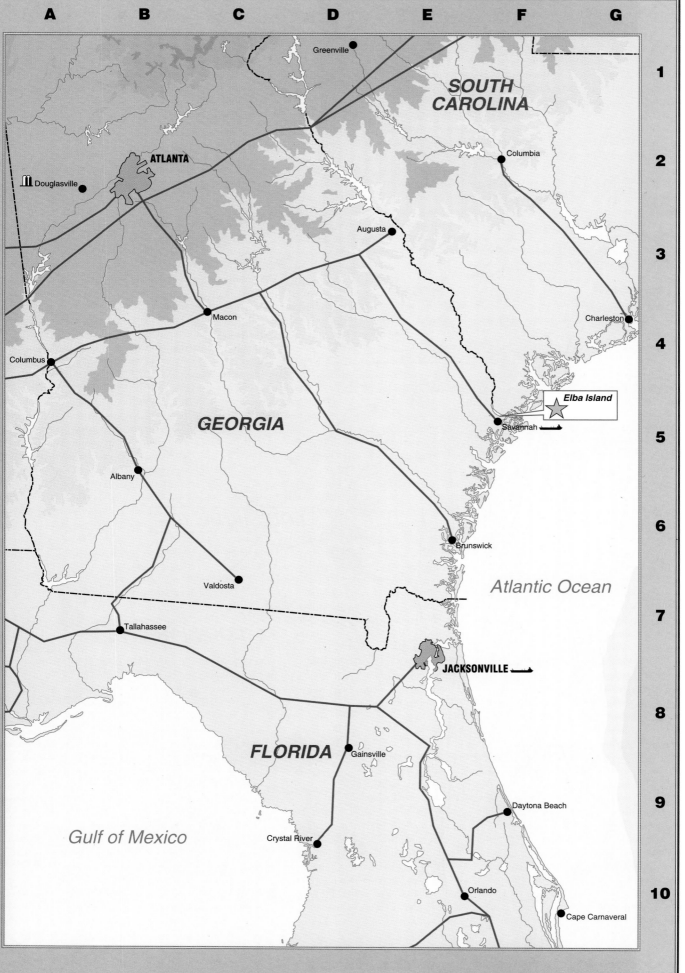

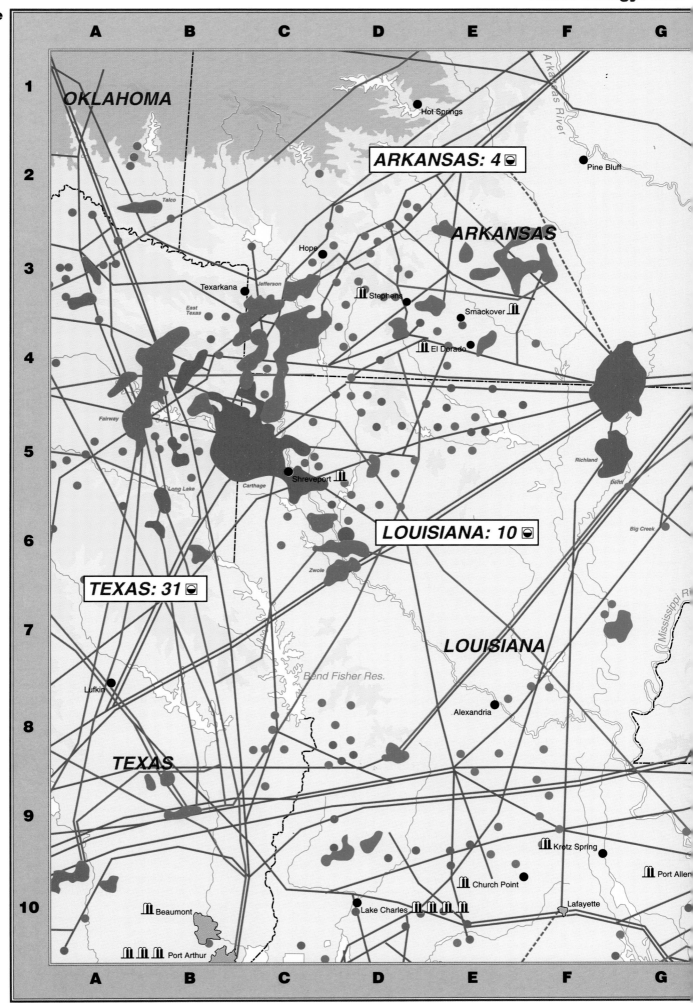

OKLAHOMA

ARKANSAS: 4 ▣

Talco

ARKANSAS

Hope

Texarkana

Jefferson

Stephens

Smackover

East
Texas

El Dorado

Fairway

Richland

Dentl

Long Lake

Carthage

Shreveport

Big Creek

LOUISIANA: 10 ▣

Zwole

TEXAS: 31 ▣

Bend Fisher Res.

LOUISIANA

Lufkin

Alexandria

TEXAS

Krotz Spring

Port Allen

Church Point

Lafayette

Beaumont

Lake Charles

Port Arthur

Hot Springs

Pine Bluff

Arkansas River

Mississippi Ri

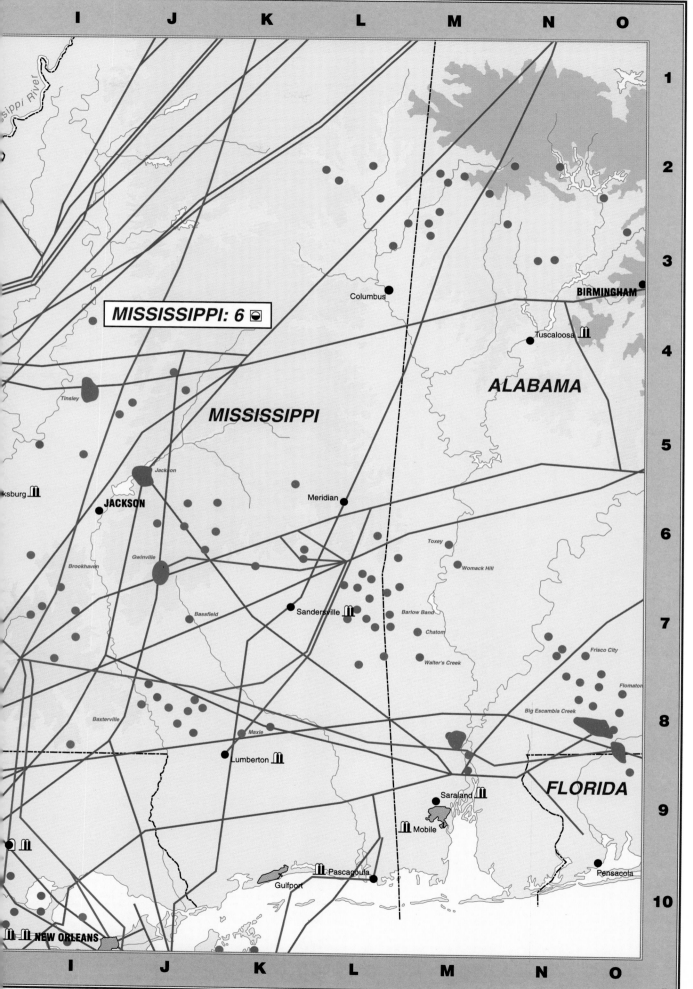

MISSISSIPPI: 6

Mississippi River

Tinsley

MISSISSIPPI

Columbus

ALABAMA

BIRMINGHAM

Tuscaloosa

Jackson

JACKSON

ksburg

Meridian

Brookhaven

Gwinville

Toxey

Womack Hill

Bassfield

Sandersville

Barlow Band

Chatom

Walter's Creek

Frisco City

Flomaton

Baxterville

Big Escambia Creek

Maxie

FLORIDA

Lumberton

Saraland

Mobile

Pascagoula

Gulfport

Pensacola

NEW ORLEANS

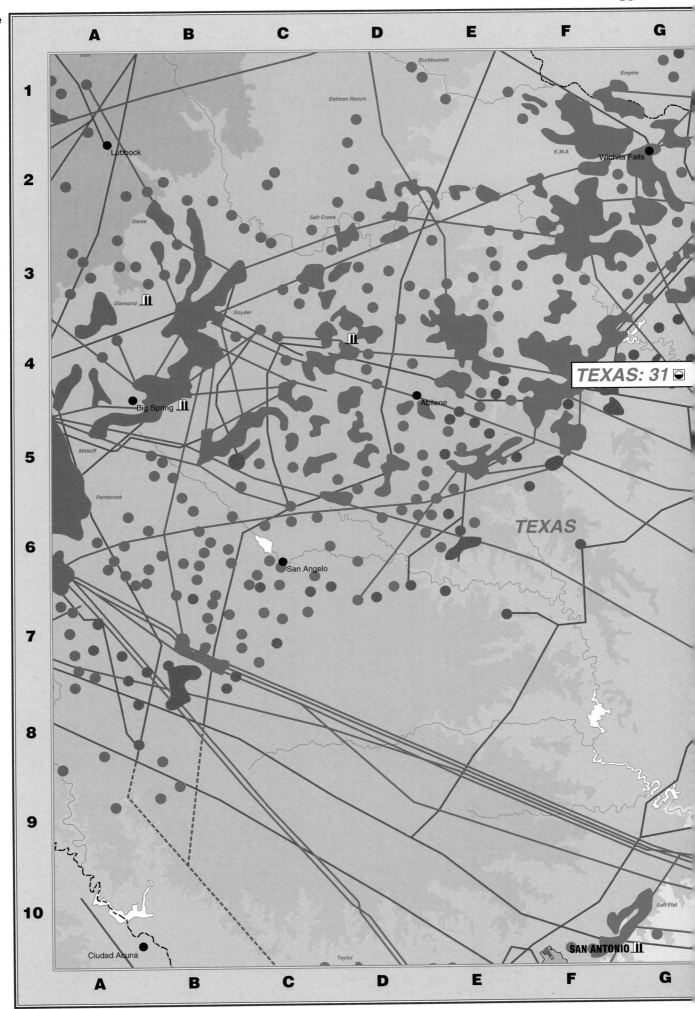

TEXAS: 31

TEXAS

Scale: 1:2,125,000

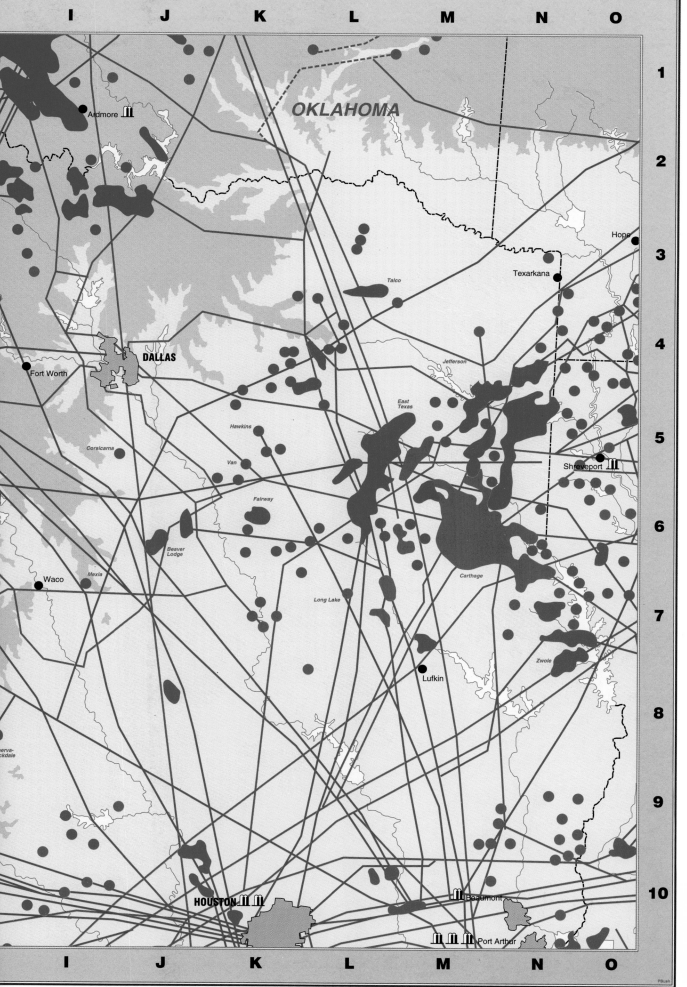

OKLAHOMA

Ardmore

Hope

Talco

Texarkana

DALLAS

Fort Worth

Jefferson

East
Texas

Hawkins

Shreveport

Corsicarna

Van

Fairway

Beaver
Lodge

Carthage

Mexia

Waco

Long Lake

Zwole

Lufkin

nerva-
ckdale

HOUSTON

Beaumont

Port Arthur

PBush

Plate
96

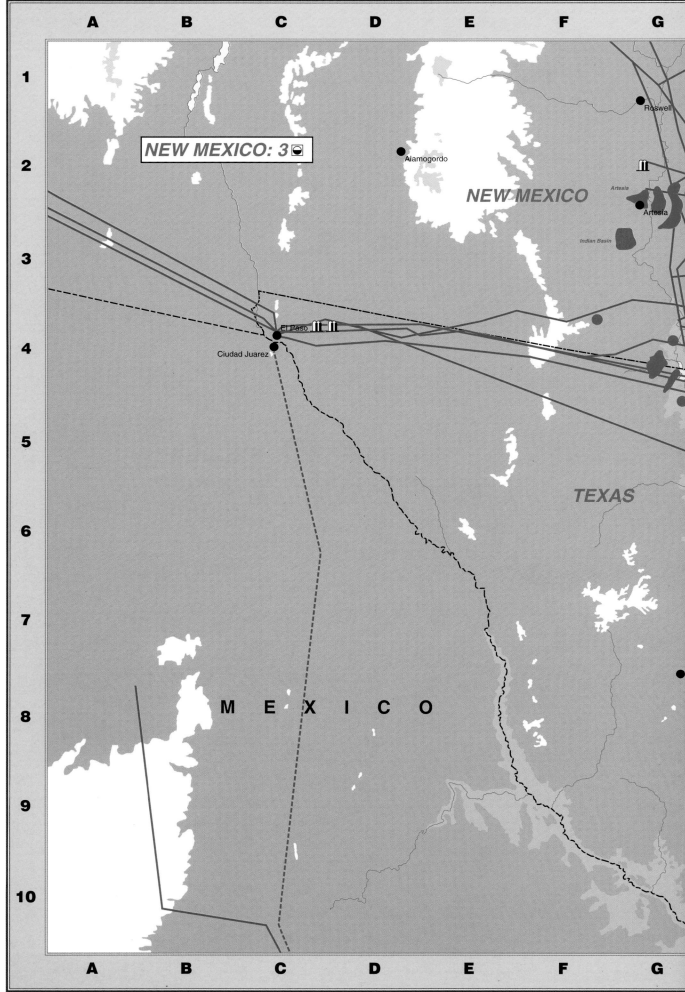

NEW MEXICO: 3

NEW MEXICO

Roswell

Alamogordo

Artesia

Artesia

Indian Basin

El Paso

Ciudad Juarez

TEXAS

M E X I C O

Scale: 1:2,240,000

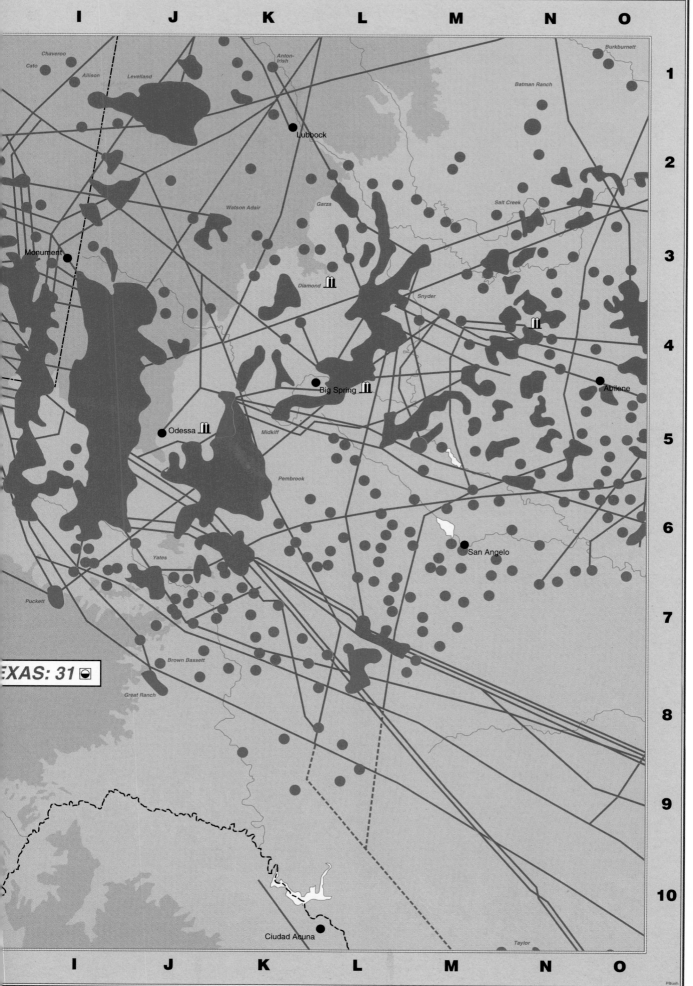

TEXAS: 31 ⬓

NORTH AMERICA

NORTH CAROLINA AND VIRGINIA

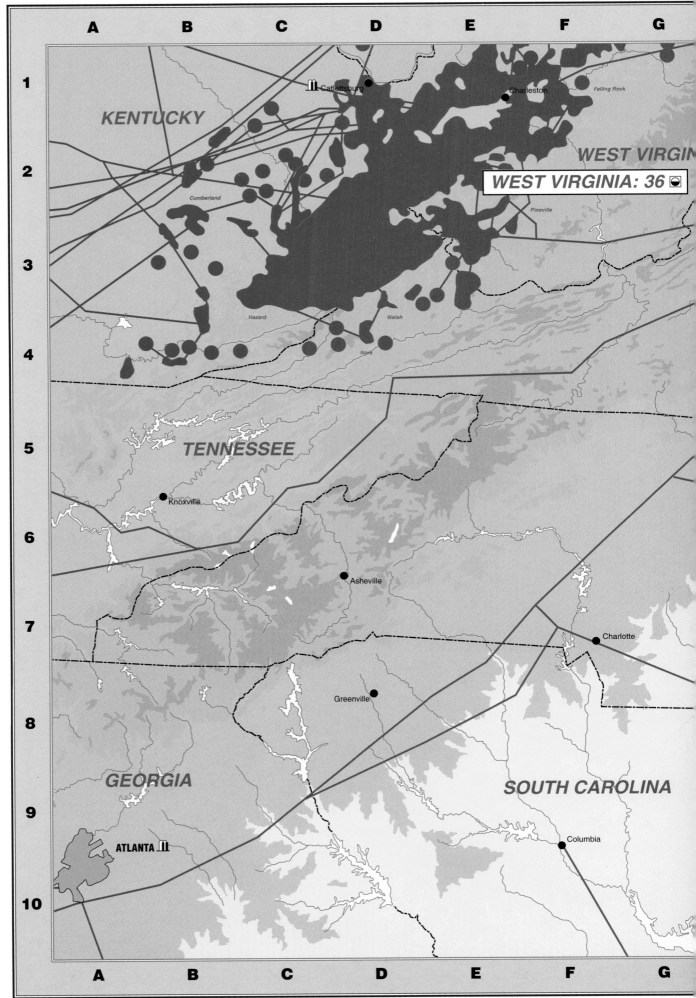

Scale: 1:2,410,000

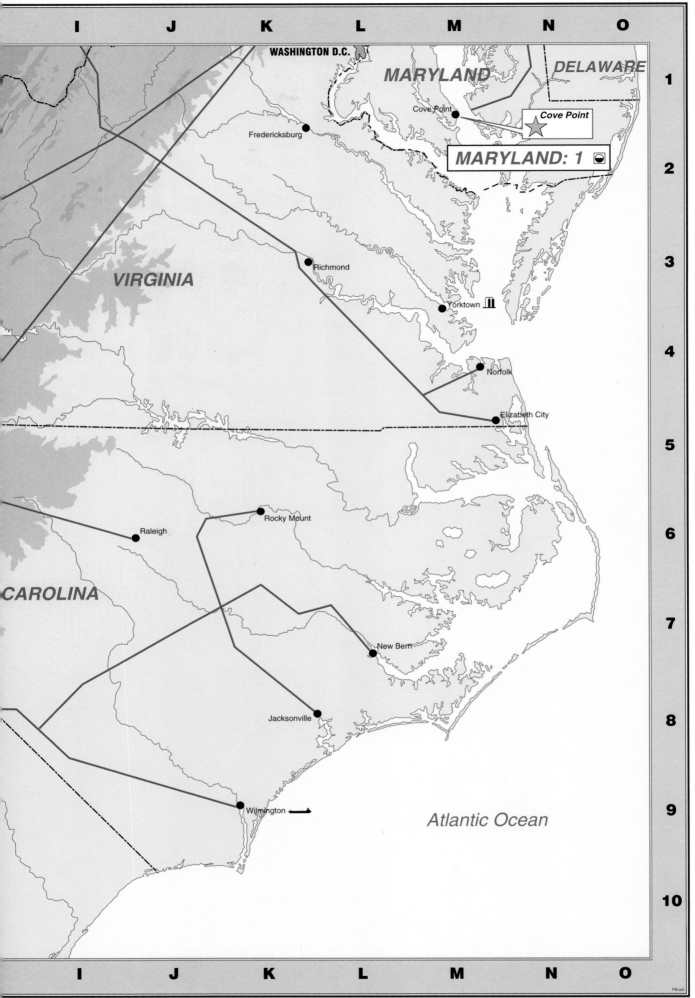

WASHINGTON D.C.

MARYLAND

DELAWARE

Cove Point

Cove Point

MARYLAND: 1

Fredericksburg

VIRGINIA

Richmond

Yorktown

Norfolk

Elizabeth City

Rocky Mount

Raleigh

CAROLINA

New Bern

Jacksonville

Wilmington

Atlantic Ocean

Plate 98

TENNESSEE AND KENTUCKY

World Energy Atlas

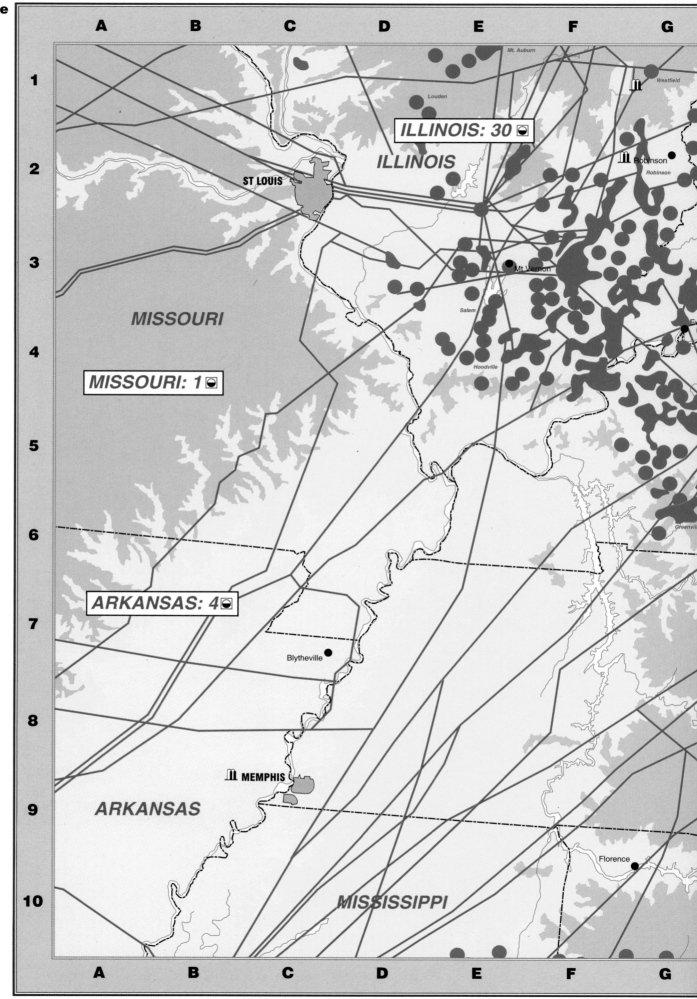

ILLINOIS: 30

MISSOURI: 1

ARKANSAS: 4

St Louis

ILLINOIS

MISSOURI

Mt. Auburn

Louden

Westfield

Robinson
Robinson

Mt Vernon

Salem

Hoodville

Greenville

Blytheville

MEMPHIS

ARKANSAS

MISSISSIPPI

Florence

Scale: 1:2,415,000

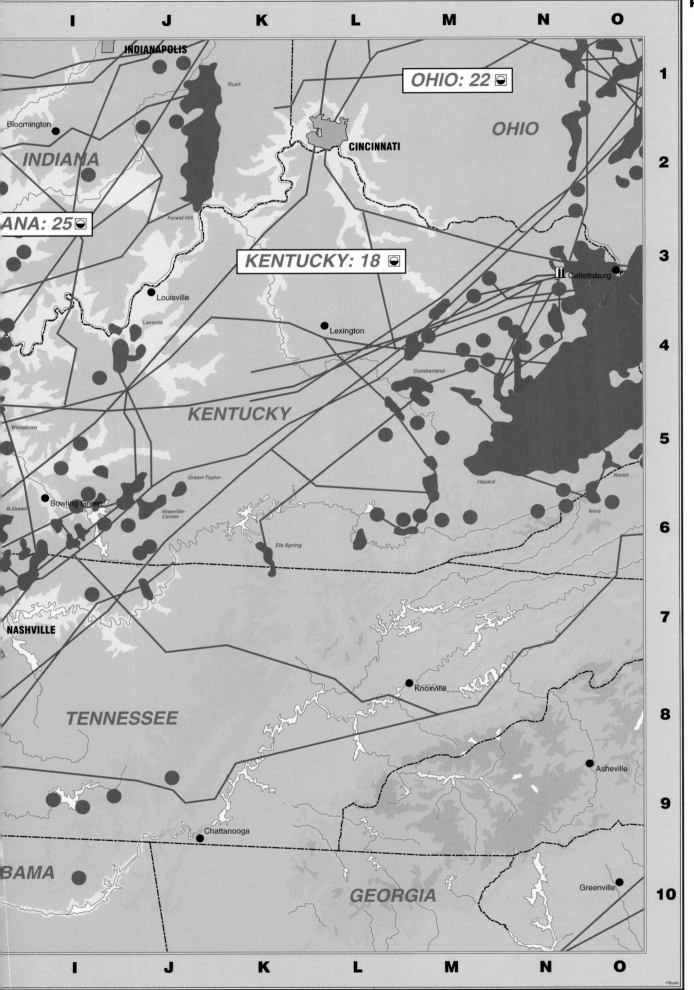

OHIO: 22

ANA: 25

KENTUCKY: 18

INDIANAPOLIS

Rush

Bloomington

INDIANA

OHIO

CINCINNATI

Forest Hill

Catlettsburg

Louisville

Laconia

Lexington

KENTUCKY

Cumberland

Wensboro

Hazard

Welsh

Green-Taylor

Bowling Green

B.Green

Hiseville-
Center

Nora

Elk Spring

NASHVILLE

Knoxville

TENNESSEE

Asheville

Chattanooga

GEORGIA

Greenville

BAMA

PBush

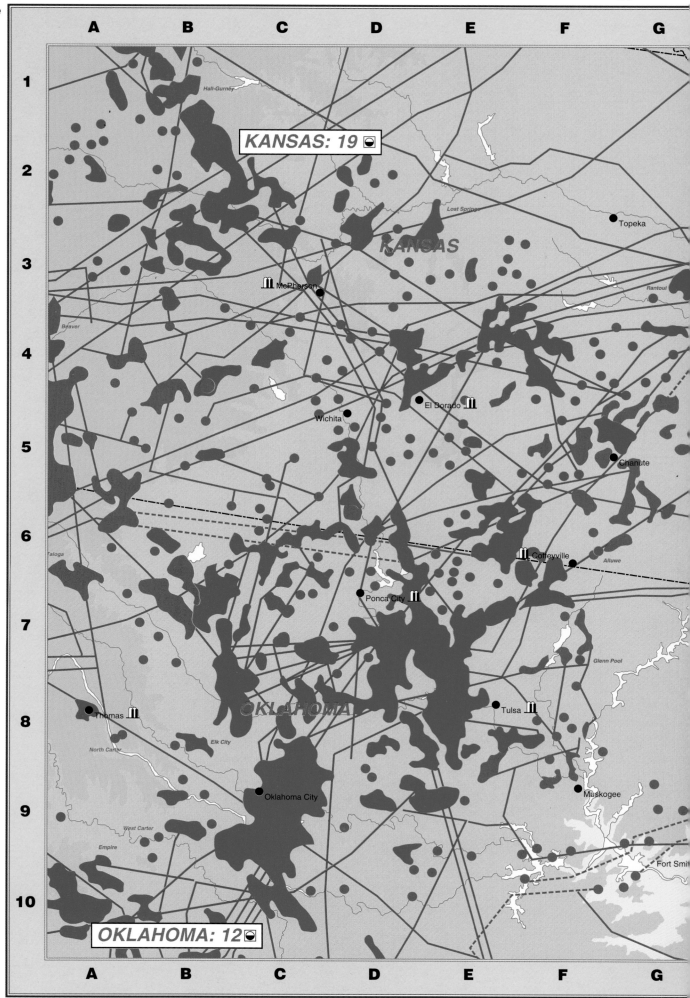

KANSAS: 19

KANSAS

OKLAHOMA

OKLAHOMA: 12

Hall-Gurney

Lost Springs

Topeka

Rantoul

McPherson

Beaver

El Dorado

Wichita

Chanute

Taloga

Coffeyville

Alluwe

Ponca City

Glenn Pool

Thomas

Tulsa

Elk City

North Carter

Muskogee

Oklahoma City

West Carter

Empire

Fort Smith

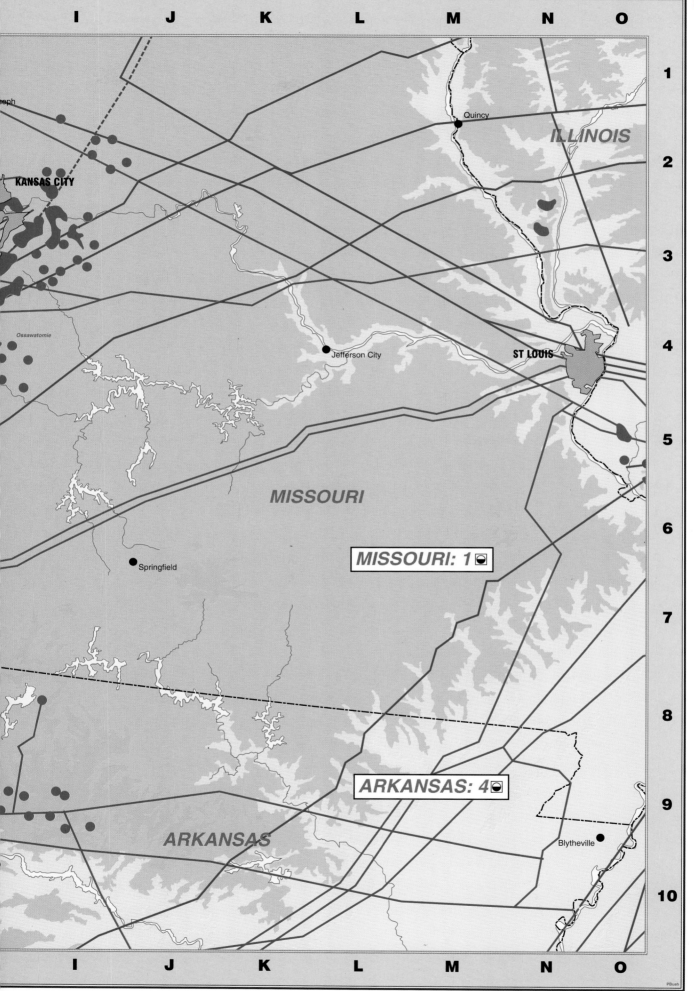

I J K L M N O

1

eph

Quincy

ILLINOIS

2

KANSAS CITY

3

Ossawatomie

Jefferson City

ST LOUIS

4

5

MISSOURI

6

MISSOURI: 1 ◨

Springfield

7

8

ARKANSAS: 4 ◨

9

ARKANSAS

Blytheville

10

I J K L M N O

PBush

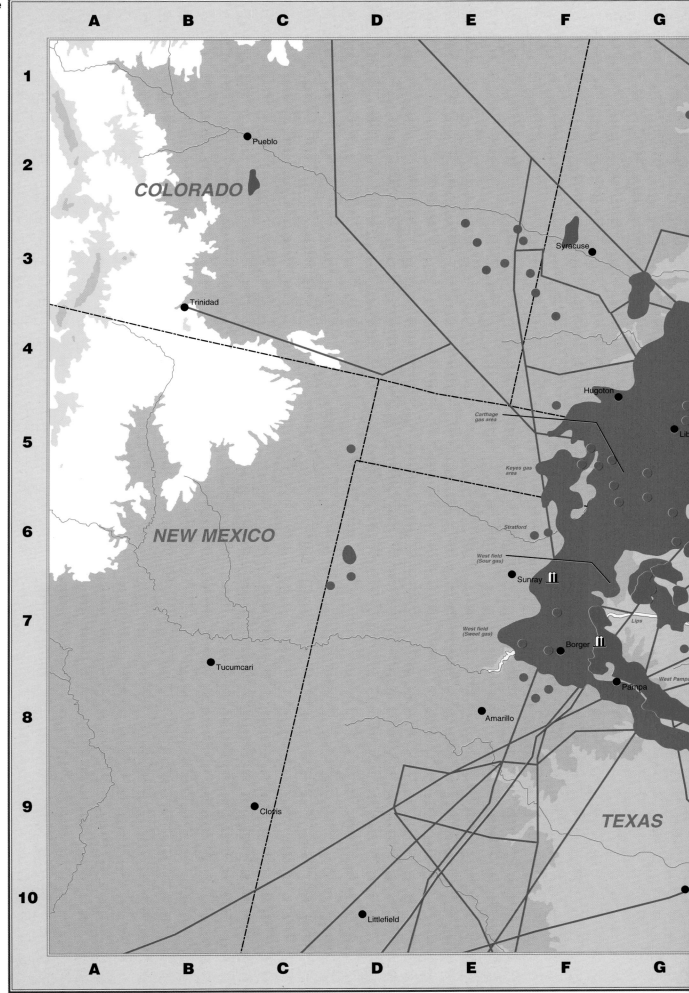

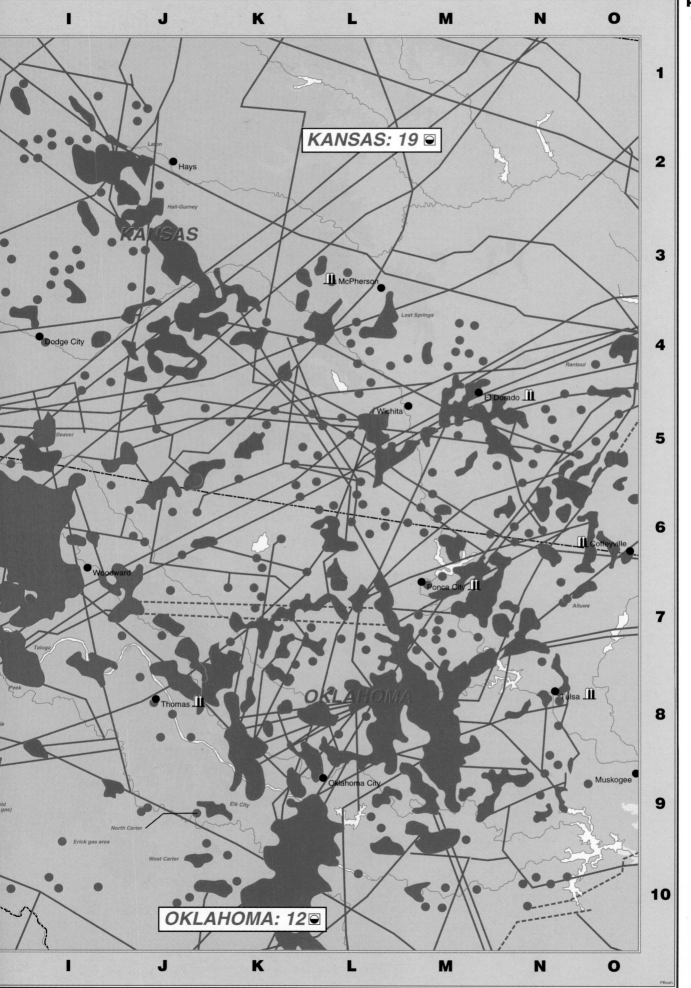

KANSAS: 19

Laton

Hays

Hall-Gurney

KANSAS

Dodge City

McPherson

Lost Springs

Beaver

Wichita

El Dorado

Rantoul

Coffeyville

Woodward

Ponca City

Alluwe

Taloga

Peek

Thomas

OKLAHOMA

Tulsa

Muskogee

Oklahoma City

Elk City

North Carter

Erick gas area

West Carter

OKLAHOMA: 12

NORTH AMERICA

PBush

©The Petroleum Economist Ltd, London 2001

Plate
101

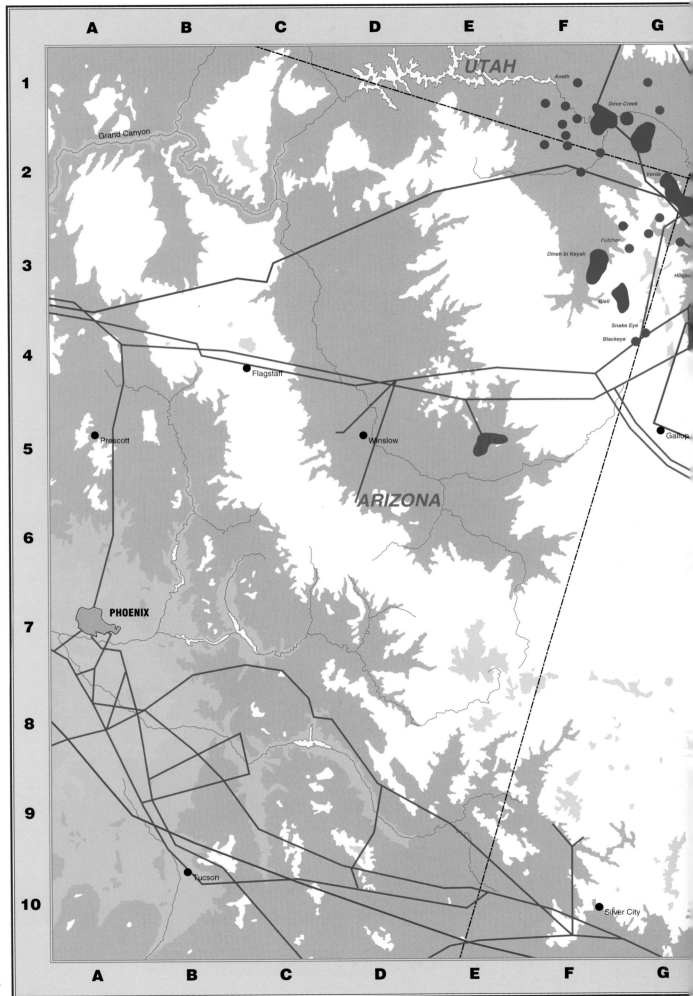

UTAH

Aneth

Dove Creek

Verde

Grand Canyon

Fulcher

Dineh bi Keyah

Hogba

Bisti

Snake Eye

Blackeye

Flagstaff

Prescott

Winslow

Gallup

ARIZONA

PHOENIX

Tucson

Silver City

Scale: 1:2,320,000

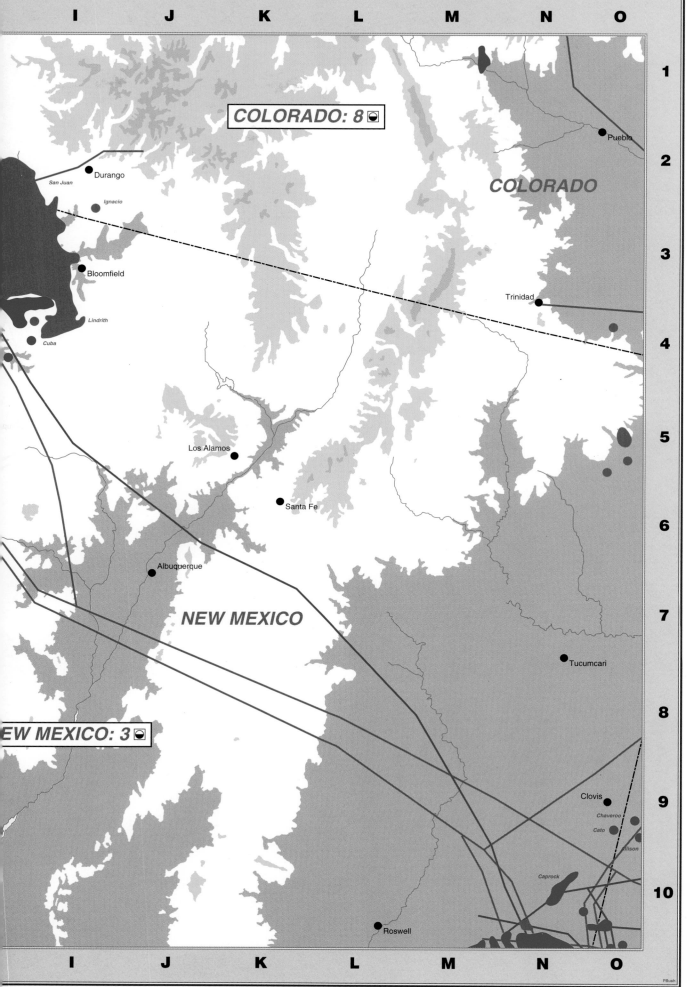

COLORADO: 8 ▣

COLORADO

Pueblo

Durango
San Juan

Ignacio

Bloomfield

Lindrith

Cuba

Trinidad

Los Alamos

Santa Fe

Albuquerque

NEW MEXICO

Tucumcari

EW MEXICO: 3 ▣

Clovis

Chaveroo

Cato

llison

Caprock

Roswell

NORTH AMERICA

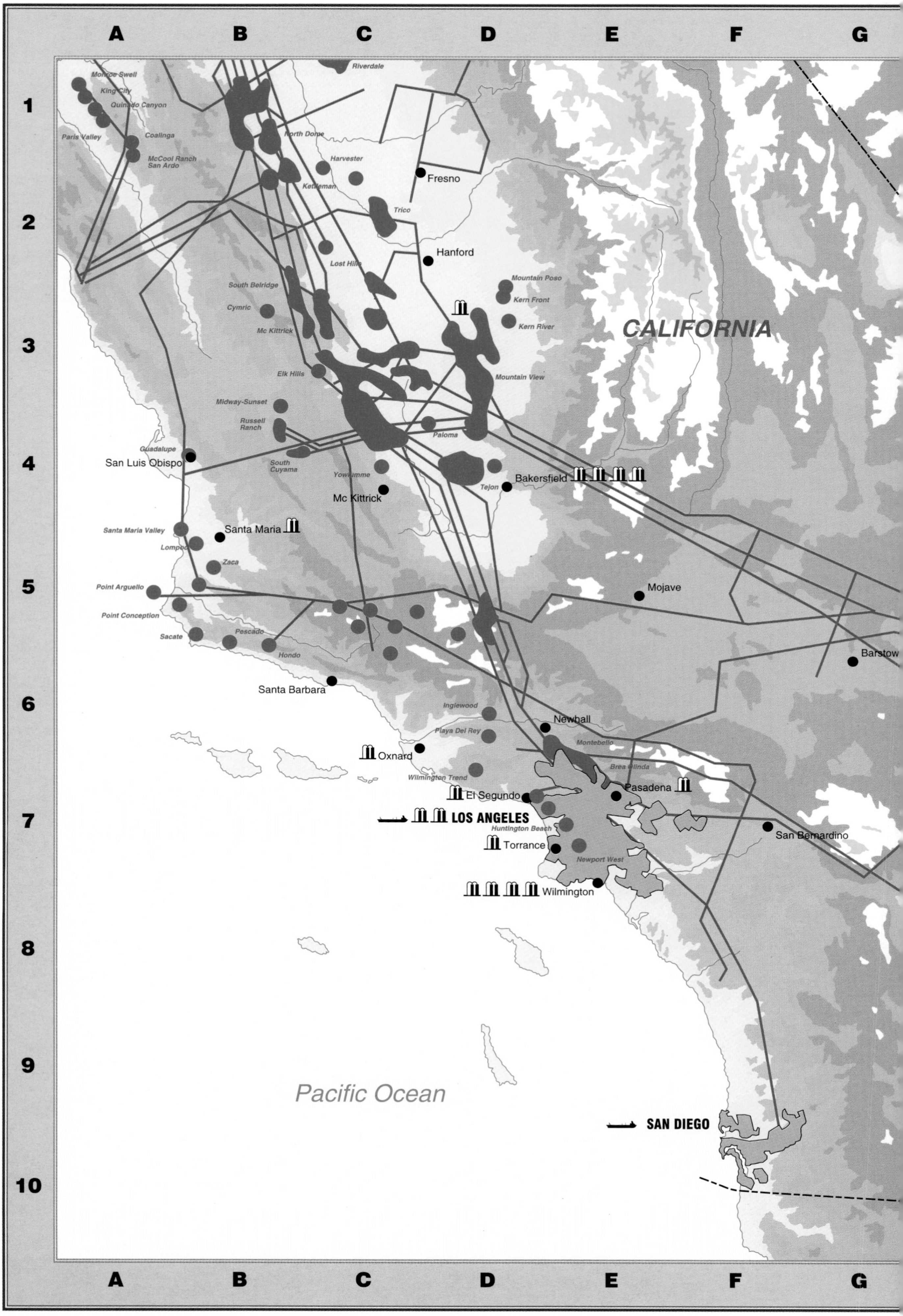

CALIFORNIA

NORTH AMERICA

Pacific Ocean

Monroe Swell
King City
Quinado Canyon
Paris Valley
Coalinga
McCool Ranch
San Ardo
Riverdale
North Dome
Harvester
Ketleman
Fresno
Trico
Lost Hills
Hanford
South Belridge
Cymric
Mc Kittrick
Mountain Poso
Kern Front
Kern River
Elk Hills
Midway-Sunset
Russell Ranch
Mountain View
Guadalupe
San Luis Obispo
South Cuyama
Yowlumme
Paloma
Tejon
Bakersfield
Mc Kittrick
Santa Maria Valley
Santa Maria
Lompoc
Zaca
Point Arguello
Point Conception
Sacate
Pescado
Hondo
Mojave
Barstow
Santa Barbara
Inglewood
Playa Del Rey
Newhall
Montebello
Brea Olinda
Oxnard
Wilmington Trend
El Segundo
Pasadena
LOS ANGELES
Huntington Beach
San Bernardino
Torrance
Newport West
Wilmington
SAN DIEGO

Scale: 1:2,385,000

SOUTHERN CALIFORNIA

Plate
102

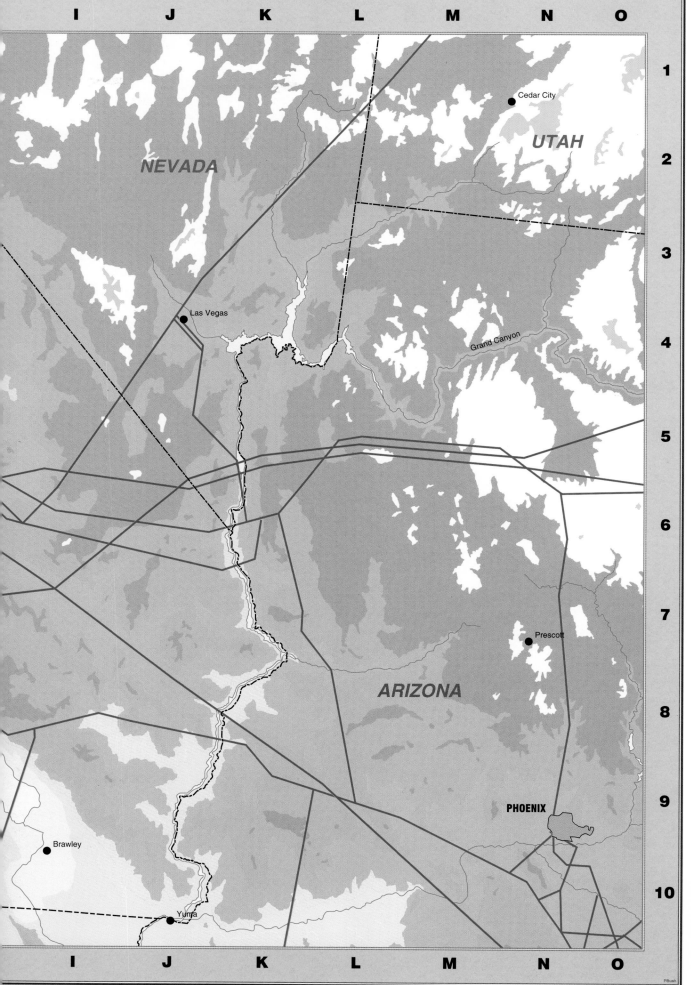

I J K L M N O

1

Cedar City

UTAH

2

NEVADA

3

Las Vegas

4

Grand Canyon

5

6

7

Prescott

ARIZONA

8

PHOENIX

9

Brawley

10

Yuma

I J K L M N O

NORTH AMERICA

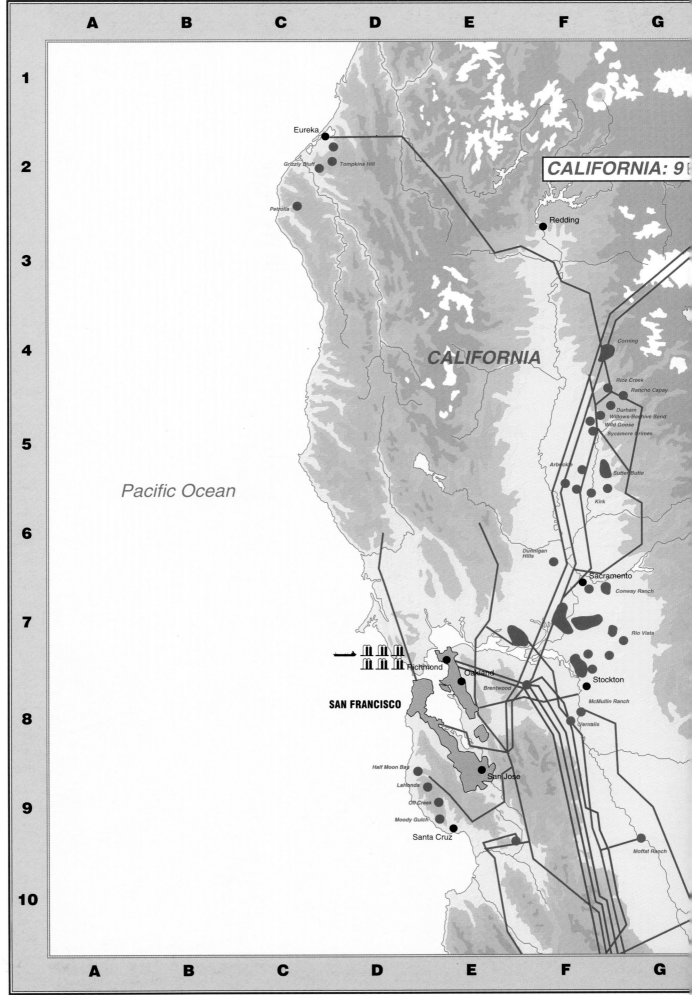

CALIFORNIA: 9

Eureka

Grizzly Bluff
Tompkins Hill

Petrolia

Redding

CALIFORNIA

Pacific Ocean

Corning

Rice Creek
Rancho Capay

Durham
Willows-Beehive Bend
Wild Goose
Sycamore Grimes

Arbuckle

Sutter Butte

Kirk

Dunnigan
Hills

Sacramento

Conway Ranch

Rio Vista

Richmond

Oakland

Brentwood

Stockton

SAN FRANCISCO

McMullin Ranch

Vernalis

Half Moon Bay

LaHonda

San Jose

Oil Creek

Moody Gulch

Santa Cruz

Moffat Ranch

Scale: 1:2,425,000

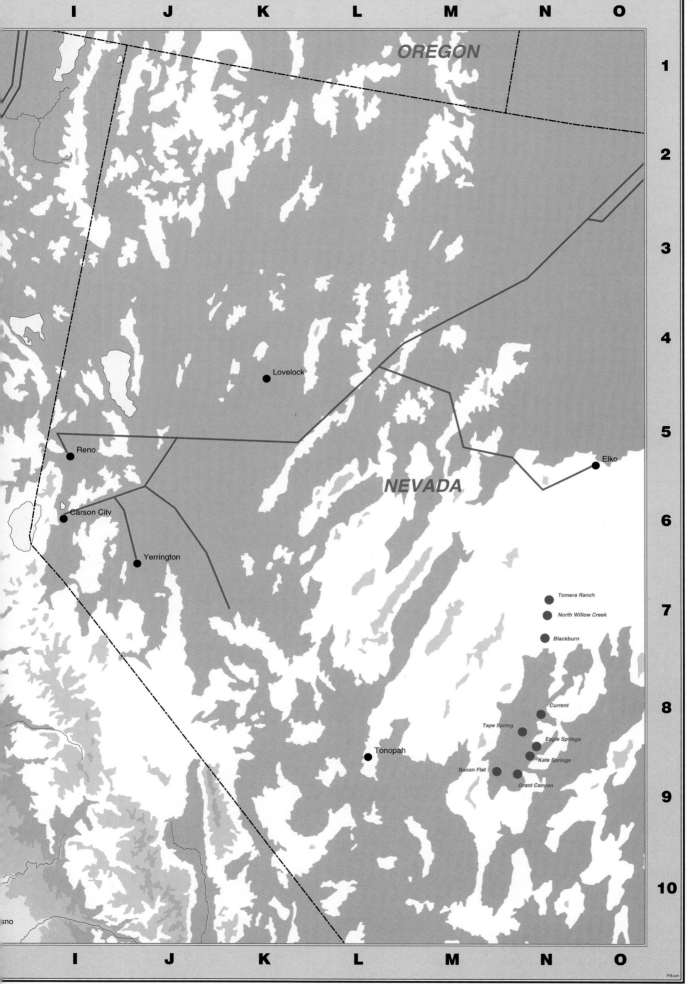

OREGON

1

2

3

4

Lovelock

5

Reno

Elko

NEVADA

Carson City

6

Yerrington

Tomera Ranch

North Willow Creek

7

Blackburn

Current

8

Tape Spring

Eagle Springs

Tonopah

Kate Springs

Bacon Flat

Grant Canyon

9

10

Plate
104

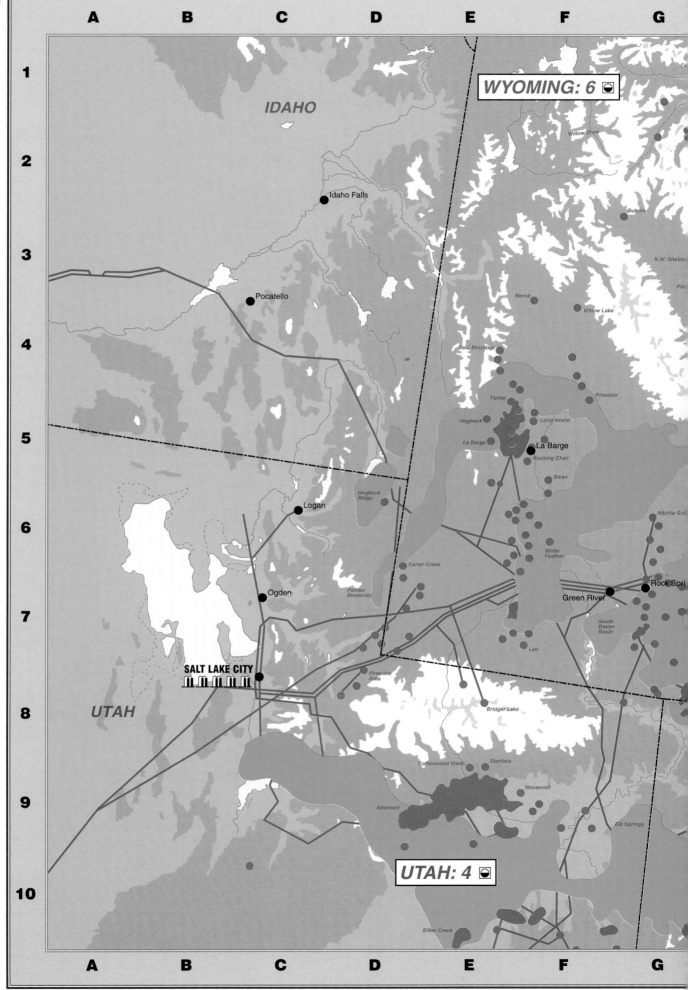

WYOMING: 6

IDAHO

Willow Draw

Dubois

N.W. Sheldo.

Pilo.

Merna

Willow Lake

Idaho Falls

Bald Mountain

Tiptop

Pinedale

Hogback

Long Island

Pocatello

La Barge

La Barge

Rocking Chair

Swan

Hogback
Ridge

Nitchie Gul.

Logan

Carter Creek

White
Feather

Rock Spri

Green River

Ogden

South
Baxter
Basin

Leo

SALT LAKE CITY

Pineview
Area

UTAH

Bridger Lake

Cottonwood Wash

Starflats

Roosevelt

Altamont

Elk Springs

UTAH: 4

Bitter Creek

Scale: 1:2,310,000

I   J   K   L   M   N   O

1

2

3

4

5

6

7

8

9

10

Sheridan

Joe Creek
Rocky Point
Recluse
Spotted Horse
Flat Draw

Manderson
Bonanza
Hidden Dome
Worland
Meyer Gulch

Dead Horse Creek
Kitty
Deadman Creek
Barton

Billy
Creek
Hilight
South Coyote Creek
Osage

Water Creek
Reno
Clareton Area
Newcastle

Kirby Creek
North
Folk
Creek
Dugout
Lone Tree
Creek

Ilion

Lost Cabin
Burke
Ranch
E. Mule Creek

Sand Draw
Glenrock
Glenrock

appy Springs
Grieve
Casper
Big Muddy
Flat Top

ge

Wertz
Spintletop
Bolton Creek

NG
Sherard
E. Mahoney

Simpson Ridge

Oil Springs

Torrington

Slavery
Rawlins
Sinclair

Espy
Diamond Dome
Chugspring

Diamond Ranch

Big Hollow

ghole

Focus Ranch
Laramie
Horse
Creek

Cheyenne

N.Craig
Lone Pine
Butler Creek
Bone
Pine Bluffs

Craig
Wellington

Fort Collins
Pierce

Tow Creek
COLORADO

Wattenberg

| **COLORADO: 8** |

DENVER

I   J   K   L   M   N   O

PBush

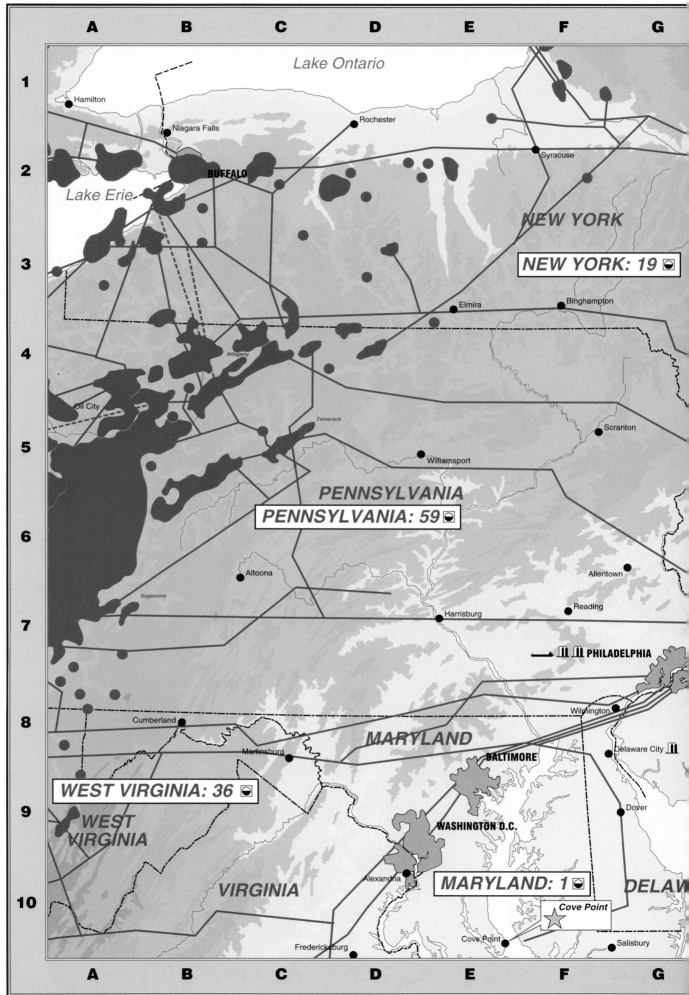

Lake Ontario

Hamilton

Niagara Falls

Rochester

Syracuse

BUFFALO

Lake Erie

NEW YORK

NEW YORK: 19

Elmira

Binghampton

Atlegany

Scranton

Oil City

Tamarack

Williamsport

PENNSYLVANIA

PENNSYLVANIA: 59

Altoona

Allentown

Sagamore

Reading

Harrisburg

PHILADELPHIA

Cumberland

Wilmington

MARYLAND

Martinsburg

BALTIMORE

Delaware City

WEST VIRGINIA: 36

WEST VIRGINIA

Dover

WASHINGTON D.C.

MARYLAND: 1

DELAW

Alexandria

VIRGINIA

Cove Point

Cove Point

Salisbury

Fredericksburg

Scale: 1:2,315,000

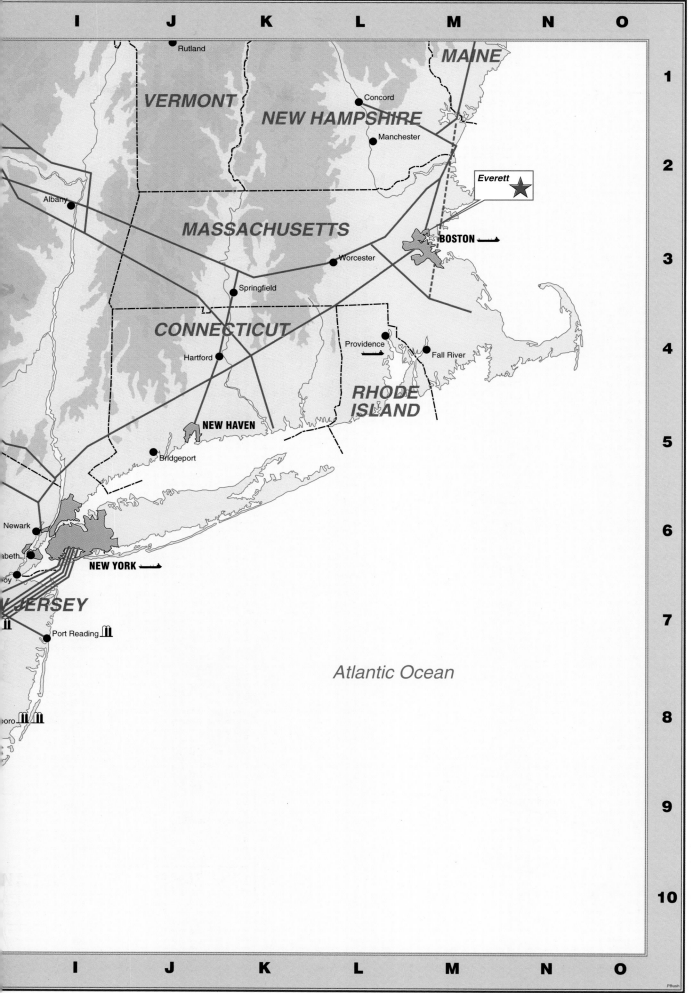

MAINE

VERMONT

NEW HAMPSHIRE

Rutland

Concord

Manchester

Everett

Albany

MASSACHUSETTS

BOSTON

Worcester

Springfield

CONNECTICUT

Hartford

Providence

Fall River

RHODE ISLAND

NEW HAVEN

Bridgeport

Newark

abeth.

oy

NEW YORK

JERSEY

Port Reading

Atlantic Ocean

oro

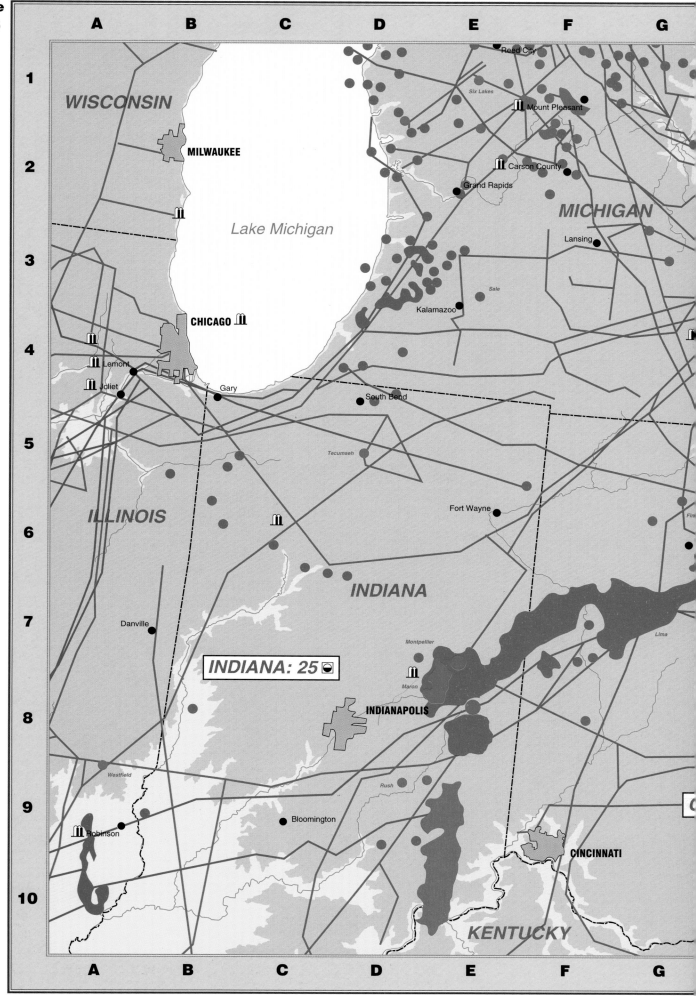

Scale: 1:2,340,000

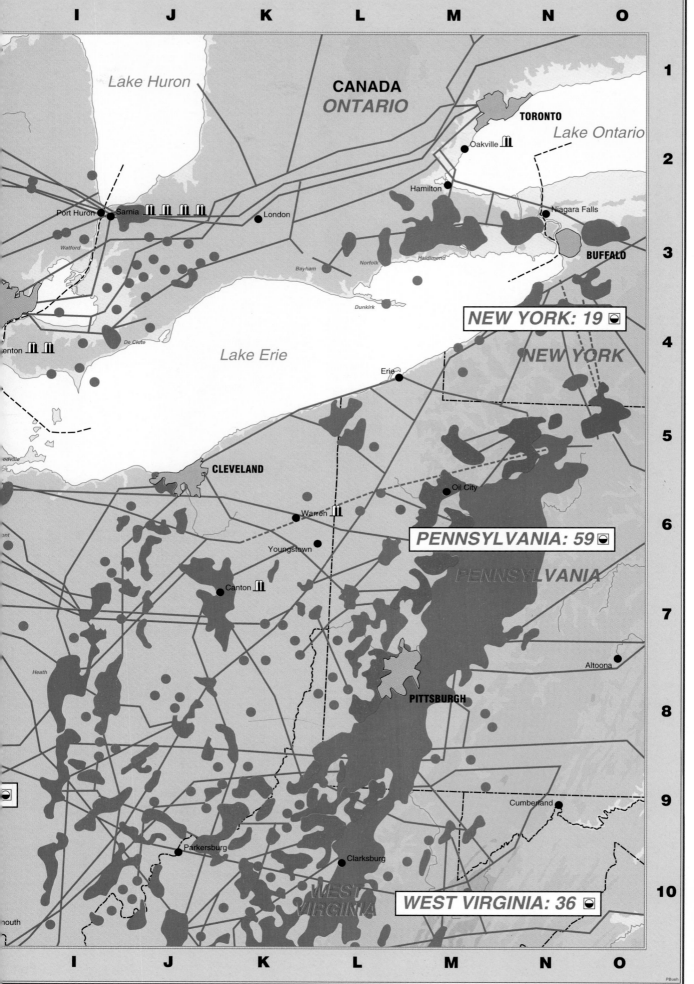

NEW YORK: 19

PENNSYLVANIA: 59

WEST VIRGINIA: 36

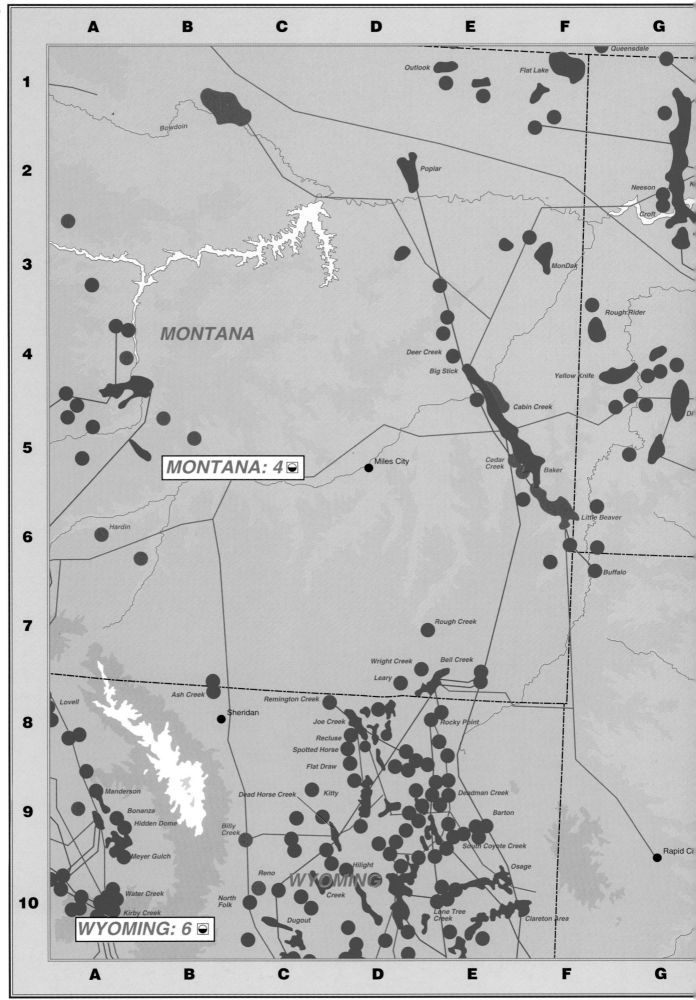

Scale: 1:2,470,000

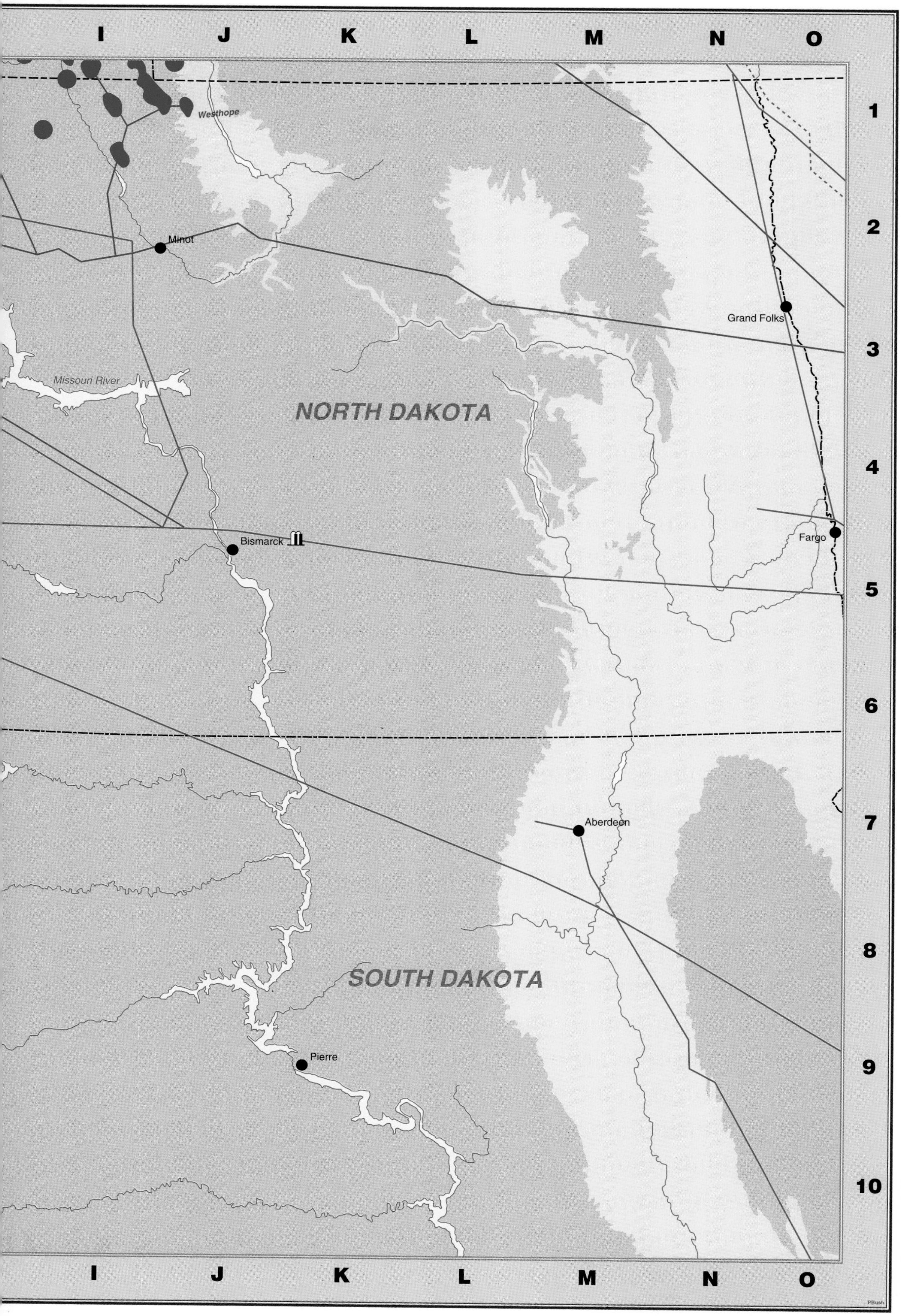

I J K L M N O

1

2

Westhope

Minot

Grand Folks

Missouri River

NORTH DAKOTA

3

4

Bismarck

Fargo

5

6

Aberdeen

7

8

SOUTH DAKOTA

9

Pierre

10

I J K L M N O

NORTH AMERICA

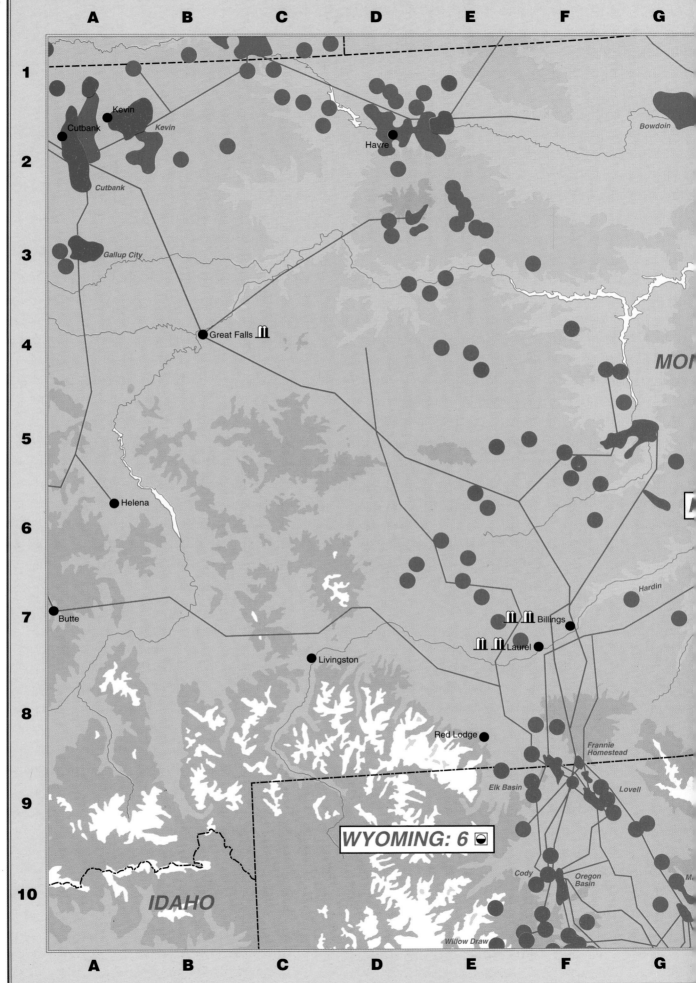

MONTANA

Kevin

Cutbank

Kevin

Cutbank

Bowdoin

Havre

Gallup City

Great Falls

MON

Helena

Hardin

Butte

Billings

Laurel

Livingston

Red Lodge

Frannie
Homestead

Elk Basin

Lovell

WYOMING: 6

Cody

Oregon
Basin

M

IDAHO

Willow Draw

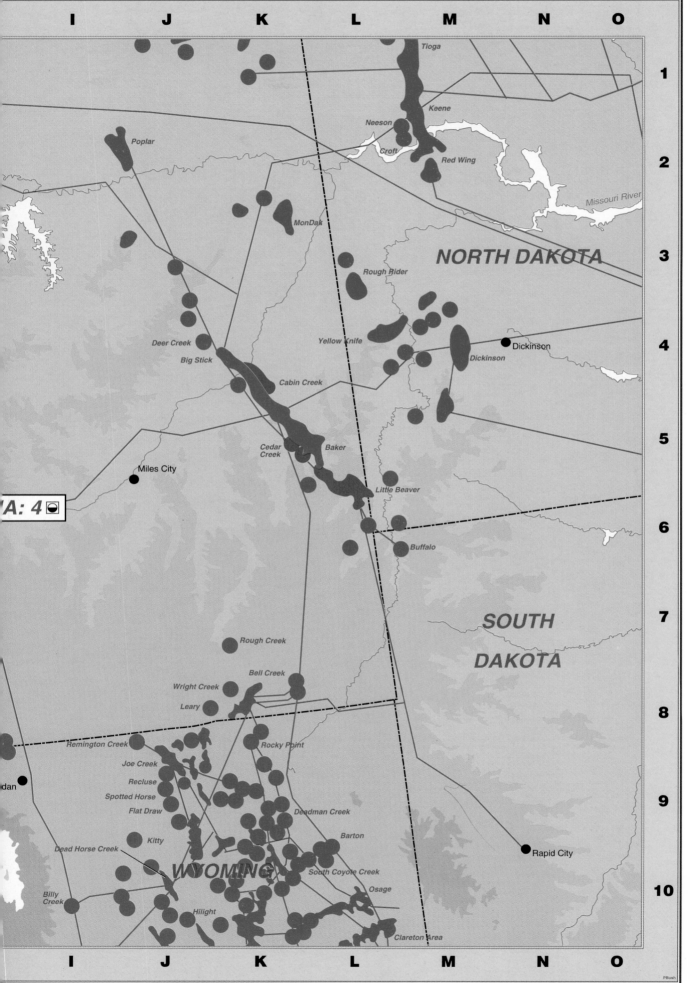

I J K L M N O

1

Tioga

Keene

Neeson

Poplar

Croft

Red Wing

2

Missouri River

MonDak

NORTH DAKOTA

3

Rough Rider

Deer Creek

Yellow Knife

4

Dickinson

Big Stick

Dickinson

Cabin Creek

5

Cedar
Creek

Baker

A: 4 ▣

Miles City

Little Beaver

6

Buffalo

SOUTH

7

Rough Creek

DAKOTA

Bell Creek

Wright Creek

8

Leary

Remington Creek

Rocky Point

Joe Creek

dan

Recluse

9

Spotted Horse

Flat Draw

Deadman Creek

Kitty

Barton

Dead Horse Creek

WYOMING

South Coyote Creek

Rapid City

Osage

10

Billy
Creek

Hilight

Clareton Area

I J K L M N O

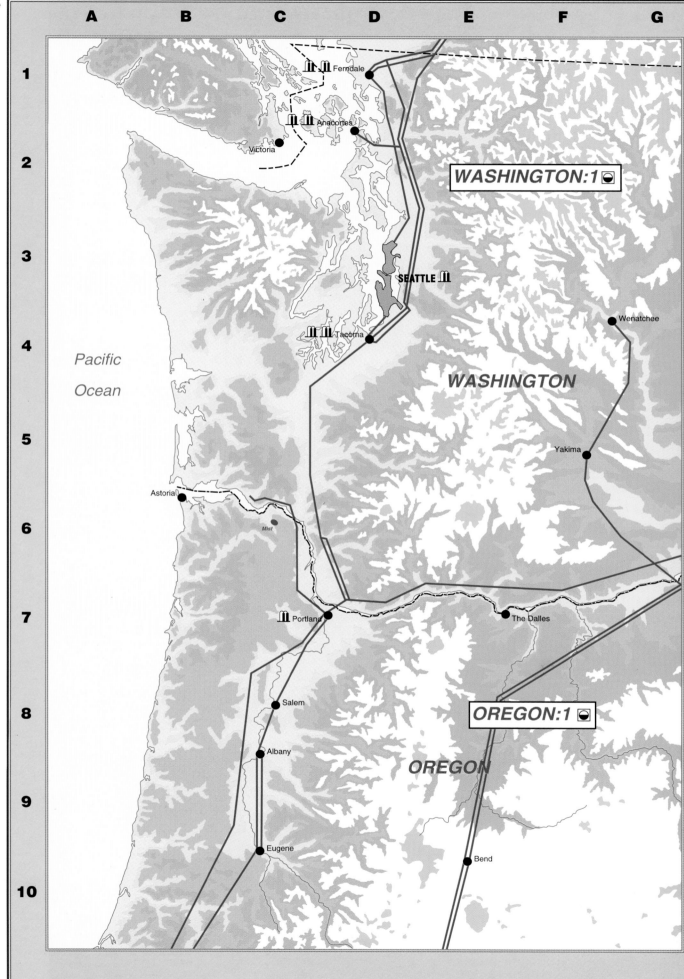

Pacific

Ocean

WASHINGTON:1

OREGON:1

WASHINGTON

OREGON

Ferndale

Anacortes

Victoria

SEATTLE

Tacoma

Wenatchee

Yakima

Astoria

Mist

Portland

The Dalles

Salem

Albany

Eugene

Bend

Scale: 1:2,112,000

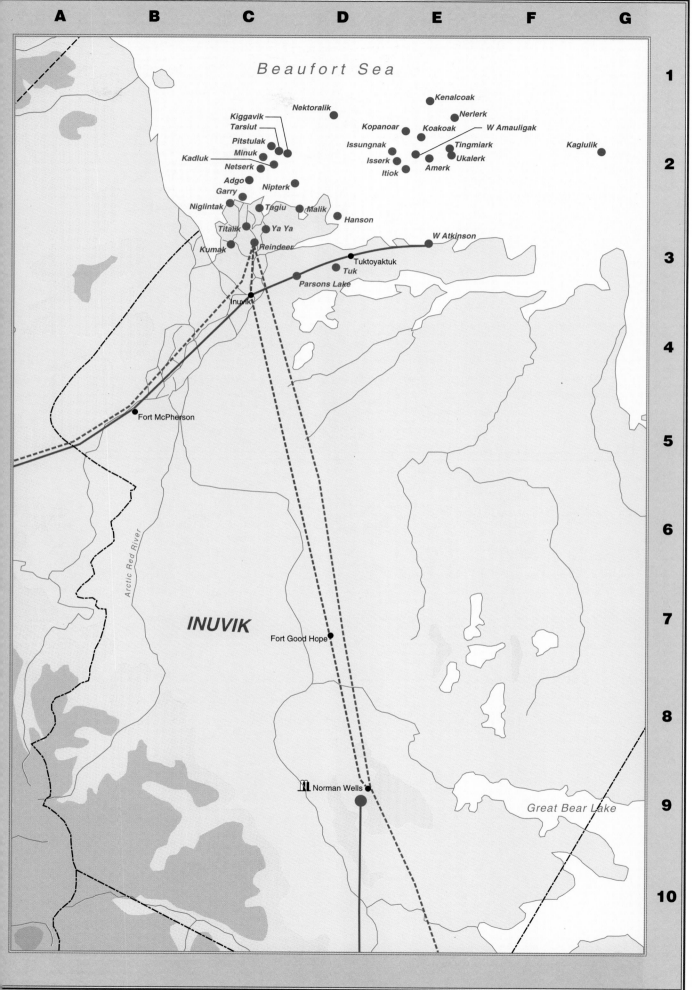

Beaufort Sea

A B C D E F G

1

Kenalcoak

Nektoralik
Kiggavik
Tarsiut
Nerlerk
Pitstulak
Kopanoar
Koakoak
W Amauligak
Minuk
Kadluk
Issungnak
Tingmiark
Kaglulik
Netserk
Isserk
Ukalerk
Adgo
Itiok
Amerk
Garry
Nipterk
Niglintak
Tagiu
Malik
Hanson
Titalik
Ya Ya
W Atkinson
Kumak
Reindeer
Tuktoyaktuk
Tuk
Parsons Lake
Inuvik

2

3

Fort McPherson

4

5

Arctic Red River

6

INUVIK

7

Fort Good Hope

8

Norman Wells

Great Bear Lake

9

10

cale: 1:3,980,000

©**The Petroleum Economist Ltd, London** 2001

NORTH AMERICA

Plate
111

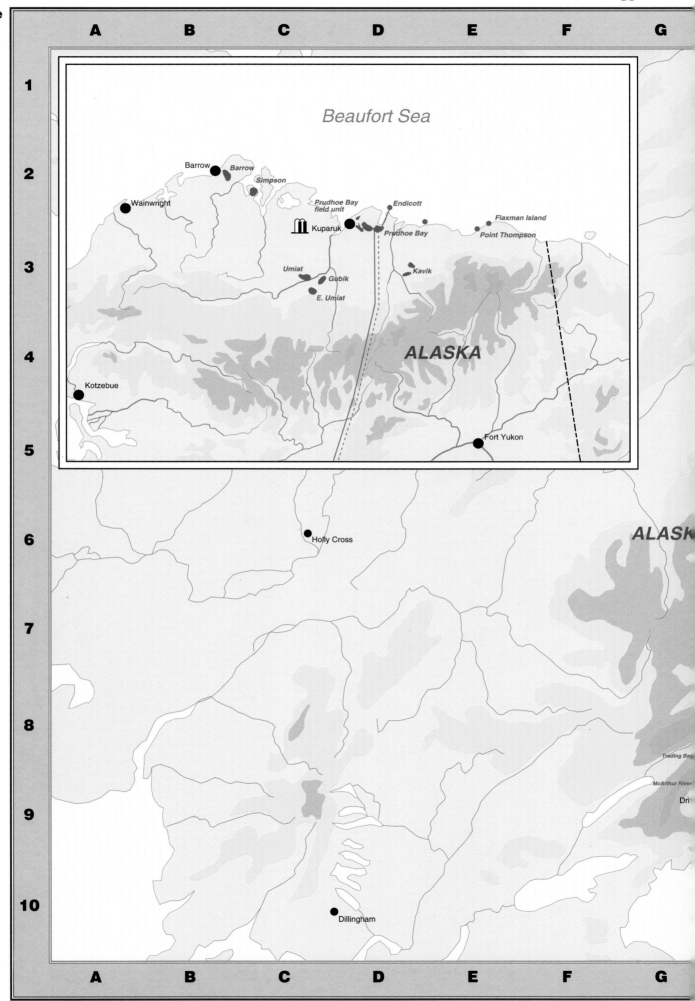

Beaufort Sea

Barrow
Barrow
Simpson
Wainwright
Prudhoe Bay field unit
Endicott
Flaxman Island
Kuparuk
Prudhoe Bay
Point Thompson
Umiat
Kavik
Gubik
E. Umiat
ALASKA
Kotzebue
Fort Yukon
Holly Cross
ALASK
Trading Bay
McArthur River
Dri
Dillingham

Scale: 1:3,754,000 (Inset 1:6,570,000)

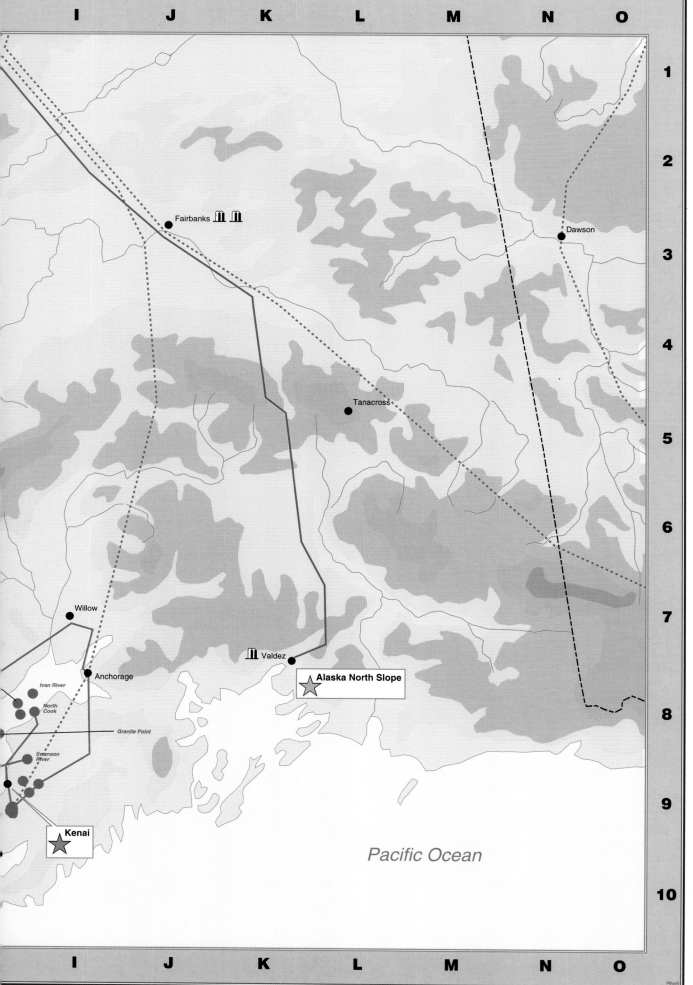

I J K L M N O

1
2
3
4
5
6
7
8
9
10

Fairbanks

Dawson

Tanacross

Willow

Anchorage

Ivan River

North Cook

Granite Point

Swanson River

Valdez

Alaska North Slope

Kenai

Pacific Ocean

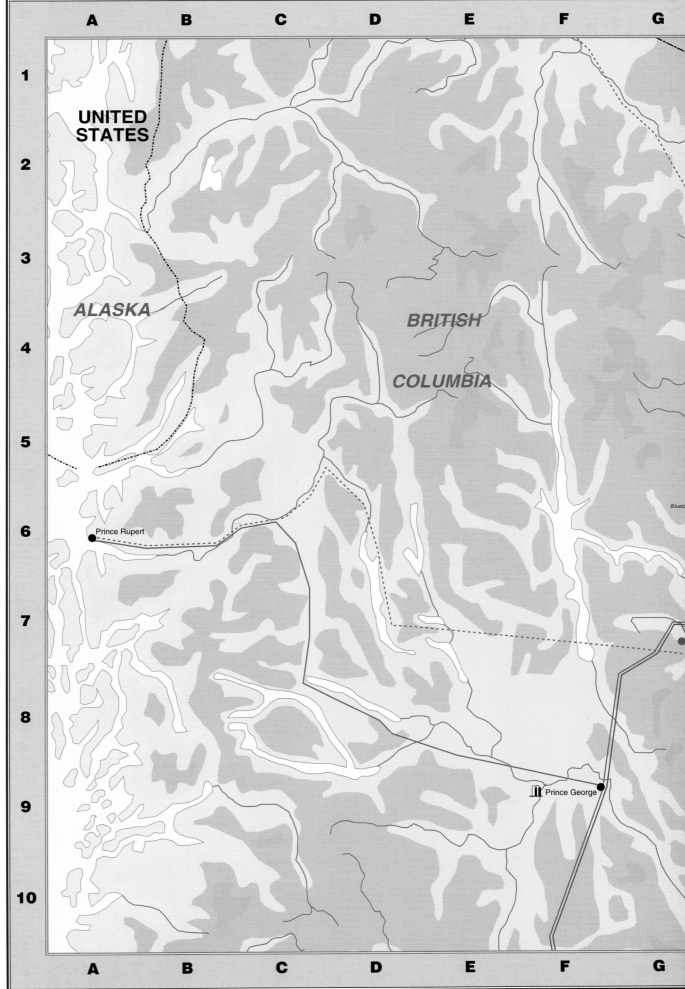

UNITED
STATES

ALASKA

BRITISH

COLUMBIA

Bluebe

Prince Rupert

Prince George

Scale: 1:3,500,000

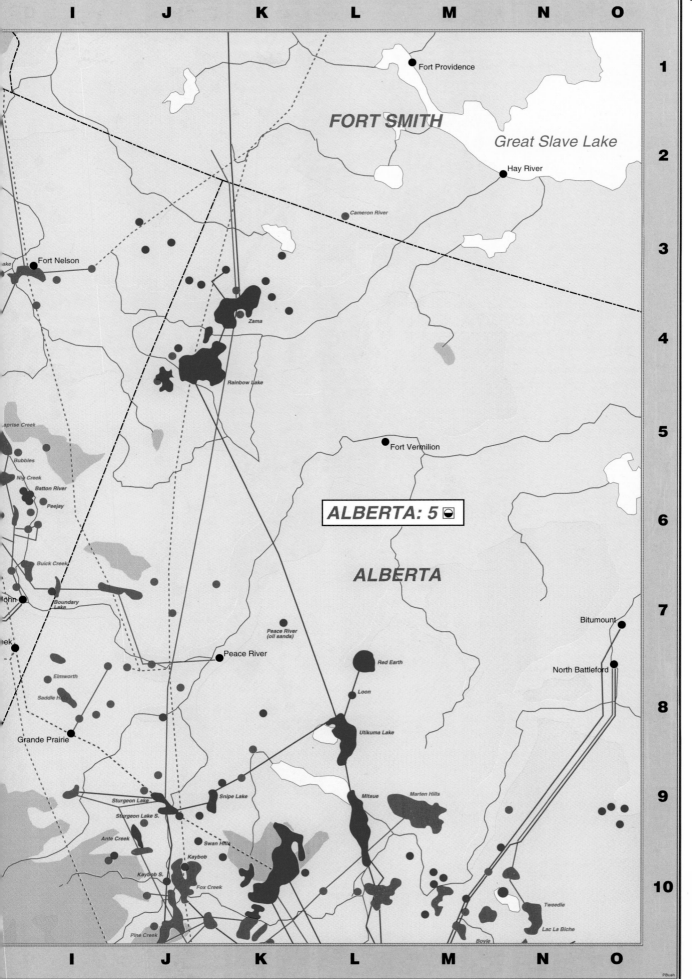

I J K L M N O

1 Fort Providence

FORT SMITH

Great Slave Lake

2 Hay River

Cameron River 3

Fort Nelson

Zama 4

Rainbow Lake

aprise Creek 5 Fort Vermilion

Bubbles

Nig Creek

Batton River

Peejay **ALBERTA: 5** ⬖ 6

Buick Creek **ALBERTA**

ohn Boundary
Lake 7 Bitumount

ek Peace River
(oil sands)

Peace River Red Earth North Battleford

Elmworth Loon

Saddle Hills 8

Grande Prairie Utikuma Lake

Sturgeon Lake Snipe Lake Mitsue Marten Hills 9
Sturgeon Lake S.

Ante Creek Swan Hills

Kaybob

Kaybob S. Tweedie

Fox Creek 10

Pine Creek Lac La Biche

Boyle

I J K L M N O

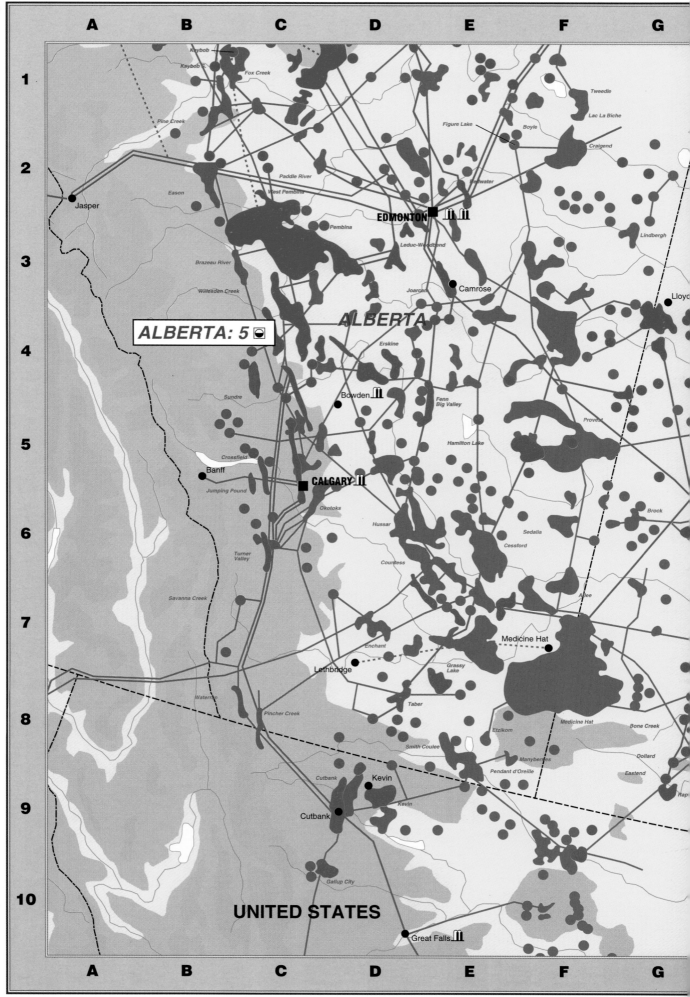

ALBERTA: 5

Scale: 1:3,580,000

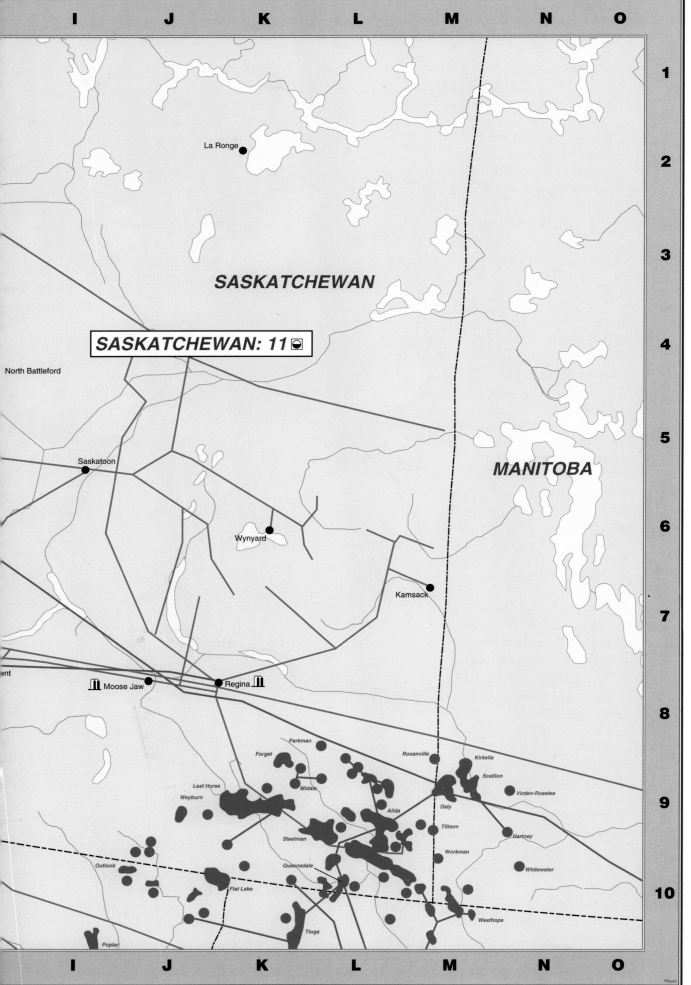

I J K L M N O

1
2
3

SASKATCHEWAN

SASKATCHEWAN: 11 ◖

4

North Battleford

5

Saskatoon

MANITOBA

La Ronge

Wynyard

6

Kamsack

7

Moose Jaw   Regina

8

Parkman
Forget   Rooanville   Kirkella
Last Horse   Midale   Scallion
Weyburn   Virden-Roselea
               Alida   Daly
Steelman   Tiltson   Hartney
Queensdale   Workman
Outlook   Whitewater
        Flat Lake
                 Tioga   Westhope
Poplar

9

10

I J K L M N O

NORTH AMERICA

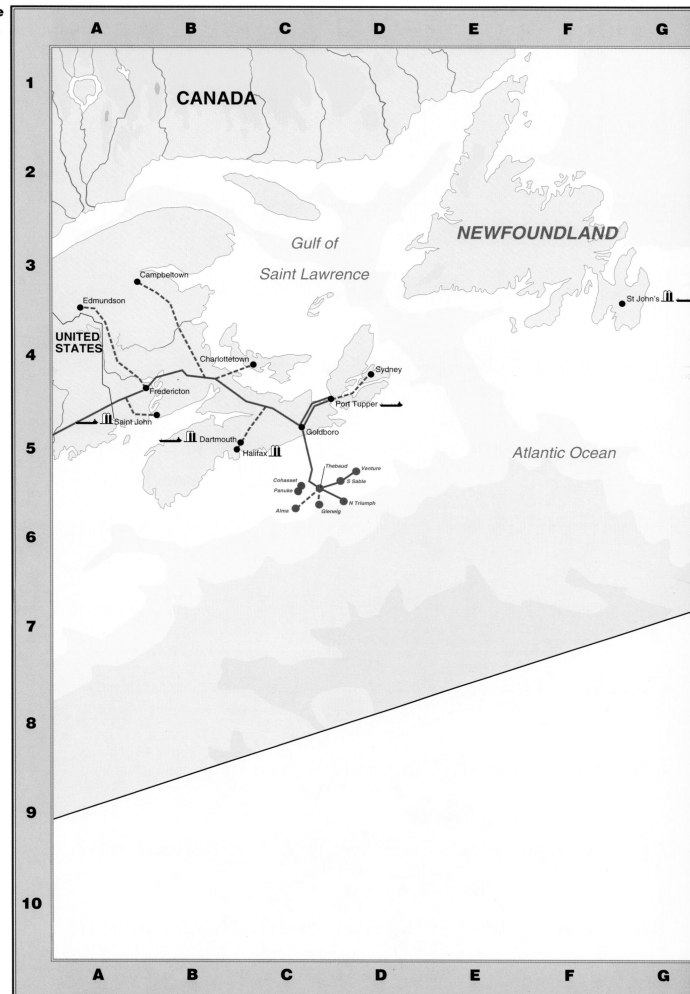

CANADA

Gulf of

Saint Lawrence

NEWFOUNDLAND

St John's

Campbeltown

Edmundson

UNITED
STATES

Charlottetown

Fredericton

Sydney

Port Tupper

Saint John

Goldboro

Dartmouth

Halifax

Atlantic Ocean

Thebaud
Venture

Cohasset
S Sable

Panuke

N Triumph

Alma
Glenelg

Scale: 1:8,200,000

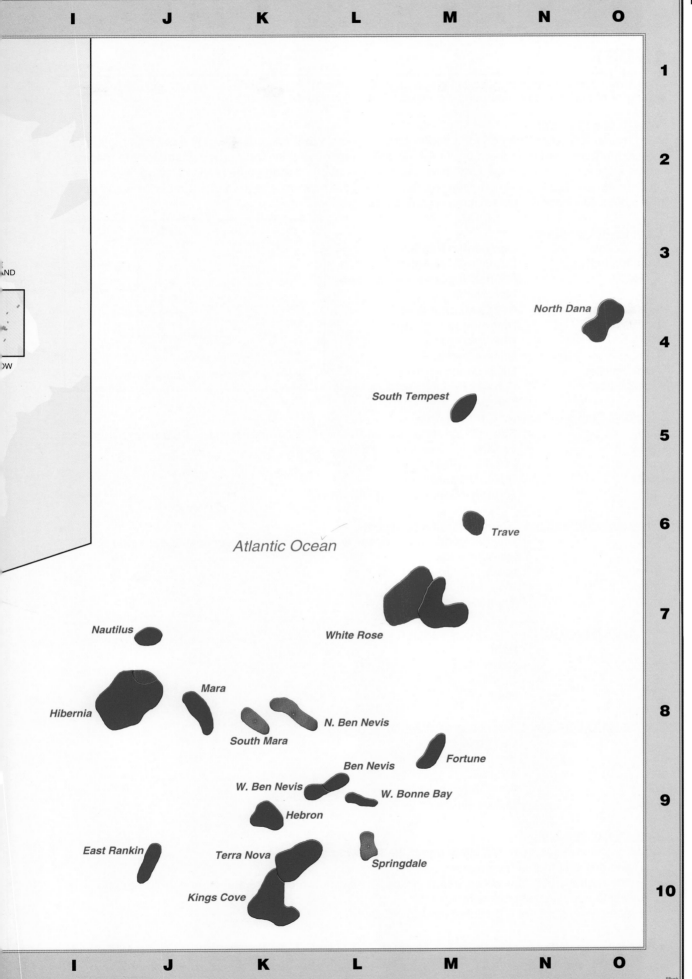

North Dana

South Tempest

Trave

Atlantic Ocean

White Rose

Nautilus

Mara

Hibernia

N. Ben Nevis

South Mara

Fortune

Ben Nevis

W. Ben Nevis

W. Bonne Bay

Hebron

East Rankin

Terra Nova

Springdale

Kings Cove

NORTH AMERICA

INDEX (vertical, left margin)

INDEX

The index contains all geographical place names and features. The index does not include a listing of the oil and gas field names as these would exceed 40,000 entries.

How to use the index
Find the specific place name in the Name column, look in the Plate column to find out which plate or plates the place name appears on. In the Grid Reference column, find out which square the place name appears on. Locate the plate from the contents page. Once you have the plate open, use the grid reference, starting with the letter (running along the bottom) and then the number (running up the sides), to locate the place name you have selected.

Country Abbreviations

D.R. Congo	Democratic Republic of Congo
Dominican Rep.	Dominican Republic
FYROM	Former Yugoslav Republic of Macedonia
Russian Fed.	Russian Federation
UAE	United Arab Emirates
UK	United Kingdom
US	United States
Neth. Antilles	Netherlands Antilles
Yugloslavia	Federal Republic of Yugoslavia

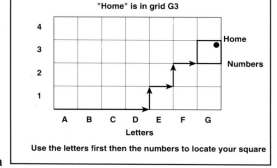

"Home" is in grid G3

Use the letters first then the numbers to locate your square

Regional Status (all following place name)

aut.	Subordinate Autonomous District/Autonomous Region (FSU only)
prov.	Province (Canada and [FSU – Oblast])
rep.	Republic (FSU only)
state	State (US/Australia)
terr.	Territory (Canada and [FSU – Kray])

Geographical Features (all following place names)

City	City (included only in cases where city name is identical to a country name)
Is.	Island/Islands
lake	Lake
mtns.	Mountains
river	River

Compass Directions (largely follows usage on plates)

E.	East
N.	North
S.	South
W.	West

US States (where two different places of identical name)

CA	California
SC	South Carolina
VA	Virginia
WV	West Virginia
Mass.	Massachusetts

Country Column Status

Country Column has been left blank under the following conditions:
1. Place name is that of the country;
2. Place name is that of a water feature divided between two or more states, and/or has been classified as international waters; and
3. Place name is that of a disputed territory.

Name	Country	Plate	Grid Ref
A			
Aachen	Germany	2	G8
Aachen	Germany	9	K1
Aachen	Germany	11	A4
Aba	Nigeria	46	K5
Abadan	Iran	33	J5
Abakan	Russian Fed.	31	D9
Aberdeen	UK	2	F3
Aberdeen	UK	5	A9
Aberdeen	US	107	L6
Abez	Russian Fed.	25	G5
Abijan	Cote D'Ivoire	45	D3
Abilene	US	95	D4
Abilene	US	96	N4
Abkhazia	Georgia	16	G5
Abkhazia rep.	Georgia	20	K6
Abrau-Dyurso	Russian Fed.	20	G4
Abu Dhabi	UAE	34	I4
Abu Dhabi	UAE	34	H5
Abu Dhabi	UAE	35	G8
Abu Dhabi	UAE	35	I6
Abu Musa rep.	UAE	34	I2
Abu Musa rep.	UAE	35	J2
Abuju	Nigeria	45	J2
Acajutla	El Salvador	76	A6
Accra	Ghana	45	F3
Achinsk	Russian Fed.	31	D7
Achi-Su	Russian Fed.	18	D1
Ad Damman	Saudi Arabia	33	K8
Ad Damman	Saudi Arabia	34	E3
Adana	Turkey	16	E9
Adana	Turkey	17	B8
Addis Ababa	Ethiopia	52	F6
Adelaide	Australia	70	D7
Aden	Yemen	38	B9
Adiyaman	Turkey	17	F7
Adrar	Algeria	42	E8
Adri	Libya	44	D8
Adriatic Sea		10	F4
Adygeya rep.	Russian Fed.	16	F5
Adygeya rep.	Russian Fed.	20	H6
Adzharia rep.	Georgia	17	J1
Adzharia rep.	Georgia	16	H6
Adzharia rep	Georgia	20	L9
Aegean Sea		10	J7
Afghanistan		23	K8
Afghanistan		24	L9
Afghanistan		56	A2
Afghanistan		60	A2
Afipsky	Russian Fed.	20	I4
Aflou	Algeria	42	G3
Ag Theodori	Greece	10	I8
Agdam	Azerbaijan	18	D5
Agdash	Azerbaijan	18	D4
Aggeneis	South Africa	54	B8
Aguasay	Venezuela	77	J5
Ahmadabad	India	56	C5
Ahmadabad	India	60	D9
Ahnet Tassili	Algeria	42	G10
Ahwaz	Iran	33	J4
Ain Sukhna	Egypt	43	J5
Ain Temouchent	Algeria	42	D2
Ajaccio	France	9	K8
Ajaccio	France	10	B3
Ajaokuta	Nigeria	45	J2
Akhalkalaki	Georgia	16	H6
Akhalkalaki	Georgia	17	L10
Akhalkalaki	Georgia	20	N9
Akhaltsikhe	Georgia	17	K1
Akhaltsikhe	Georgia	20	M9
Akhmeta	Georgia	16	I5
Akhmeta	Georgia	18	B2
Akhsu	Azerbaijan	18	E4
Akhtubinsk	Russian Fed.	19	A2
Akhtubinsk	Russian Fed.	21	E7
Akmene	Lithuania	11	I1
Akmene	Lithuania	13	A4
Aksai	Russian Fed.	22	M9
Akstafa	Azerbaijan	16	I6
Akstafa	Azerbaijan	17	N1
Akstafa	Azerbaijan	18	B4
Aksu	China	61	C6
Aktau	Kazakhstan	19	H9
Aktau	Kazakhstan	23	B6
Aktau (Shevchenko)	Kazakhstan	16	L4
Aktivneset	Norway	6	K2
Aktivneset	Norway	8	C1
Aktyubinsk	Kazakhstan	23	C1
Al 'Amarah	Iraq	33	H4
Al Ghalil	Oman	34	L3
AL GHALIL	Oman	37	C1
Al Halaniyat Is. (Kuria Muria Is.)	Oman	37	C9
Al Halaniyat Is. (Kuria Muria Is.) rep.	Oman	34	L9
Al Hasakah	Syria	33	C1
Al Hufuf	Saudi Arabia	33	L9
Al Hufuf	Saudi Arabia	34	E4
Al Jawf	Saudi Arabia	33	D7
Al Jazirah	Iraq	33	D2
Al Kufrah	Libya	52	A1
Al Kut	Iraq	33	H4
Al Manamah	Bahrain	33	L8
Al Manamah	Bahrain	34	F3
Al Manamah	Bahrain	35	A4
Al Manamah	Bahrain	36	A4
Al Mukalla	Yemen	38	F7
Al Mussayib	Iraq	33	G4
Al Quwayri	Iraq	33	E1
Alabama state	US	94	M4
Alabama state	US	98	G9
Alagir	Russian Fed.	18	A1
Alagir	Russian Fed.	20	N6
Alamogordo	US	96	D1
Åland Is	Sweden	13	A1
Åland Is	Finland	2	N3
Alaska state	US	111	F6
Alaska state	US	112	A3
Alaska	Zimbabwe	53	A9
Alaska	Zimbabwe	54	E4
Alaverdi	Armenia	17	M2
Alaverdi	Armenia	18	A4
Albania		10	H5
Albany	Australia	72	C10
Albany	US	93	A5
Albany	US	105	I2
Albany	US	109	B8
Ålborg	Denmark	2	J4
Albuquerque	US	101	I6
Albury	Australia	71	C6
Aldan	Russian Fed.	30	E4
Aldan river	Russian Fed.	30	F1
Aleksandriya	Ukraine	22	F6
Aleksandrov	Russian Fed.	13	G4
Aleksandrov Gay	Russian Fed.	13	K7
Aleksandrov Gay	Russian Fed.	15	D7
Aleksandrov Gay	Russian Fed.	21	G4
Aleksandrovka	Ukraine	22	E6
Aleksandrovsk-Sakhalinskiy	Russian Fed.	29	B1
Aleksandrovsk-Sakhalinskiy	Russian Fed.	30	J8
Alekseyevka	Russian Fed.	21	K1
Aleppo	Syria	33	A2
Ålesund	Norway	2	J1
Ålesund	Norway	6	N1
Ålesund	Norway	8	F1
Alexander Bay	South Africa	54	A7
Alexandra	Egypt	43	G2
Alexandria	US	94	D7
Alexandria	US	105	C9
Alexandroupolis	Greece	10	K6
Alexandroupolis	Greece	16	A7
Alga	Kazakhstan	23	C2
Algeria		42	C9
Algiers	Algeria	42	H1
Ali Bayramiy	Azerbaijan	16	K6
Ali Bayramiy	Azerbaijan	18	F5
Ali Bayramiy	Azerbaijan	23	A9
Aliaga	Turkey	10	L7
Aliaga	Turkey	16	A8
Alicante	Spain	9	E9
Alice Springs	Australia	70	B1
Alitus	Lithuania	11	I2
Alitus	Lithuania	13	B5
Aliveri	Greece	10	J8
Allentown	US	105	F6
Almalyk	Uzbekistan	23	K5
Almalyk	Uzbekistan	24	L3
Almaty	Kazakhstan	23	M2
Almaty	Kazakhstan	61	B5
Almendralejo	Spain	9	B7
Almeria	Spain	42	D1
Almería	Spain	9	C10
Almetyevsk	Russian Fed.	13	L4
Almetyevsk	Russian Fed.	14	B8
Almetyevsk	Russian Fed.	15	D2
Alor Is rep.	Indonesia	63	K9
Alor Island	Indonesia	69	B6
Alpine	US	96	G7
Altagracia de Orituco	Venezuela	77	B3
Altona	Australia	71	B7
Altoona	US	105	B6
Altoona	US	106	O7
Alushta	Ukraine	11	M10
Alushta	Ukraine	16	D4
Alushta	Ukraine	20	D4
Amarillo	US	100	E7
Amazon River	Brazil	78	D7
Amazon River	Brazil	78	K7
Ambarli	Turkey	10	L6
Ambarli	Turkey	16	A7
Ambes	France	9	F4
Ambroiyevka	Ukraine	22	K8
Amga river	Russian Fed.	30	G2
Amguid	Algeria	42	I9
Amman	Jordan	33	A5
Amol	Iran	18	K10
Amrumbank	Germany	3	N1
Amsterdam	Netherlands	2	G7
Amsterdam	Netherlands	3	K6
Amsterdam	Netherlands	11	A2
Amu Darya river	Uzbekistan	24	D4
Amuay	Venezuela	76	J7
Amur river	Russian Fed.	30	H9
An Nafud	Saudi Arabia	33	D7
An Nafud	Saudi Arabia	39	E1
An Najaf	Iraq	33	G4
An Nasiriyah	Iraq	33	H5
Anacortes	US	109	C1
Ananyev	Ukraine	10	N1
Ananyev	Ukraine	11	K7
Ananyev	Ukraine	13	D10
Ananyev	Ukraine	16	B2
Ananyev	Ukraine	22	C7
Anapa	Russian Fed.	20	F4
Anchorage	US	111	I7
Andaman Is.	India	56	I9
Andaman Is.	India	63	A4
Andaman Sea		56	I8
Andaman Sea		63	A3
Andizhan	Uzbekistan	23	K5
Andizhan	Uzbekistan	24	N2
Andorra		9	G6
Angara river	Russian Fed.	31	H8
Angara river	Russian Fed.	61	J1
Angarsk	Russian Fed.	31	H9
Angola		45	M9
Angola		54	A2
Angola (Cabinda)		45	L8
Angola (Cabinda)		48	F7
Angola (Cabinda)		49	E2
Angoulême	France	9	G4
Aniva Bay	Russian Fed.	29	C9
Ankara	Turkey	16	C7
Annaba	Algeria	10	A7
Annaba	Algeria	42	K1
Anqing	China	61	N10
Anqing	China	62	E9
Anshan	China	62	F5
Antigua & Barbuda		76	L5
Antilla	Cuba	76	H2
Antipovka	Russian Fed.	19	A1
Antipovka	Russian Fed.	21	D5
Antofagasta	Chile	82	B1
Antofagasta	Chile	84	A8
Antwerp	Belgium	2	G8
Antwerp	Belgium	3	J10
Antwerp	Belgium	9	J1
Anyang	China	61	M8
Anyang	China	62	C7
Aonla	India	56	E3
Aosta	Italy	9	K5
Aosta	Italy	10	B1
Aoulef	Algeria	42	F8
Apeldoorn	Netherlands	3	L7
Aqaba	Jordan	33	A7
Aqaba	Jordan	39	A1
Ar Raqqah	Syria	33	B2
Arabian Sea		56	A5
Aracaju	Brazil	81	E6
Arad	Romania	10	I1
Arad	Romania	11	G8
Arafura Sea		63	N10
Arafura Sea	Australia	69	F6
Arak	Iran	33	J1
Arak	Algeria	42	H10
Araks	Azerbaijan	18	E6
Araks river	Azerbaijan	16	J7
Aral Sea		23	E4
Aralsk river	Azerbaijan	23	A9
Arandai	Indonesia	63	N8
Arandai	Indonesia	69	G2
Aransas Pass	US	89	G5
Arar	Saudi Arabia	33	D6
Ararat	Armenia	17	N4
Ararat	Armenia	18	A6
Aras	Turkey	17	K3
Araucaria	Brazil	80	B5
Araya Peninsula	Venezuela	77	J1
Arbil	Iraq	33	F1
Ardabil	Iran	18	F8
Ardmore	US	95	I1
Arendal	Norway	2	J3
Arequipa	Peru	84	A5
Argentina		82	C3
Århus	Denmark	2	J5
Arica	Chile	84	A6
Aries	South Africa	54	B8
Arima	Trinidad	79	F5
Arizona state	US	101	C5
Arizona state	US	102	K8
Arkansas state	US	94	D2
Arkansas state	US	98	A9
Arkansas state	US	99	I9
Arkansas River	US	94	E1
Arkhangelsk	Russian Fed.	25	A7
Arkhangelsk prov.	Russian Fed.	25	A9
Arkhara	Russian Fed.	30	F9
Armavir	Russian Fed.	16	G4
Armavir	Russian Fed.	20	K3
Armenia		16	H6

World Energy Atlas

Petroleum Economist

XIII

INDEX

Name	Country	Plate	Grid Ref
Berezovka	Moldova	22	C8
Berezovo	Russian Fed.	25	H6
Berezovo	Russian Fed.	27	C6
Bergen	Norway	2	I2
Bergen	Norway	5	L1
Bergen	Norway	6	M7
Bergen	Norway	8	E5
Bergen Bank	Norway	5	H1
Bergen Bank	Norway	6	I7
Bergen Bank	Norway	8	A6
Berghausen	Germany	9	N4
Berghausen	Germany	11	C6
Berlin	Germany	2	K8
Berlin	Germany	11	D3
Bern	Switzerland	9	K4
Bern	Switzerland	11	A6
Betim	Brazil	80	D3
Beyneu	Kazakhstan	16	M2
Beyneu	Kazakhstan	19	L6
Beyneu	Kazakhstan	23	C5
Beziers	France	9	H6
Bezmein	Turkmenistan	23	F9
Bezmein	Turkmenistan	24	C9
Bhutan		56	H4
Bicaz	Romania	10	L1
Bicaz	Romania	11	I8
Bicaz	Romania	16	A3
Bie Plateau	Angola	54	A2
Big Spring	US	86	H1
Big Spring	US	95	A4
Big Spring	US	96	K4
Bijaipur	India	56	E4
Bilbao	Spain	9	E5
Billings	US	107	
Billings	US	108	E6
Billyakh	Russian Fed.	30	C1
Billyakh	Russian Fed.	31	M2
Bindura	Zimbabwe	53	B8
Bindura	Zimbabwe	54	E4
Binghampton	US	105	F3
Bintulu	Malaysia	63	H6
Bintulu	Malaysia	64	B4
Bir Ali	Yemen	38	E8
Birmingham	UK	2	D6
Birmingham	US	94	N3
Bishkek	Kyrgyzstan	23	L3
Bishkek	Kyrgyzstan	61	A5
Biskra	Algeria	42	J2
Bismarck	US	107	
Bitumount	Canada	112	N7
Biysk	Russian Fed.	31	C9
Bizai	Kazakhstan	16	N2
Bizai	Kazakhstan	19	M5
Bizai	Kazakhstan	23	D4
Bizerta	Tunisia	42	M1
Black Sea		16	C5
Black Sea		17	E10
Black Sea		20	C6
Black Volta *river*	Ghana	45	F1
Blagoveshchensk	Russian Fed.	20	F3
Blagoveshchensk	Russian Fed.	30	D8
Blantyre	Malawi	53	B8
Blantyre	Malawi	54	F3
Blaregnies	Belgium	2	F8
Blaregnies	Belgium	9	J1
Blida	Algeria	42	H1
Bloemfontein	South Africa	54	C8
Bloomfield	US	101	I3
Bloomington	US	98	H1
Bloomington	US	106	C9
Bludenz	Austria	9	L4
Bludenz	Austria	11	A7
Blue Nile *river*	Sudan	52	E5
Bluff	New Zealand	73	A9
Blytheville	US	98	C7
Blytheville	US	99	N9
Bo	Sierra Leone	45	A2
Bo Hai Gulf		62	E6
Boa Vista	Brazil	78	G3
Bobo Dioulasso	Burkina Faso	45	E1
Bogata	Colombia	78	A2
Bogata	Colombia	85	E2
Boknafjord	Norway	5	L4
Boknafjord	Norway	8	E8
Bol.Uzen *river*	Russian Fed.	21	F3
Bolin	China	62	F2
Bolivia		84	B4
Bolnisi	Georgia	17	M1
Bolnisi	Georgia	18	A3
Bologna	Italy	9	L7
Bologna	Italy	10	D2
Bologna	Italy	11	B9
Bombay (Mumbai)	India	37	E7
Bonao	Dominican Rep.	76	J3
Bongaigaon	India	56	H4
Bonn	Germany	2	H8
Bonn	Germany	9	K1
Bonn	Germany	11	A4
Bonny	Nigeria	45	J4
Bonny Island	Nigeria	45	J4
Bonny Island	Nigeria	46	J7
Bonny Terminal	Nigeria	46	K7
Bontang/Santan	Indonesia	63	H7
Bontang/Santan	Indonesia	64	D7
Bor	Yugoslavia	10	J3
Bor	Yugoslavia	11	G10
Bordeaux	France	9	G4
Bordj Tarat	Algeria	42	L10
Borger	US	100	E7
Borispol	Ukraine	11	L5
Borispol	Ukraine	13	D8
Borispol	Ukraine	16	C1
Borispol	Ukraine	22	D3
Borneo	Indonesia/ Malaysia	63	H7
Borneo	Indonesia/ Malaysia	64	C6
Bornholm Is.	Denmark	2	K6
Bornholm Is.	Denmark	11	E1
Borok	Russian Fed.	13	G3
Borovaya	Ukraine	22	K6
Borovichi	Russian Fed.	13	E3
Borzhomi	Georgia	17	L10
Borzhomi	Georgia	20	N8
Bosnia-Herzegovina		10	G2
Bosnia-Herzegovina		11	E9
Bosporus	Turkey	10	M6
Bosporus	Turkey	16	B6
Bostandyk	Kazakhstan	19	D1
Bostandyk	Kazakhstan	21	G5
Boston	US	105	L2
Botlek	Netherlands	3	J8
Botosani	Romania	10	L1
Botosani	Romania	11	I7
Botosani	Romania	13	C10
Botosani	Romania	16	A2
Botswana		54	B5
Bou Saada	Algeria	42	I2
Bouake	Cote D'Ivoire	45	D2
Boucau	Spain	9	F5
Boulogne	France	2	F8
Boulogne	France	9	I1
Bourbonne	France	2	F10
Bourbonne	France	9	J3
Bowden	Canada	113	C4
Bowling Green	US	98	H5
Boyarka	Ukraine	22	C3
Braga	Portugal	9	B5
Braila	Romania	10	M2
Braila	Romania	11	J9
Braila	Romania	16	A4
Brasilia	Brazil	80	C1
Brasilia	Brazil	81	A8
Brasov	Romania	10	L2
Brasov	Romania	11	I9
Brasov	Romania	16	A4
Bratislava	Slovak Rep.	11	E6
Brawley	US	102	H9
Brazil		78	F9
Brazil		80	A2
Brazil		81	A4
Brazil		84	C1
Brazzaville	Congo (Brazzaville)	45	M8
Breda	Netherlands	3	K8
Bremen	Germany	2	I7
Bremen	Germany	11	B2
Bressay Bank	UK	5	D3
Bressay Bank	UK	6	E10
Brest	France	2	B8
Brest	France	9	F1
Brest	Belarus	11	H4
Brest	Belarus	13	B7
Bridgeport	US	105	I5
Brighton	Trinidad	79	D7
Brindisi	Italy	10	G5
Brisbane	Australia	71	E2
Bristol	UK	2	D7
British Columbia	Canada	112	D3
Brno	Czech Rep.	11	E6
Broadhaven Bay	Ireland	2	B4
Brody	Ukraine	11	I5
Brody	Ukraine	13	B8
Brody	Ukraine	16	A1
Broome	Australia	72	E2
Brunei		63	G5
Brunswick	US	93	E6
Brussels	France	2	G8
Brussels	Belgium	9	J1
Bryansk	Russian Fed.	11	M3
Bryansk	Russian Fed.	13	E6
Bryansk prov.	Russian Fed.	13	E6
Bryukovetsk	Russian Fed.	20	H2
Bubiyan Is. *rep.*	Kuwait	34	C1
Bubiyan Is.*rep.*	Kuwait	33	J6
Bubnovsk	Russian Fed.	21	A4
Bucaramanga	Colombia	76	I10
Bucaramanga	Colombia	78	B1
Bucaramanga	Colombia	85	E1
Buchanan	Liberia	45	A3
Bucharest	Romania	10	L3
Bucharest	Romania	11	I10
Bucharest	Romania	16	A4
Budapest	Hungary	10	H1
Budapest	Hungary	11	F7
Budennovsk	Russian Fed.	16	H4
Budennovsk	Russian Fed.	20	N4
Budy	Ukraine	22	I5
Buenaventura	Colombia	85	C3
Buenos Aires	Argentina	82	F7
Buffalo	US	105	B2
Buffalo	US	106	N3
Bujumbura	Burundi	53	A3
Bukavu	D.R. Congo	53	A3
Bukhara	Uzbekistan	23	H7
Bukhara	Uzbekistan	24	H6
Bulawayo	Zimbabwe	53	A9
Bulawayo	Zimbabwe	54	E4
Bulgaria		10	J4
Bulgaria		16	A5
Bunbury	Australia	72	B9
Buncefield	UK	3	C8
Bundaberg	Australia	71	E1
Buqayq	Saudi Arabia	33	K8
Buqayq	Saudi Arabia	34	E4
Buraydah	Saudi Arabia	33	G9
Buraydah	Saudi Arabia	34	A4
Bureyo *river*	Russian Fed.	30	F8
Burgas	Bulgaria	10	L4
Burgas	Bulgaria	16	A6
Burgos	Spain	9	D6
Burma (Myanmar)		56	I5
Burme/Devonport	Australia	71	C9
Bursa	Turkey	10	M6
Bursa	Turkey	16	B7
Buru	Indonesia	69	C3
Buru *rep.*	Indonesia	63	L8
Burundi		53	A3
Bushehr	Iran	33	L6
Bushehr	Iran	34	F1
Butte	US	108	A7
Buynaksk	Russian Fed.	18	C1

C

Name	Country	Plate	Grid Ref
Cabaiguan	Cuba	76	F2
Cabinda	Angola (Cabinda)	50	D1
Cabo Frio	Brazil	80	B10
Cadereyta	Mexico	86	H6
Cádiz	Spain	9	A9
Caen	France	2	E8
Caen	France	9	H1
Cagayan de Oro	Philippines	63	K4
Cagliari	Italy	9	J10
Cagliari	Italy	10	B6
Cainpana	Argentina	82	F6
Cairo	Egypt	43	I4
Cajamarca	Peru	85	C8
Calais	France	2	F7
Calais	France	9	I1
Calcutta	India	56	G5
Caleta Cordova	Argentina	83	C3
Caleta Olivia	Argentina	83	C4
Calgary	Canada	113	C5
Cali	Colombia	85	D3
California *state*	US	102	E3
California *state*	US	103	D3
Callantshoog	Netherlands	2	G7
Callantshoog	Netherlands	11	A2
Callantsoog	Netherlands	3	K5
Cambodia		56	L8
Cambodia		63	E3
Cambodia		65	C1
Cambridge	UK	3	D7
Camden	US	105	G7
Cameron	US	91	C2
Cameroon		45	K4
Cameroon		46	N7
Cameroon		51	D1
Campbeltown	Canada	114	A3
Campeche	Mexico	86	M9
Campina Grande	Brazil	81	E4
Campo Grande	Brazil	80	A3
Campo Grande	Brazil	84	F7
Campos	Brazil	80	E3
Campos dos Goytacazes	Brazil	80	C7
Camrose	Canada	113	D3
Can	Turkey	10	L7
Can	Turkey	16	A7
Canada		106	K1
Cananea	Mexico	86	C1
Canberra	Australia	71	D6
Cangzhou	China	61	N7
Cangzhou	China	62	F4
Canoas	Brazil	80	B6
Canton	US	106	J6
Canvey Island	UK	2	E7
Canvey Island/ Shell Haven/ Coryton	UK	3	D9
Cap Lopez	Gabon	45	J6
Cap Lopez Terminal	Gabon	47	B1
Cape Bon	Tunisia	10	B8
Cape Carnaveral	US	92	D4
Cape Carnaveral	US	93	F10
Cape Horn		83	C8

©The Petroleum Economist Ltd, London 2001

XVII

INDEX

INDEX

INDEX

INDEX

Name	Country	Plate	Grid Ref
Riyadh	Saudi Arabia	34	C5
Roanoke	US	97	G3
Robinson	US	98	F1
Robinson	US	106	A9
Rochester	US	105	C1
Rock Springs	US	104	F6
Rocky Mount	US	97	J5
Romania		10	J2
Romania		11	G9
Romania		16	A2
Rome	Italy	9	L9
Rome	Italy	10	D4
Ronneby	Sweden	2	L5
Ronneby	Sweden	11	E1
Rosario	Philippines	63	I2
Rosario	Argentina	82	E6
Rossosh	Russian Fed.	22	L4
Rostock	Germany	2	J7
Rostock	Germany	11	D2
Rostov prov.	Russian Fed.	13	H10
Rostov prov.	Russian Fed.	16	G2
Rostov-on-Don	Russian Fed.	13	H10
Rostov-on-Don	Russian Fed.	16	F2
Rostov-on-Don	Russian Fed.	22	L9
Roswell	US	96	F1
Roswell	US	101	L10
Rota	Spain	9	A9
Rota	Spain	42	A1
Rotterdam	Netherlands	2	F7
Rotterdam	Netherlands	3	J7
Rouen	France	2	E8
Rouen	France	9	I2
Roussines	France	9	H4
Rovno	Ukraine	11	J5
Rovno	Ukraine	13	C8
Rovno	Ukraine	16	A1
Rovuma river	Tanzania	53	D6
Rozenburg	Netherlands	3	J8
Rozhdestvensk	Russian Fed.	20	L3
Rtishchevo	Russian Fed.	21	B1
Rub al Khali (Empty Quarter)	Saudi Arabia	38	D3
Rudnichny	Russian Fed.	13	L1
Rudnichny	Russian Fed.	14	A4
Rügen Is.	Germany	11	D2
Ruse	Bulgaria	10	L3
Ruse	Bulgaria	16	A5
Russian Fed.		13	H1
Russian Fed.		21	A4
Russian Fed.		61	H1
Russian Fed.		62	A1
Rustavi	Georgia	16	I6
Rustavi	Georgia	17	N1
Rustavi	Georgia	18	B3
Rutland	US	105	J1
Ruwais	UAE	33	N9
Ruwais	UAE	34	H4
Ruwais	UAE	35	F7
Rwanda		53	A3
Ryazan	Russian Fed.	13	H5
Ryazan prov.	Russian Fed.	13	H5
Rybinsk Reservoir	Russian Fed.	13	F3
Rybnista	Moldova	22	B7
Rzhev	Russian Fed.	11	M1
Rzhev	Russian Fed.	13	F4

S

Name	Country	Plate	Grid Ref
S Balyk	Russian Fed.	25	K7
S Balyk	Russian Fed.	27	H7
S Bug river	Ukraine	22	C6
s' Gravenhage	Netherlands	3	J7
S Ossetia aut.	Georgia	16	H5
Saaremaa	Estonia	13	A3
Saaremaa Is.	Estonia	2	N4
Sabah	Malaysia	63	I5
Sabine Pass	US	91	B2
Sabirabad	Azerbaijan	18	E5
Sachkhere	Georgia	20	N7
Sacramento	US	103	F6
Safid Rud river	Iran	18	H10
Saginaw	US	106	G1
Sagiz	Kazakhstan	19	J2
Sagiz	Russian Fed.	21	M6
Sagyramo	Georgia	16	I6
Sagyramo	Georgia	17	N1
Sagyramo	Georgia	18	A3
Saida	Algeria	42	F2
Saimaa	Finland	13	D1
Saint John	Canada	114	A4
Sai-Utes	Kazakhstan	16	L3
Sai-Utes	Kazakhstan	19	J7
Sai-Utes	Kazakhstan	23	C6
Sakai	Japan	62	K7
Sakaide	Japan	62	I7
Sakhalin Inlet	Russian Fed.	28	A1
Sakhalin Island	Russian Fed.	30	J9
Sakhalinskiy Zaliu	Russian Fed.	30	I7
Saki	Ukraine	20	C3
Salalah	Oman	34	J10
Salaleh	Oman	37	B10
Salamanca	Mexico	86	G8

Name	Country	Plate	Grid Ref
Salaya	India	37	A1
Salaya	India	56	B5
Salaya	Pakistan	60	C10
Saldanha Bay	South Africa	54	A9
Salekhard	Russian Fed.	25	H5
Salekhard	Russian Fed.	26	C9
Salekhard	Russian Fed.	27	C3
Salem	US	109	C7
Salerno	Italy	9	N10
Salerno	Italy	10	E5
Salisbury	US	105	F10
Salt Lake City	US	104	B7
Salta	Argentina	82	D2
Salta	Argentina	84	C9
Salto	Jamaica	80	A7
Salvador	Brazil	81	D7
Salween river	Myanmar	63	B1
Salween river	Myanmar	56	J6
Salzburg	Austria	9	N4
Salzburg	Austria	11	C6
Samar rep.	Philippines	63	K3
Samara	Russian Fed.	13	K5
Samara	Russian Fed.	14	B10
Samara	Russian Fed.	15	D4
Samara prov.	Russian Fed.	13	K5
Samara prov.	Russian Fed.	14	B9
Samara prov.	Russian Fed.	15	D4
Samaria	Mexico	86	M3
Samarkand	Uzbekistan	23	J6
Samarkand	Uzbekistan	24	J5
Sambu Island	Indonesia	63	D7
Sambu Island rep.	Indonesia	66	B2
Samsun	Turkey	16	E6
Samsun	Turkey	17	C1
Samsun	Turkey	20	E9
San Angelo	US	95	C6
San Angelo	US	96	M6
San Antonio	US	89	E2
San Antonio	US	95	E10
San Bernardino	US	102	F7
San Carlos de Bariloche	Argentina	82	A10
San Carlos de Bariloche	Argentina	83	B1
San Cristobal	Venezuela	76	I10
San Cristobal	Venezuela	85	E1
San Diego	US	102	E9
San Eufemia	Italy	10	F7
San Fernando	Trinidad	79	D7
San Francisco	US	103	C7
San Jose	Guatemala	76	A6
San Jose	Costa Rica	76	D9
San Jose	US	103	E8
San Jose del Guaviare	Colombia	78	B4
San Jose del Guaviare	Colombia	85	E3
San Juan	Puerto Rico	76	L3
San Julian	Argentina	83	C5
San Lorenzo	Venezuela	76	J9
San Lorenzo	Argentina	82	E6
San Luis	Argentina	82	C6
San Luis Obispo	US	102	A4
San Luis Potos	Mexico	86	G7
San Marino		9	M7
San Marino		10	D3
San Marino		11	B9
San Miguel de Tucuman	Argentina	82	D3
San Miguel de Tucuman	Argentina	84	C10
San Rocque	Spain	9	B10
San Salvador	El Salvador	76	B6
San Salvo	Italy	9	N9
San Salvo	Italy	10	E4
San Sebastian	Argentina	83	B7
Sana'a	Yemen	38	B7
Sandakan	Malaysia	63	I5
Sandakan	Malaysia	64	E2
Sandefjord	Norway	2	J3
Sandersville	US	94	K6
Sanghar	Pakistan	56	B4
Sanghar	Pakistan	60	C8
Sangre Grande	Trinidad	79	F5
Santa Barbara	Venezuela	77	K4
Santa Barbara	US	102	B5
Santa Cruz	Bolivia	84	C6
Santa Cruz	US	103	D9
Santa Fe	Argentina	82	E5
Santa Fe	US	101	K5
Santa Maria	Brazil	80	A6
Santa Maria	US	102	B4
Santa Marta	Colombia	76	H7
Santa Marta	Colombia	76	H7
Santander	Spain	9	E5
Santiago	Chile	82	A6
Santiago de Cuba	Cuba	76	G3
Santiago del Estero	Argentina	82	D3
Santo Domingo	Dominican Rep.	76	J4
Santos	Brazil	80	C4
Sanya	China	56	N6
Sanya	China	63	F1

Name	Country	Plate	Grid Ref
Sao Francisco do Sul	Brazil	80	B5
Sao Jose dos Campos	Brazil	80	C4
Sao Luis de Maranhao	Brazil	81	B2
Sao Mateus	Brazil	80	E2
Sao Mateus	Brazil	81	D9
Sao Paulo	Brazil	80	C4
Sao Sebastiao	Brazil	80	D4
Sao Tome	Sao Tome & Principe	45	I6
Sao Tome & Principe		45	I5
Sapporo	Japan	62	K4
Sapugaskanda	Sri Lanka	56	E10
Sarajevo	Bosnia-Herzegovina	10	H3
Sarajevo	Bosnia-Herzegovina	11	E10
Saraland	US	94	L9
Saransk	Russian Fed.	13	J5
Saransk	Russian Fed.	15	B4
Saratov	Russian Fed.	13	J7
Saratov	Russian Fed.	15	B6
Saratov	Russian Fed.	21	D3
Saratov prov.	Russian Fed.	13	J6
Saratov Reservoir	Russian Fed.	21	F1
Sarawak	Malaysia	63	H6
Sarawak	Malaysia	64	B5
Sardinia	Italy	9	J9
Sardinia	Italy	10	B5
Sarnia	Canada	106	I2
Sarny	Ukraine	22	A10
Sarroch	Italy	10	B6
Sarykamys	Kazakhstan	13	N10
Sarykamys	Kazakhstan	16	L2
Sarykamys	Kazakhstan	19	J5
Sarykamys	Kazakhstan	21	M9
Sarykamys	Kazakhstan	23	C4
Sarytash	Kazakhstan	19	H8
Sasebo	Japan	62	H8
Saskatchewan state	Canada	113	J3
Saskatoon	Canada	113	H5
Sasolburg	South Africa	54	D7
Sassandra	Cote D'Ivoire	45	C3
Satu Mare	Romania	10	J1
Satu Mare	Romania	11	H7
Satu Mare	Romania	13	A10
Saudi Arabia		33	E8
Saudi Arabia		34	A6
Saudi Arabia		35	B9
Saudi Arabia		36	A10
Saudi Arabia		38	A2
Saudi Arabia		39	D1
Savannah	US	93	E4
Savannakhet	Laos	56	L7
Savannakhet	Laos	63	E1
Savona	Italy	9	K6
Savona	Italy	10	B2
Savona	Italy	11	A8
Sawqirah Bay		34	L9
Sawqirah Bay	Oman	37	D8
Sayda	Germany	2	J9
Sayda	Germany	9	O2
Sayda	Germany	11	C4
Scarborough	Tobago	79	I2
Schlüchtern	Germany	2	I9
Schlüchtern	Germany	9	M2
Schlüchtern	Germany	11	B4
Schwedt	Germany	2	K7
Schwedt	Germany	11	E2
Scranton	US	105	F4
Sea of Okhotsk	Russian Fed.	28	E2
Sea Island rep.	Kuwait	33	J6
Sea Island rep.	Kuwait	34	D1
Sea of Azov		16	E3
Sea of Azov		20	F1
Sea of Azov		22	J9
Sea of Japan		62	I5
Sea of Okhotsk	Russian Fed.	30	L5
Seattle	US	109	D3
Sebha	Libya	44	E8
Secunderabad	India	56	E7
Segamat	Malaysia	63	D6
Segamat	Malaysia	65	B9
Segamat	Malaysia	67	F4
Selebi-Phikwe	Botswana	53	A10
Selebi-Phikwe	Botswana	54	D5
Selenga river	Russian Fed.	31	I10
Selenge Mörön river	Mongolia	61	J2
Selenge Mörön river	Mongolia	62	A1
Semipalatinsk	Kazakhstan	31	A10
Senboku	Japan	62	K7
Sendai	Japan	62	L6
Senipah	Indonesia	63	I7
Senipah	Indonesia	64	E7
Seoul	South Korea	62	H6
Seram	Indonesia	69	E3
Seram rep.	Indonesia	63	M8
Serengeti	Tanzania	53	C3
Serenje	Zambia	53	A7
Serenje	Zambia	54	E2

INDEX

Name	Country	Plate	Grid Ref
Tulle	France	9	H4
Tulsa	US	99	E7
Tulsa	US	100	N7
Tuma	Russian Fed.	13	H5
Tumaco	Colombia	85	B4
Tumanyan	Armenia	17	M2
Tumanyan	Armenia	18	A4
Tumen Delta		62	I4
Tunbs *rep.*	Iran	34	J2
Tunbs *rep.*	Iran	35	J1
Tunis	Tunisia	10	B8
Tunis	Tunisia	42	M1
Tunisia		10	A10
Tunisia		42	K3
Tunisia		44	A2
Tunja	Colombia	78	A2
Tunja	Colombia	85	E2
Tura	Russian Fed.	31	G2
Turbot Bank	UK	4	A1
Turbot Bank	UK	5	B8
Turbot Bank	UK	7	E10
Turin	Italy	9	K6
Turin	Italy	10	B1
Turkey		16	C8
Turkey		17	A4
Turkey		33	A1
Turkmenbashi	Turkmenistan	16	L6
Turkmenbashi	Turkmenistan	18	K4
Turkmenbashi	Turkmenistan	23	C8
Turkmenistan		16	M6
Turkmenistan		18	L3
Turkmenistan		23	D8
Turkmenistan		24	D7
Turku	Finland	13	A1
Turkwe *river*	Kenya	53	C2
Turkwel *river*	Kenya	52	F9
Turpan	China	61	F5
Turukhansk	Russian Fed.	31	C1
Tuscaloosa	US	94	M3
Tuticorin	India	56	D9
Tuticorin	India	58	A9
Tuxpan	Mexico	86	I8
Tuy	Spain	9	B5
Tuymazy	Russian Fed.	13	M4
Tuymazy	Russian Fed.	14	D8
Tuymazy	Russian Fed.	15	F2
Tver	Russian Fed.	11	N1
Tver	Russian Fed.	13	F4
Tver *prov.*	Russian Fed.	13	E4
Tyrnyauz	Russian Fed.	16	H5
Tyrnyauz	Russian Fed.	20	M6
Tyrrhenian Sea		9	K9
Tyrrhenian Sea		10	C5
Tyulei	Uzbekistan	19	N7
Tyumen	Russian Fed.	25	J4
Tyumen *prov.*	Russian Fed.	25	G6
Tyumen *prov.*	Russian Fed.	27	C5
Tyung *river*	Russian Fed.	31	M2

U

Name	Country	Plate	Grid Ref
UAE		37	A2
UAE		34	I5
Ubari	Libya	44	D9
Uberaba	Brazil	80	C2
Uchami	Russian Fed.	31	F3
Udachny	Russian Fed.	31	J1
Uddevalla	Sweden	2	K4
Udmurtia *rep.*	Russian Fed.	13	L3
Udmurtia *rep.*	Russian Fed.	14	B6
Udmurtia *rep.*	Russian Fed.	15	D1
Udskaya Guba	Russian Fed.	30	H6
Uele *river*	D.R. Congo	52	A8
Ufa	Russian Fed.	13	M4
Ufa	Russian Fed.	14	E8
Uganda		52	D9
Uganda		53	B2
Uil	Kazakhstan	19	J1
Uil	Russian Fed.	21	M5
Ujung Pandang	Indonesia	63	I9
Ukhta	Russian Fed.	14	A1
Ukhta	Russian Fed.	25	E7
Ukraine		11	J6
Ukraine		13	C2
Ukraine		16	A2
Ukraine		22	B7
Ulan Bator	Mongolia	61	K3
Ulan Bator	Mongolia	62	B2
Ulan-Ude	Russian Fed.	31	I9
Ulsan	South Korea	62	H7
Ulyanovsk *prov.*	Russian Fed.	13	J5
Ulyanovsk *prov.*	Russian Fed.	14	A9
Ulyanovsk *prov.*	Russian Fed.	15	B4
Umeå	Sweden	2	O1
Umm Al Nar	UAE	34	I4
Umm Al Nar	UAE	35	J6
Umm Bab	Qatar	33	L9
Umm Bab	Qatar	34	F4
Umm Bab	Qatar	35	B6
Umm Bab	Qatar	36	B7
Umm Qasr	Iraq	33	I5
Umm Qasr	Iraq	34	C1

Name	Country	Plate	Grid Ref
Umm Said	Qatar	33	M9
Umm Said	Qatar	34	G4
Umm Said	Qatar	35	D6
Umm Said	Qatar	36	D7
Unecha	Russian Fed.	11	L3
Unecha	Russian Fed.	13	E6
Unggi	North Korea	62	H4
United Kingdom		2	D4
Unst Basin	UK	6	D5
Unst Basin	UK	7	G1
Upington	South Africa	54	B7
Ural *river*	Kazakhstan	13	L7
Ural *river*	Kazakhstan	15	F6
Ural *river*	Russian Fed.	21	N1
Ural *river*	Kazakhstan	21	J4
Uralsk	Kazakhstan	13	L7
Uralsk	Kazakhstan	15	E6
Uralsk	Kazakhstan	21	I2
Uralsk	Kazakhstan	23	A1
Urengoy	Russian Fed.	25	K3
Urengoy	Russian Fed.	26	I7
Urengoy	Russian Fed.	27	H1
Urgench	Uzbekistan	23	G6
Urgench	Uzbekistan	24	D5
Uritsk	Russian Fed.	21	C2
Uruguaiana	Brazil	80	A6
Ürümqi	China	61	E5
Ushuaia	Argentina	83	C8
Ushumun	Russian Fed.	30	E7
Usinsk	Russian Fed.	25	E6
Ussuri *river*	China	62	I3
Ust'-Bol'sheretsk	Russian Fed.	30	M7
Ust-Ilimsk	Russian Fed.	31	H6
Ust-Kamenogorsk	Kazakhstan	31	A10
Ust-Kut	Russian Fed.	31	H7
Ust-Labinsk	Russian Fed.	20	I3
Ustyurt Plateau	Kazakhstan	16	M3
Utah *state*	US	101	E1
Utah *state*	US	102	M1
Utah *state*	US	104	A8
Utsira Ground	Norway	5	H5
Utsira Ground	Norway	8	A9
Uusikaupunki	Finland	2	O3
Uusikaupunki	Finland	13	A1
Uva	Russian Fed.	13	L3
Uva	Russian Fed.	14	B6
Uva	Russian Fed.	15	E1
Uvs Nuur	Mongolia	61	G2
Uzbekistan		19	M8
Uzbekistan		23	E6
Uzbekistan		24	C3
Uzhgorod	Ukraine	11	H6
Uzhgorod	Ukraine	13	A9
Uzice	Yugoslavia	10	H3
Uzice	Yugoslavia	11	F10
Uzin	Ukraine	22	D4

V

Name	Country	Plate	Grid Ref
Vaal *river*	South Africa	54	C7
Vado	Italy	9	K6
Vado	Italy	10	B2
Valdai	Russian Fed.	13	E3
Valdez	US	111	K7
Valdivia	Chile	82	A9
Valdivia	Chile	83	A1
Valdosta	US	93	B6
Valencia	Spain	9	E8
Valencia	Venezuela	76	K8
Valladolid	Spain	9	D6
Valle La Pascua	Venezuela	77	C5
Valletta	Malta	10	D9
Valparaiso	Chile	82	A6
Valuyki	Russian Fed.	22	K4
Van	Turkey	17	L6
Vanatsor	Armenia	17	M2
Vanatsor	Armenia	18	A4
Varberg	Sweden	2	K4
Vardenis	Armenia	17	N3
Vardenis	Armenia	18	B5
Varna	Bulgaria	10	M4
Varna	Bulgaria	16	A5
Västerås	Sweden	2	L3
Västervik	Sweden	2	L4
Vaygach Island	Russian Fed.	25	E3
Velikiye Luki	Russian Fed.	11	K1
Velikiye Luki	Russian Fed.	13	D4
Velke Kapuzany	Slovak Rep.	11	G6
Velke Kapuzany	Slovak Rep.	13	A9
Venezuela		76	K10
Venezuela		78	D1
Venezuela		79	A4
Venezuela		79	A10
Venice	Italy	9	M6
Venice	Italy	10	E1
Venice	Italy	11	B8
Venisay *river*	Russian Fed.	31	D4
Ventspils	Latvia	2	N5
Ventspils	Latvia	13	A3
Veracruz	Mexico	86	J9
Verkhnedneprovsk	Ukraine	22	F6
Vermont *state*	US	105	I1

Name	Country	Plate	Grid Ref
Veselov Reservoir	Russian Fed.	20	K1
Veselov Reservoir	Russian Fed.	22	N9
Vicksburg	US	94	H5
Victoria	US	89	G3
Victoria Falls		54	C4
Victoria *state*	Australia	70	F6
Victoria *state*	Australia	71	A6
Viedma	Argentina	83	E1
Vienna	Austria	11	E6
Vientiane	Laos	56	K6
Vientiane	Laos	63	D1
Vietnam		56	M8
Vietnam		63	F2
Vietnam		65	E2
Vigo	Spain	9	B5
Viking Bank	Norway	6	H6
Viking Bank	Norway	8	A4
Viktorovski	Russian Fed.	31	E4
Villarrica	Paraguay	80	A5
Villarrica	Paraguay	84	F9
Vilnius	Lithuania	11	I2
Vilnius	Lithuania	13	B5
Vilyuy *river*	Russian Fed.	30	D1
Vilyuy *river*	Russian Fed.	31	N2
Vindecy	France	9	I4
Vinh	Vietnam	56	M6
Vinh	Vietnam	63	E1
Vinnitsa	Ukraine	11	J6
Vinnitsa	Ukraine	13	C9
Vinnitsa	Ukraine	16	A1
Vinnitsa	Ukraine	22	B5
Virginia *state*	US	97	I3
Virginia *state*	US	105	B9
Vishakhapatnam	India	56	F7
Vishakhapatnam	India	58	F1
Vishni Volochok	Russian Fed.	13	F3
Vitebsk	Belarus	11	K1
Vitebsk	Belarus	13	D5
Vitim	Russian Fed.	30	A3
Vitim	Russian Fed.	31	K5
Vitim *river*	Russian Fed.	30	A7
Vitim *river*	Russian Fed.	31	K9
Vitoria	Brazil	80	E2
Vitoria		81	D10
Vivi *river*	Russian Fed.	31	E1
Vizirka	Ukraine	20	A1
Vizirka	Ukraine	22	C9
Vladikavkaz	Russian Fed.	16	H5
Vladikavkaz	Russian Fed.	18	A1
Vladimir	Russian Fed.	13	G4
Vladimir *prov.*	Russian Fed.	13	G4
Vladimirovka	Russian Fed.	22	J8
Vladivostok	Russian Fed.	62	I4
Vlissingen	Netherlands	2	G7
Vlissingen	Netherlands	3	I9
Vlissingen	Netherlands	9	J1
Vlorë	Albania	10	H6
Volga Delta	Russian Fed.	16	J3
Volga Delta	Russian Fed.	19	D6
Volga Delta	Russian Fed.	23	A5
Volga *river*	Russian Fed.	13	G3
Volga *river*	Russian Fed.	13	J9
Volga *river*	Russian Fed.	15	C9
Volga *river*	Russian Fed.	19	A2
Volga *river*	Russian Fed.	21	C7
Volga-Don Canal	Russian Fed.	13	J9
Volga-Don Canal	Russian Fed.	15	A9
Volga-don Canal	Russian Fed.	16	H1
Volga-don Canal	Russian Fed.	21	B7
Volga-Ural	Russian Fed.	13	M5
Volgodonsk	Russian Fed.	13	I10
Volgodonsk	Russian Fed.	15	A10
Volgodonsk	Russian Fed.	16	G2
Volgodonsk	Russian Fed.	21	A8
Volgograd	Russian Fed.	13	I9
Volgograd	Russian Fed.	15	A9
Volgograd	Russian Fed.	16	H1
Volgograd	Russian Fed.	21	C7
Volgograd prov.	Russian Fed.	13	I8
Volgograd *prov.*	Russian Fed.	16	G1
Volgograd Reservoir	Russian Fed.	19	A2
Volgograd Reservoir	Russian Fed.	21	C6
Volkhov	Russian Fed.	13	E2
Volnogorsk	Ukraine	22	F6
Vologda	Russian Fed.	13	G2
Vologda *prov.*	Russian Fed.	13	G10
Volsk	Russian Fed.	13	K6
Volsk	Russian Fed.	15	C5
Volsk	Russian Fed.	21	E1
Volta Redonda	Brazil	80	C4
Vorkuta	Russian Fed.	25	G4
Vorkuta	Russian Fed.	26	A8
Vorkuta	Russian Fed.	27	A2
Voronezh	Russian Fed.	13	H7
Voronezh	Russian Fed.	22	L2
Voronezh *prov.*	Russian Fed.	13	H7
Vratsa	Bulgaria	10	J4
Vredendal	South Africa	54	A8
Vuktyl	Russian Fed.	25	F7
Vung Tau	Vietnam	56	M9
Vung Tau	Vietnam	63	E4
Vung Tau	Vietnam	65	F1

LIST OF THE WORLD'S DEEPWATER OIL AND GAS FIELDS

APPENDIX

Country	Operator	Field Name	Date Discovered	Date on Stream
Angola	BP	Plutonio (Block 18)	06/03/99	01/01/05
Angola	ExxonMobil	Chocalho (Kizomba Block 15)	03/01/99	01/01/05
Angola	ExxonMobil	Hungo (Kizomba Block 15)	05/01/98	01/01/04
Angola	ExxonMobil	Xikomba (Kizomba Block 15)	06/01/99	10/01/05
Angola	TotalFinaElf	Dalia I (Block 17)	08/01/97	12/31/04
Angola	TotalFinaElf	Girassol B (Block 17)	04/01/96	12/01/01
Angola	TotalFinaElf	Girassol C (Block 17)	10/01/96	10/01/05
Australia	Woodside	Enfield	04/21/99	01/01/05
Brazil	Enterprise	Bijupira	02/01/90	07/01/03
Brazil	Petrobras	Albacora Leste	01/01/94	10/01/03
Brazil	Petrobras	Albacora Leste Pilot	01/01/94	06/02/98
Brazil	Petrobras	Area do 1-RJS-424	03/01/93	01/01/05
Brazil	Petrobras	Area do 1-RJS-425	01/01/90	01/01/04
Brazil	Petrobras	Area do 1-RJS-497 (Caratinga Pilot)	10/01/94	09/30/97
Brazil	Petrobras	Area do 1-RJS-539 (BS-500 Santos) Pilot	09/01/99	07/01/03
Brazil	Petrobras	Area do 4-RJS-495 (Caratinga Pilot)	04/01/94	09/30/97
Brazil	Petrobras	Barracuda	07/01/89	09/30/97
Brazil	Petrobras	Bijupira Pilot	02/01/90	08/01/93
Brazil	Petrobras	Caratinga	01/01/94	10/01/03
Brazil	Petrobras	Caratinga Pilot	01/01/94	09/30/97
Brazil	Petrobras	Espadarte (Area do 1-RJS-499)	09/01/94	09/01/00
Brazil	Petrobras	Marimba East (Phase 1)	01/01/96	12/01/98
Brazil	Petrobras	Marimba Leste	01/01/96	01/01/01
Brazil	Petrobras	Marlim	02/01/85	03/16/91
Brazil	Petrobras	Marlim Leste	01/01/94	01/01/04
Brazil	Petrobras	Marlim Leste Pilot	01/01/94	08/01/98
Brazil	Petrobras	Marlim South	11/01/87	06/01/01
Brazil	Petrobras	Marlim South (Module 1) Pilot	11/01/87	04/29/94
Brazil	Petrobras	Marlim South (Module 4) Pilot	11/01/87	08/13/97
Brazil	Petrobras	Marlim West Area do 4-RJS-396D	10/01/93	12/01/99
Brazil	Petrobras	Roncador Pilot	10/01/96	01/25/99
Brazil	Petrobras	Salema	03/01/90	08/01/03
Brazil	Petrobras	Salema Pilot	03/01/90	08/01/93
Brazil	Petrobras	Voador North (Marlim Area 4-RJS-403)	05/19/89	08/01/98
Brazil	Petrobras	Voador South (Marlim Area 4-RJS-377)	08/01/87	07/23/98
Brazil	Chevron-Texaco	Frade (Area do 1-RJS-366)	12/01/86	01/01/05
Congo	TotalFinaElf	Bilondo	02/01/98	01/01/05
Congo	TotalFinaElf	Moho	10/01/95	07/01/04
Egypt	British Gas/EGPC/Edison	Saffron (Med)	06/01/98	01/01/03
Egypt	British Gas/EGPC/Edison	Scarab (Med)	07/01/98	07/01/03
Egypt	British Gas/EGPC/Edison	Simian (Med)	07/01/99	01/01/05
Equatorial Guinea	ExxonMobil	Topacio	01/01/96	05/01/97
Equatorial Guinea	Triton	Ceiba	10/06/99	11/22/00
Gaza Offshore	British Gas	Gaza Marine	09/30/00	01/01/05
Indonesia	Unocal	Merah Besar	01/01/97	01/01/04
Indonesia	Unocal	West Seno	08/17/98	12/15/02
Israel	British Gas	Or 1 (Med)	10/31/99	01/01/04
Israel	Samedan/Noble	Noa 1 (Med)	06/01/99	01/01/05
Italy	Agip-Eni	Aquila	04/16/81	03/04/98
Ivory Coast	Canadian Natural Resources	Baobab (Ci-40)	03/01/01	01/01/05
Nigeria	ExxonMobil	Erha (Opl 209)	02/01/99	01/01/05
Nigeria	Shell	Bonga (Oml 118) (Ex Opl 212)	03/01/96	11/11/03
Nigeria	Chevron-Texaco	Agbami (Opl 216)	11/01/98	12/31/04
Nigeria	Chevron-Texaco	Ikija (Opl 216)	05/07/00	01/01/05
Nigeria	TotalFinaElf	Akpo (Opl 246) Eps	05/01/00	01/01/03
Philippines	Shell	Malampaya	05/01/92	10/01/01
Philippines	Shell	Malampaya Oil Rim	04/01/00	01/01/03
Philippines	Shell	Malampaya Oil Rim Ewt	04/01/00	10/01/01
United Kingdom	BP	Alligin (Ex Foinaven North)	07/21/95	01/01/04
United Kingdom	BP	Cuillin Central (Northeast Foinaven)	10/01/94	01/01/03
United Kingdom	BP	Cuillin South (Northwest Foinaven)	09/01/94	01/01/05
United States	Agip-Eni	Ewing Bank 921 & 964-5 Morpeth	01/01/92	10/11/98
United States	Agip-Eni	Green Canyon 037	03/01/97	01/01/03
United States	Agip-Eni	Green Canyon 039	01/01/87	01/01/05
United States	Agip-Eni	Green Canyon 082	01/01/96	01/01/04
United States	Agip-Eni	Green Canyon 254-3 & 297-8 Allegheny	07/01/92	10/18/99
United States	Agip-Eni	Mississippi Canyon 546 & 502-503 Leo	05/02/86	01/01/05
United States	Amerada Hess	Garden Banks 200 Northwestern	09/09/98	11/30/00
United States	Amerada Hess	Garden Banks 260 & 259 Baldpate	11/01/91	09/14/98
United States	Anadarko	Green Canyon 608 Marco Polo	04/14/00	01/01/04
United States	Anadarko	Mississippi Canyon 755 & 711 Gomez	10/01/87	10/01/04
United States	BP	Desoto Canyon 133 & 177 Kings Peak	04/01/93	07/01/02
United States	BP	Green Canyon 243 Aspen	03/01/01	01/01/03
United States	BP	Green Canyon 244-245 & 200-201 Troika	08/01/94	11/11/97
United States	BP	Green Canyon 644-645 Holstein	03/01/99	01/01/04
United States	BP	Green Canyon 698-700 & 742-744 Atlantis	01/01/98	01/01/05
United States	BP	Green Canyon 825-827 & 781-783 Mad Dog	04/01/99	12/31/04
United States	BP	Mississippi Canyon 028 & 72 Pompano II	01/01/86	05/01/96
United States	BP	Mississippi Canyon 084-085 & 129 King	01/01/93	12/31/01
United States	BP	Mississippi Canyon 173 & 217 Kings Peak	01/01/92	07/01/02
United States	BP	Mississippi Canyon 520 Herschel(Na Kika)	04/01/97	07/01/03
United States	BP	Mississippi Canyon 607 Anstey E(Na Kika)	01/01/98	01/01/04
United States	BP	Mississippi Canyon 778 &822 Crazy Horse	07/04/99	01/01/05
United States	BP	Mississippi Canyon 778 Crazy Horse Test	07/04/99	07/01/03
United States	BP	Viosca Knoll 914 Nile	01/01/97	06/01/01
United States	BP	Viosca Knoll 915 & 871 Marlin	07/01/93	11/21/99
United States	Burlington	East Breaks 599 Hack Wilson	04/02/01	01/01/05
United States	Chevron-Texaco	Garden Banks 254	08/01/93	01/01/05
United States	Chevron-Texaco	Green Canyon 205 & 160-161 Genesis	05/01/89	01/28/99
United States	Chevron-Texaco	Green Canyon 237-236 Typhoon	01/01/99	07/15/01
United States	Conoco	Garden Banks 783 Magnolia(Entrada East)	05/01/99	01/01/05
United States	Conoco	Green Canyon 141 Grand Canyon	09/01/87	01/01/03
United States	Conoco	Green Canyon 184 Jolliet	10/01/83	11/08/89
United States	Devon Energy - Santa Fe Snyder	Garden Banks 372 Knight	06/01/97	10/01/04

Depletion Date	Reserves (TOE)	Water Depth (m)	Development Type	Plate
01/01/23	40,000,000	1362	Floating Production	50 - Northwest Angola
01/01/25	38,700,000	1147	Subsea Satellite To Floating Production	50 - Northwest Angola
01/01/29	93,720,000	1202	Floating Production	50 - Northwest Angola
10/01/13	18,350,000	1355	Floating Production	50 - Northwest Angola
01/01/30	119,000,000	1360	Floating Production	50 - Northwest Angola
01/01/32	108,100,000	1360	Floating Production	50 - Northwest Angola
10/01/30	47,052,200	1375	Subsea Satellite To Floating Production	50 - Northwest Angola
01/01/15	10,666,667	520	Floating Production	
07/01/18	17,175,364	735	Floating Production	80 - Southeast Brazil & Uruguay/Campos Basin
10/01/23	110,000,000	1200	Floating Production	80 - Southeast Brazil & Uruguay/Campos Basin
06/01/03	800,000	1109	Subsea Satellite To Floating Production	80 - Southeast Brazil & Uruguay/Campos Basin
01/01/20	13,333,333	1056	Floating Production	80 - Southeast Brazil & Uruguay/Campos Basin
01/01/14	4,000,000	925	Floating Production	80 - Southeast Brazil & Uruguay/Campos Basin
10/01/03	2,000,000	977	Subsea Satellite To Floating Production	80 - Southeast Brazil & Uruguay/Campos Basin
07/01/06	1,000,000	1595	Floating Production	80 - Southeast Brazil & Uruguay/Campos Basin
10/01/03	2,000,000	1053	Subsea Satellite To Floating Production	80 - Southeast Brazil & Uruguay/Campos Basin
10/01/27	109,900,000	843	Floating Production	80 - Southeast Brazil & Uruguay/Campos Basin
08/01/02	2,800,000	735	Floating Production	80 - Southeast Brazil & Uruguay/Campos Basin
10/01/23	25,551,000	922	Floating Production	80 - Southeast Brazil & Uruguay/Campos Basin
10/01/03	1,000,000	922	Subsea Satellite To Floating Production	80 - Southeast Brazil & Uruguay/Campos Basin
09/01/16	30,000,000	940	Floating Production	80 - Southeast Brazil & Uruguay/Campos Basin
01/01/01	1,000,000	700	Floating Production	80 - Southeast Brazil & Uruguay/Campos Basin
01/01/17	12,333,300	700	Subsea Satellite To Floating Production	80 - Southeast Brazil & Uruguay/Campos Basin
01/01/25	339,000,000	835	Floating Production	80 - Southeast Brazil & Uruguay/Campos Basin
01/01/24	25,000,000	1250	Floating Production	80 - Southeast Brazil & Uruguay/Campos Basin
01/01/03	1,500,000	1250	Subsea Satellite To Floating Production	80 - Southeast Brazil & Uruguay/Campos Basin
06/01/26	195,600,000	1080	Floating Production	80 - Southeast Brazil & Uruguay/Campos Basin
12/31/00	2,235,000	1027	Subsea Satellite To Floating Production	80 - Southeast Brazil & Uruguay/Campos Basin
08/01/01	1,023,500	1709	Floating Production	80 - Southeast Brazil & Uruguay/Campos Basin
01/01/05	2,666,667	700	Subsea Satellite To Floating Production	80 - Southeast Brazil & Uruguay/Campos Basin
01/01/01	1,333,333	1853	Floating Production	80 - Southeast Brazil & Uruguay/Campos Basin
08/01/17	5,324,871	550	Subsea Satellite To Floating Production	80 - Southeast Brazil & Uruguay/Campos Basin
08/01/02	1,066,700	551	Subsea Satellite To Floating Production	80 - Southeast Brazil & Uruguay/Campos Basin
08/01/09	2,031,446	563	Subsea Satellite To Floating Production	80 - Southeast Brazil & Uruguay/Campos Basin
08/01/09	7,513,666	611	Floating Production	80 - Southeast Brazil & Uruguay/Campos Basin
01/01/30	61,000,000	1141	Floating Production	80 - Southeast Brazil & Uruguay/Campos Basin
01/01/19	19,763,000	546	Subsea Satellite To Floating Production	48 - Congo
07/01/19	41,100,000	800	Floating Production	48 - Congo
01/01/33	51,716,000	610	Subsea Satellite To Onshore Facility	43 - Egypt
07/01/28	42,313,000	610	Subsea Satellite To Onshore Facility	43 - Egypt
01/01/30	23,507,300	790	Subsea Satellite To Onshore Facility	43 - Egypt
05/01/11	4,266,700	579	Subsea Satellite To Floating Production	45 - Gulf of Guinea
01/01/16	55,175,400	700	Floating Production	45 - Gulf of Guinea
01/01/25	20,750,000	603	Subsea Satellite To Onshore Facility	43 - Egypt
01/01/29	35,500,000	500	Floating Production	63 - South East Asia
01/01/27	63,500,000	853	Floating Production	63 - South East Asia
01/01/20	8,230,000	695	Subsea Satellite To Onshore Facility	43 - Egypt
01/01/17	7,760,000	779	Subsea Satellite To Onshore Facility	43 - Egypt
03/01/05	3,000,000	850	Floating Production	10 - Southern Europe
01/01/22	20,000,000	1484	Floating Production Or Subsea (Alternative)	45 - Gulf of Guinea
01/01/25	134,000,000	1350	Floating Production	46 - Nigeria
11/01/28	117,540,000	1015	Floating Production	46 - Nigeria
01/01/30	138,420,000	1433	Floating Production	46 - Nigeria
01/01/25	32,350,000	1849	Subsea Satellite To Floating Production	46 - Nigeria
01/01/06	4,000,000	1375	Floating Production	46 - Nigeria
10/01/31	97,000,000	820	Fixed Production Platform And Subsea	63 - South East Asia
01/01/09	6,666,667	845	Floating Production	63 - South East Asia
01/01/02	400,000	845	Floating Production	63 - South East Asia
01/01/11	2,000,000	514	Subsea Satellite To Floating Production	7 - UK Atlantic Margin
01/01/11	2,666,667	510	Subsea Satellite To Floating Production	7 - UK Atlantic Margin
01/01/11	1,867,000	530	Subsea Satellite To Floating Production	7 - UK Atlantic Margin
01/01/09	10,375,000	518	Floating Production	91 - Louisiana Gulf Coast
01/01/09	666,667	617	Subsea Satellite To Floating Production	91 - Louisiana Gulf Coast
01/01/09	500,000	700	Subsea Satellite To Fixed Production	91 - Louisiana Gulf Coast
01/01/09	501,740	750	Subsea Satellite To Fixed Production	91 - Louisiana Gulf Coast
11/01/09	7,000,000	971	Floating Production	91 - Louisiana Gulf Coast
01/01/15	6,300,000	762	Floating Production	91 - Louisiana Gulf Coast
01/01/11	3,605,078	534	Subsea Satellite To Fixed Production	91 - Louisiana Gulf Coast
01/01/19	19,000,000	503	Fixed Production Platforms Only	91 - Louisiana Gulf Coast
01/01/20	28,700,000	1310	Floating Production	91 - Louisiana Gulf Coast
01/01/20	14,350,000	872	Floating Production	91 - Louisiana Gulf Coast
07/01/12	3,350,000	2038	Subsea Satellite To Fixed Production	91 - Louisiana Gulf Coast
01/01/15	20,230,600	945	Floating Production Or Subsea (Alternative)	91 - Louisiana Gulf Coast
01/01/13	31,052,200	829	Subsea Satellite To Fixed Production	91 - Louisiana Gulf Coast
01/01/24	34,000,000	1220	Floating Production	91 - Louisiana Gulf Coast
01/01/25	34,000,000	1400	Floating Production	91 - Louisiana Gulf Coast
01/01/30	60,000,000	1800	Floating Production	91 - Louisiana Gulf Coast
05/01/16	12,350,000	568	Subsea Satellite To Fixed Production	91 - Louisiana Gulf Coast
01/01/10	6,274,000	1621	Subsea Satellite To Floating Production	91 - Louisiana Gulf Coast
07/01/12	2,940,000	1980	Subsea Satellite To Fixed Production	91 - Louisiana Gulf Coast
07/01/12	8,665,000	2055	Subsea Satellite To Floating Production	91 - Louisiana Gulf Coast
01/01/12	7,052,000	2134	Subsea Satellite To Floating Production	91 - Louisiana Gulf Coast
01/01/30	135,000,000	1856	Floating Production	91 - Louisiana Gulf Coast
01/01/05	2,000,000	1850	Floating Production	91 - Louisiana Gulf Coast
06/01/11	6,350,000	1067	Subsea Satellite To Floating Production	91 - Louisiana Gulf Coast
12/01/14	13,530,000	986	Floating Production	91 - Louisiana Gulf Coast
01/01/13	6,273,625	961	Subsea Satellite To Floating Production	91 - Louisiana Gulf Coast
01/01/10	1,568,400	585	No Development Scheme Announced Yet	91 - Louisiana Gulf Coast
01/01/19	21,330,000	792	Floating Production	91 - Louisiana Gulf Coast
08/01/09	14,115,655	642	Floating Production	91 - Louisiana Gulf Coast
01/01/20	23,300,000	1433	Floating Production Or Subsea (Alternative)	91 - Louisiana Gulf Coast
01/01/13	4,000,000	523	Floating Production Or Subsea (Alternative)	91 - Louisiana Gulf Coast
01/01/04	9,400,000	536	Floating Production	91 - Louisiana Gulf Coast
10/01/10	1,410,000	530	Subsea Satellite To Fixed Production	91 - Louisiana Gulf Coast

XXXII

APPENDIX

Country	Operator	Field Name	Date Discovered	Date on Stream
United States	Devon Energy - Santa Fe Snyder	Green Canyon 111 & 112 Stellaria	07/01/97	12/01/99
United States	Devon Energy - Santa Fe Snyder	Green Canyon 114 Gretchen	12/01/99	07/01/02
United States	Dominion	Mississippi Canyon 773 Devils Tower	01/01/00	07/01/03
United States	Enserch	Garden Banks 344 Jason	12/01/00	01/01/05
United States	Enserch	Garden Banks 386 Llano	12/01/97	10/01/04
United States	Enserch	Garden Banks 386 Llano Ewt	12/01/97	07/01/02
United States	ExxonMobil	Green Canyon 160	03/01/90	01/01/05
United States	ExxonMobil	Green Canyon 166 Bison	01/01/86	01/01/03
United States	ExxonMobil	Mississippi Canyon 211 Mica	09/01/90	08/01/01
United States	ExxonMobil	Alaminos Canyon 024 Madison	01/01/99	01/01/02
United States	ExxonMobil	Alaminos Canyon 025 & 26 Hoover	03/01/97	09/30/00
United States	ExxonMobil	Alaminos Canyon 065 South Diana	04/01/97	01/01/04
United States	ExxonMobil	East Breaks 945-946 & 988-989 Diana	07/01/90	05/31/00
United States	ExxonMobil	East Breaks 949 Marshall	10/02/98	01/01/02
United States	ExxonMobil	East Breaks 992 Rockefeller	07/01/96	01/01/05
United States	Kerr-McGee	East Breaks 602-601 & 646 Nansen	10/06/99	11/01/01
United States	Kerr-McGee	East Breaks 642 West Boomvang	11/01/99	01/01/02
United States	Kerr-McGee	East Breaks 643 North Boomvang	12/01/97	01/01/02
United States	Kerr-McGee	East Breaks 688 East Boomvang	11/01/88	01/01/02
United States	Kerr-McGee	Garden Banks 244	07/01/97	01/01/04
United States	Kerr-McGee	Garden Banks 668 Gunnison	06/05/00	01/01/03
United States	Kerr-McGee	Viosca Knoll 826 Neptune	08/21/89	03/17/97
United States	Kerr-McGee	Viosca Knoll 869 & 825 Thor	06/01/84	10/01/98
United States	Kerr-McGee	Viosca Knoll 870 Thor Southeast	01/01/86	01/01/03
United States	Marathon	Ewing Bank 963 Arnold	08/01/96	05/25/98
United States	Marathon	Mississippi Canyon 348 Camden Hills	08/01/99	07/01/02
United States	Mariner Energy	Ewing Bank 966 Black Widow	06/16/98	10/29/00
United States	Mariner Energy	Green Canyon 472-473 & 517 King Kong	04/03/89	12/31/01
United States	Mariner Energy	Mississippi Canyon 674 &718 Pluto/Bs&T	07/01/96	12/29/99
United States	Murphy	Green Canyon 338 Front Runner	01/16/01	01/01/05
United States	Murphy	Mississippi Canyon 538 & 582 Medusa	10/01/99	10/01/02
United States	Ocean	Mississippi Canyon 496 Zia	12/01/98	01/01/05
United States	Samedan/Noble	East Breaks 421 & 464 Lost Ark	02/09/01	07/01/02
United States	Shell	Garden Banks 341 Habanero	02/01/99	10/01/03
United States	Shell	Garden Banks 426-427 & 470-471 Auger	08/21/87	04/15/94
United States	Shell	Garden Banks 471 Cardamom	01/01/96	10/24/98
United States	Shell	Garden Banks 516 Serrano (Sorano)	11/01/96	09/01/01
United States	Shell	Garden Banks 559 Oregano	04/21/99	12/01/01
United States	Shell	Garden Banks 602 Macaroni	01/01/94	08/24/99
United States	Shell	Green Canyon 110 Rocky	10/01/84	08/01/95
United States	Shell	Green Canyon 113 & 157 Angus	07/01/97	09/05/99
United States	Shell	Green Canyon 116-117 & 72-73 Popeye	07/01/85	01/11/96
United States	Shell	Green Canyon 155 & 156 Manatee	01/01/99	10/01/02
United States	Shell	Green Canyon 158 & 202 Brutus	12/01/88	09/01/01
United States	Shell	Green Canyon 248 Glider	01/01/96	01/01/03
United States	Shell	Green Canyon 296	09/01/96	01/01/03
United States	Shell	Mississippi Canyon 383 Keppler(Na Kika)	11/06/87	07/01/03
United States	Shell	Mississippi Canyon 429 Ariel (Na Kika)	01/01/96	07/01/03
United States	Shell	Mississippi Canyon 522 Fourier(Na Kika)	01/01/91	07/01/03
United States	Shell	Mississippi Canyon 657 Coulomb(Na Kika)	03/31/88	07/01/05
United States	Shell	Mississippi Canyon 686/7 & 730/1 Mensa	06/01/87	07/12/97
United States	Shell	Mississippi Canyon 764 King	02/01/98	04/19/00
United States	Shell	Mississippi Canyon 765 Princess	07/01/00	01/01/04
United States	Shell	Mississippi Canyon 807-806 & 763 Mars	01/01/89	07/08/96
United States	Shell	Mississippi Canyon 809-810 & 854 Ursa	01/01/91	03/08/99
United States	Shell	Mississippi Canyon 853 Venus	01/01/92	01/01/03
United States	Shell	Mississippi Canyon 899 Crosby/Flathead	05/01/98	10/01/01
United States	Shell	Mississippi Canyon 934 & 935 Europa	03/01/94	01/31/00
United States	Shell	Mississippi Canyon 942 Morgus	01/01/99	01/01/03
United States	Shell	Viosca Knoll 872 Einset	11/01/98	11/01/01
United States	Shell	Viosca Knoll 956-957 & 912 Ram-powell	07/24/85	09/06/97
United States	Chevron-Texaco	Atwater Valley 063 Champlain	05/04/00	01/01/05
United States	Chevron-Texaco	Mississippi Canyon 292 Gemini	07/01/95	06/02/99
United States	Chevron-Texaco	Mississippi Canyon 638 Narcissus	01/01/97	01/01/05
United States	Chevron-Texaco	Viosca Knoll 786 Petronius	08/01/95	07/31/00
United States	TotalFinaElf	Mississippi Canyon 243 Matterhorn	01/01/91	10/01/03
United States	TotalFinaElf	Mississippi Canyon 305 Aconcagua	03/21/99	07/01/02
United States	TotalFinaElf	Viosca Knoll 1003 Ida/Fastball	01/01/00	12/31/01
United States	BP	Garden Banks 782 Entrada(Magnolia West)	04/24/00	01/01/05
United States	BP	Mississippi Canyon 126/7 Horn Mountain	08/01/99	01/01/03
United States	BP	Mississippi Canyon 941 Mirage (Ex Zeus)	07/01/91	01/01/05
United States	Walter	Ewing Bank 1006	01/01/97	03/15/99
United States	Walter	Mississippi Canyon 443	01/01/98	01/01/02

Depletion Date	Reserves (TOE)	Water Depth (m)	Development Type	Plate
01/01/10	3,600,000	536	Subsea Satellite To Fixed Production	91 - Louisiana Gulf Coast
07/01/10	940,000	818	Subsea Satellite To Fixed Production	91 - Louisiana Gulf Coast
07/01/19	12,900,000	1710	Floating Production	91 - Louisiana Gulf Coast
01/01/15	7,020,000	648	No Development Scheme Announced Yet	91 - Louisiana Gulf Coast
10/01/19	32,543,500	792	Floating Production Or Subsea (Alternative)	91 - Louisiana Gulf Coast
07/01/04	1,000,000	792	Floating Production	91 - Louisiana Gulf Coast
	500,000	891	No Development Scheme Announced Yet	91 - Louisiana Gulf Coast
01/01/13	6,350,000	767	Floating Production Or Subsea (Alternative)	91 - Louisiana Gulf Coast
08/01/16	20,000,000	1326	Subsea Satellite To Fixed Production	91 - Louisiana Gulf Coast
01/01/12	2,431,220	1479	Subsea Satellite To Floating Production	91 - Louisiana Gulf Coast
06/01/20	21,710,000	1463	Floating Production	91 - Louisiana Gulf Coast
01/01/12	4,900,000	1490	Subsea Satellite To Floating Production	91 - Louisiana Gulf Coast
06/01/20	19,354,000	1416	Subsea Satellite To Floating Production	91 - Louisiana Gulf Coast
01/01/12	3,826,600	1334	Subsea Satellite To Floating Production	91 - Louisiana Gulf Coast
01/01/12	1,450,000	1483	Subsea Satellite To Floating Production	91 - Louisiana Gulf Coast
01/01/17	17,406,676	1122	Floating Production	91 - Louisiana Gulf Coast
01/01/10	1,830,000	1067	Subsea Satellite To Floating Production	91 - Louisiana Gulf Coast
01/01/13	11,368,124	1065	Floating Production	91 - Louisiana Gulf Coast
01/01/12	6,940,000	1287	Subsea Satellite To Floating Production	91 - Louisiana Gulf Coast
01/01/12	1,568,406	610	Floating Production Or Subsea (Alternative)	91 - Louisiana Gulf Coast
01/01/18	31,368,000	960	Floating Production	91 - Louisiana Gulf Coast
01/01/17	21,134,000	588	Floating Production	91 - Louisiana Gulf Coast
10/01/14	9,000,000	564	Floating Production Or Subsea (Alternative)	91 - Louisiana Gulf Coast
01/01/09	1,333,333	732	Subsea Satellite To Floating Production	91 - Louisiana Gulf Coast
06/01/05	3,686,000	533	Subsea Satellite To Fixed Production	91 - Louisiana Gulf Coast
07/01/17	12,420,000	2195	Subsea Satellite To Fixed Production	91 - Louisiana Gulf Coast
11/01/05	2,117,540	579	Subsea Satellite To Floating Production	91 - Louisiana Gulf Coast
01/01/14	11,283,500	1163	Subsea Satellite To Floating Production	91 - Louisiana Gulf Coast
11/01/07	3,066,700	849	Subsea Satellite To Fixed Production	91 - Louisiana Gulf Coast
01/01/20	20,000,000	1067	Subsea Satellite To Floating Production	91 - Louisiana Gulf Coast
01/01/15	14,900,000	678	Floating Production	91 - Louisiana Gulf Coast
01/01/15	8,000,000	500	Subsea Satellite To Floating Production	91 - Louisiana Gulf Coast
07/01/15	5,187,400	823	Subsea Satellite To Floating Production	91 - Louisiana Gulf Coast
10/01/18	13,642,000	610	Subsea Satellite To Floating Production	91 - Louisiana Gulf Coast
05/01/14	29,350,000	872	Floating Production	91 - Louisiana Gulf Coast
01/01/09	5,141,000	869	Extended Reach Drilling And/Or Subsea	91 - Louisiana Gulf Coast
09/01/10	6,700,000	961	Subsea Satellite To Floating Production	91 - Louisiana Gulf Coast
01/01/10	3,940,000	1034	Subsea Satellite To Floating Production	91 - Louisiana Gulf Coast
09/01/09	10,430,000	1123	Subsea Satellite To Floating Production	91 - Louisiana Gulf Coast
08/01/02	834,551	544	Subsea Satellite To Floating Production	91 - Louisiana Gulf Coast
10/01/11	8,533,333	625	Subsea Satellite To Fixed Production	91 - Louisiana Gulf Coast
01/01/10	8,855,665	630	Subsea Satellite To Fixed Production	91 - Louisiana Gulf Coast
01/01/11	3,372,000	700	Subsea Satellite To Fixed Production	91 - Louisiana Gulf Coast
09/01/16	26,660,000	910	Floating Production	91 - Louisiana Gulf Coast
01/01/18	18,035,000	1013	Subsea Satellite To Floating Production	91 - Louisiana Gulf Coast
01/01/08	666,667	1195	Subsea Satellite To Floating Production	91 - Louisiana Gulf Coast
07/01/14	7,500,000	1755	Subsea Satellite To Floating Production	91 - Louisiana Gulf Coast
07/01/13	5,500,000	1912	Floating Production	91 - Louisiana Gulf Coast
07/01/13	4,394,000	2118	Subsea Satellite To Floating Production	91 - Louisiana Gulf Coast
07/01/15	7,052,200	2292	Subsea Satellite To Floating Production	91 - Louisiana Gulf Coast
07/01/12	17,125,250	1650	Subsea Satellite To Fixed Production	91 - Louisiana Gulf Coast
05/01/15	8,333,300	1001	Subsea Satellite To Floating Production	91 - Louisiana Gulf Coast
01/01/20	27,052,200	1000	Floating Production Or Subsea (Alternative)	91 - Louisiana Gulf Coast
07/01/31	94,100,000	896	Floating Production	91 - Louisiana Gulf Coast
01/01/20	53,315,000	1158	Floating Production	91 - Louisiana Gulf Coast
01/01/11	4,000,000	1155	Subsea Satellite To Floating Production	91 - Louisiana Gulf Coast
10/01/11	10,821,000	1341	Subsea Satellite To Floating Production	91 - Louisiana Gulf Coast
02/01/15	21,333,333	1185	Subsea Satellite To Floating Production	91 - Louisiana Gulf Coast
01/01/11	4,000,000	1200	Subsea Satellite To Floating Production	91 - Louisiana Gulf Coast
01/01/12	2,350,000	768	Subsea Satellite To Floating Production	91 - Louisiana Gulf Coast
10/01/22	35,960,000	981	Floating Production	91 - Louisiana Gulf Coast
01/01/15	12,350,000	1337	Floating Production Or Subsea (Alternative)	91 - Louisiana Gulf Coast
06/01/09	7,586,000	1034	Subsea Satellite To Fixed Production	91 - Louisiana Gulf Coast
	784,200	1296	No Development Scheme Announced Yet	91 - Louisiana Gulf Coast
08/01/20	12,500,000	535	Fixed Production Platforms Only	91 - Louisiana Gulf Coast
10/01/18	15,400,000	864	Floating Production	91 - Louisiana Gulf Coast
07/01/16	13,750,000	2156	Subsea Satellite To Fixed Production	91 - Louisiana Gulf Coast
01/01/12	4,500,000	1000	Subsea Satellite To Floating Production	91 - Louisiana Gulf Coast
01/01/20	20,000,000	1415	Floating Production Or Subsea (Alternative)	91 - Louisiana Gulf Coast
01/01/18	23,370,000	1646	Floating Production	91 - Louisiana Gulf Coast
01/01/17	16,666,700	1177	Floating Production Or Subsea (Alternative)	91 - Louisiana Gulf Coast
04/01/04	1,570,000	574	Subsea Satellite To Fixed Production	91 - Louisiana Gulf Coast
01/01/09	536,800	639	Subsea Satellite To Fixed Production	91 - Louisiana Gulf Coast

XXXIII

APPENDIX

Source: *Infield*

Notes

Notes

Notes

APPENDIX: TERMS AND CONVERSION FACTORS

Useful Terms

Gas

LNG	Liquefied Natural Gas
LPG	Liquefied Petroleum Gas
NGL	Natural Gas Liquids
bn cm	billion cubic metres
Oil	'000 b/d (thousand barrels of oil per day)

Other weights (Coal, and other minerals)

MMt	million tonnes
m t/y	million tonnes per year

Useful Conversion factors

Distance

1 inch = 2.54 cm   1 kilometre = 0.62 miles
1 foot = 0.305 m   1 metre = 3.28 feet
1 mile = 1.61 km   1 centimetre = 0.4 inches

Volume Equivalents

	US gallon	Imperial	barrels gallon	barrels per day/ per year
1 US gallon	1.000	0.8327	0.02381	0.06523×10^{-3}
1 Imp gallon	1.201	1.0000	0.02859	0.07834×10^{-3}
1 Barrel	42.000	34.9700	1.00000	0.00274
1 Barrel per day/per year	15300.000	12764.0000	365.00000	1.00000

"Normal" Fuel Values and Equivalents*

	Coal kt	Oil kt	Oil kB	Oil b/d	Nat.Gas GL
Coal: **1000 metric tonnes (kt)**	1.000	0.700	4.900	13.400	0.840
Oil: **1000 metric tonnes (kt)**	1.430	1.000	7.000	19.100	1.200
1000 Barrels (kB)	0.204	0.143	1.000	2.740	0.172
1 barrel per day (b/d)	0.075	0.052	0.365	1.000	0.063
Natural Gas: **1 Million m^3 (GL)**	1.190	0.830	5.800	5.900	1.000

*Based on the following unit values: Coal, 7.0 teracalories per 1000 tons; oil, 10.0 teracalories (net) per 1000 tons, or 9.0 teracalories (net) per 1000 ML; natural gas, 8.3 teracalories (net) per GL; electricity, 860 teracalories per TWh.

Source: Oil and Gas Dictionary, edited by Paul Stevens, Macmillan Reference Books 1988

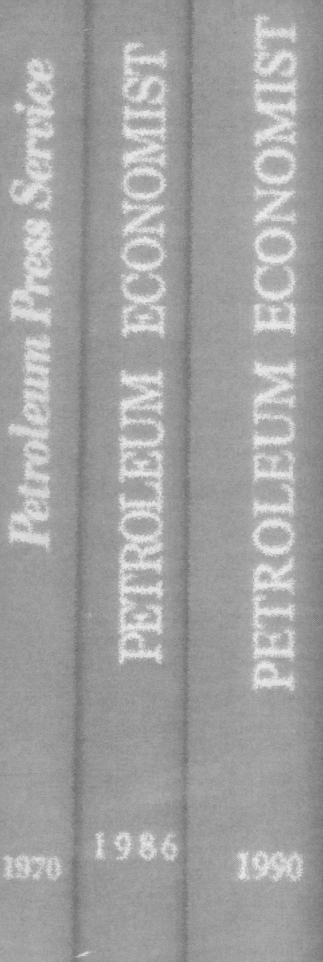